The Lost Art of 1
or The Crazy Life of Joseph T

Joseph Triska

What do you think is real or fake in this sci-fi autobiography novel?

Edited by Nichola Tyrrell
Proofread by Julie Lewthwaite
Cover & Interior Art Design: Joseph Triska
Cover & Interior Art – Technical: Craig Randall

ISBN: 978-1-7324755-0-2

Part I – The Game

Part II – The Year of the Gathering

"When governments fear the people, there is liberty. When the people fear the government, there is tyranny."
"The tree of liberty must be refreshed from time to time with the blood of patriots and tyrants."

Thomas Jefferson

Part 1: The Game

Chapter 1
The Letter

2/18/2017
Marietta, GA

Hi Ronnee,
Several sequential events happened recently that I don't fully understand. You might have experienced some of them. The more I think about them, the more questions I have. After leaving jail and a hospital at the end of January 2017, I went to the Czech Republic for a couple of weeks to forget about everything, refocus and to think about the next steps in my life. After a few days into the trip, everything went back to normal. I feel great again. I also had a lot of time to think about the past thirty-eight years of my life along with some philosophical thinking. Ronnee, I have to tell you about my life. This will hopefully help you understand why things happened the way they did.

Early Life
Joseph T. was born on June 30 1978. His parents – mom, twenty-two, and dad, twenty-three – were young and wanted to enjoy life. They were not fully ready to have a child. His grandmother, forty-one years old, an elementary school teacher, had just given final grades to her class. June 30th is always the last day of school and the beginning of the two-month summer break. A few days after he was born, the whole family, consisting of great-grandmother, grandmother, granddad, mom, dad, and aunt, took him to the summer house, located roughly fifty miles outside of Prague.

Newborn Joseph spent most of the day outdoors, including during naps, so he could listen to the birds and absorb the simplicity and beauty of nature as early as possible. He was breastfed for almost a year. In addition, the women went to the woods on a regular basis to pick berries, so he could get some extra vitamins. They were always cooking and baking, making everything from scratch. Everyone took turns to hold him in their arms and to sing to him before bedtime. He was treated like a prince by four women who loved him and wanted to spend every minute of their free time with him. This lasted for years. He can vaguely remember this, at age four. The women, especially his great-grandmother and grandmother, were in charge of the household and delegated the two men to perform other household duties. The dad, however, mostly went to Prague to do his own thing. This was understandable, since he was only twenty-three.

Joseph was sick a lot from age four to about seven. During this period he suffered from all kinds of medical problems, such as meningitis, pneumonia, appendix removal and countless ear infections, leading to adenoids removal. As mentioned before, he spent most of the springs and summers outside. This led to getting a viral infection from a tick that developed into meningitis. The disease overwhelmed him in the late spring of 1983, when he lived with his mom and stepdad in Prague 8 – Libeň. He was taken to the nearest hospital, Bulovka, located a couple of miles from the house. The child spent over a month fighting for his life, isolated and unable to see his parents, in the infection section of the hospital. He was scared to death every second that he was awake, unable to go to the restroom without nurses' help. It felt so good to be touched by another human being. He would rather pee in his pants than walk the hallways alone. The building was constructed in the early 1930s. The ceilings were high, and everything was dark, blurry and creepy. The interior design felt cold and unfriendly. This was most likely due to severe hallucinations. After the recovery, he was not the same person. According to Grandmother, the child had slower responses and was not as happy and sharp. There were no responses during the following reflex test; a person sits on a table with legs hanging freely. Then a doctor gently taps a knee with a small hammer and the leg should raise slightly on its own, without any effort. Later in life, Joseph visited many old and historical buildings, but was never as scared. It felt normal going to the newer sections of the hospital, built in the 1960s and 1970s, for examinations and other surgical procedures. It always felt weird driving by the section constructed in the 1930s. Even today, nothing could convince him to venture close by or even look at this building. Coincidently, Reinhard Heydrich, the most hated man in the country, died there of infection about forty years earlier. Look him up. He is the real jewel of humanity. :-(

After getting over the period of sickness, everything changed. Between ages seven to sixteen (1985–94) was one of the happiest periods of his life.

By 1985, his stepdad was a well-established and connected Communist Party member who managed a large restaurant/bowling bar complex in Prague 8. (Please understand that you had to be a party member, regardless of your beliefs, to hold any important position.) The socialist state-owned business model was in reality a mob hierarchy. It was all about favors, bribes, and who you knew. You could steal for yourself as much as possible as long as your superiors were happy. They did not care because they were doing the same thing. It was the only way to make any real money and differentiate from the general population, since private business ownership was illegal. The only problem was that you could not publicly show the money without risking being investigated by the secret police. My stepdad had a nice house, satellite dish, two cars and a summer house in the same village as my grandma, and was able to take a vacation several times a year. He did a great job of staying under the radar.

From a material perspective, as a child, Joseph had all the forbidden products available on the black market – Western toys, clothes, VCR and a large collection of illegal American movies. At least 90% of the country's population did not live this well.

This was a strange period to live in. I will try to describe it from both a child's and an adult's perspective, since they are so different.

A Child's Life in Communist Czechoslovakia
We, the children, were playing outside most of the time. When parents did not allow us to go out and play, it was usually due to punishment for misbehaving. This was the worst kind of punishment, far surpassing any light physical punishments we often deserved. It was normal to complete homework, go outside and play with countless friends, and return right before dinner. On Fridays and Saturdays, we were allowed to stay out until 10 p.m. (kids from about age nine and up). Throughout the country, there were tens of thousands of kids, boys and girls of all ages, playing together at any given time. Most kids had the same clothes, toys, and bicycles bought from socialist department stores. Your peers judged you by your personality and how you were able to entertain the group, not by what kind of clothes you were wearing, what you owned or what your parents had or did. The social background did not matter since, from a material perspective, everyone was pretty much at the same level. This was true for all age groups until adulthood. The government took good care of all kids. All schools, after-school activities, sports and child/adult health care were available for little or no charge. The Pioneer group

(similar to Scouts) organized weekend and two- or three-week summer camps. Joseph went almost every summer to a standing or river rafting camp. You did not have to worry about schools and places where you lived. Bad areas and school districts did not exist. Human trafficking, organized crime, and drugs also did not exist. The whole country was one large playground for kids, surrounded by barbed wire. You were not able to get in or out. It was a pretty large playground. :-) When you drove from Prague, the borders in any direction except east (six hours) were about two hours away. We, the children, were truly free and, due to the lack of law enforcement, were able to get away with almost anything (within reason). I would not trade these memories for anything. I feel sorry for all the kids in the world that were not and will not be able to experience this. This paradise island no longer exists. Here are some stories:

Mother always wanted Joseph to play a musical instrument. While attending second-grade in elementary school, he chose to play piano. Violin was the other instrument considered. His great aunt was a director of a music school, who also gave private lessons. Naturally, she was chosen as the teacher. She was a perfectionist who enjoyed her work very much. The lessons lasted for three years and ended due to Joseph's lack of interest. In preparation for the end-of-year music exhibition, usually held in a historic downtown Prague theater in front of over a hundred people, he had to memorize a classical music segment about ten minutes long. Joseph always chose Mozart, over Bach, Beethoven, Tchaikovsky, and Dvořák. Mozart's music felt the most natural and created an indescribable pleasure when played. The second event attended during this period was the Prague Spring Festival. He and his mom were going to operas and all sorts of classical concerts for the whole week. *Don Giovanni* was his favorite opera. At night, after the events ended, the streets were full of people dressed in their best. It was pure beauty to walk the historic city center at night. They always stopped at a café, sat down for a piece of cake and absorbed the incredible atmosphere of the city. Later in life, Joseph always took his new girlfriends for a night walk at around 2–3 a.m. The walk began at Wenceslas Square, led to Old Town Square, continued over Charles Bridge to Little Quarter, and ended at Prague Castle. This is the most gorgeous and romantic walk he has ever experienced. It feels like you are part of the 900-plus year history of the area. You can really feel the city and its ancestors when there is not another soul on the streets except you and your loved one. If you ever visit Prague, this is a must-do.

(I am not the best writer and an even shittier accountant. It is becoming increasingly difficult to write in third person. I will, therefore, write in first person, going forward.)

4

In the mid to late 1980s, several events occurred that forever changed my life. The VCR became the favorite toy and must-have item in Czechoslovakia. Western and especially American movies, with a few exceptions, were strictly forbidden. A forbidden movie was smuggled over the borders and re-recorded with one voice in the Czech language. The volume of the original actors' voices was lowered. Then the movie was copied endlessly and distributed to the general population via the black market. Of course, the quality was sometimes very bad. People faced prison sentences if caught with this kind of VHS tape. Some movies, such as *The Witches of Eastwick*, with Jack Nicholson, passed through a censorship committee and were allowed in the theaters. I remember seeing this movie for the first time when I was about ten years old, at an outdoor movie theatre located a couple of miles from the summer house. The Moon was almost full and the atmosphere was just right to see this movie. It was a very powerful movie that I can see over and over again. I begged my aunt, who is eleven years older than me, to go see this movie with me again. We ended up going several times in a row.

The really good movies, such as the Rambos and Rockys, were not allowed. You could not see them in theaters; however, everybody knew the characters. Everyone talked about *Rocky IV* once the movie spread around the country. During that time, I was attending a language elementary school where my grandmother was a teacher. I had to travel across half of Prague to get there. I asked people of all ages and genders at subway stations, tram stops or inside a particular public transportation unit: "Have you seen *Rocky IV*?" The usual response was, "Yes, and he got that Russian bastard really good this time." (Please note that Czechs and all of occupied Eastern Europe hated the Russian government, not necessarily its citizens.) I even asked my favorite teacher about *Rocky IV* and received a similar response. Had I told this to the police, his teaching career would have been over.

The whole country and Eastern Europe fell in love with American movies. They fell in love with fairy tales, beautiful ones. The USA had a huge propaganda advantage. Correct me if I am wrong, but I don't think there were any Russian movies and music the Americans craved. I truly believe VCR was the number one weapon that helped the United States win the Cold War, not the bullshit politicians. The Rambos, Rockys, Terminators, Highlanders, Witches of Eastwicks, Indiana Joneses, Star Wars and many more were the bullets. I wish Antonia was also reading this. She would have agreed with me 100%.

There were other "hot" battles fought during the Cold War. They were fought in the sports arenas, especially in hockey. For example, the 1987 Canada vs USSR World Junior Hockey Championship in Piešťany,

Czechoslovakia, still holds the world record for the longest hockey player fight. My parents and their friends were always cheering for the team that played against the Soviets. Sometimes, I asked why they didn't cheer for the Russians. I never received an answer. Maybe they thought I was not old enough to understand the answer. I asked, because I was receiving conflicting information. At school, we were being told that the Russians would be our protectors and friends forever. I still did not receive much of an answer after the explanation. These really were interesting times to live in. Everything was about sarcasm and double-sided meaning.

On Friday, November 17 1989, the Velvet Revolution started. The first student protest at Národní Třída boulevard in Prague ended when the police attacked the demonstrators. On the following Monday, there were flyers all over the public transportation network urging people to protest. For the next two weeks I went to the protests almost daily, right after school. The demonstrations were held at Wenceslas Square or Leteňská Pláň. I remember this period day by day. The atmosphere was incredible; the whole country was emotionally supercharged and everyone was positive, happy, and excited, especially when discussing this matter. I saw and heard Václav Havel multiple times speaking to the excited crowd. I was hardly able to breathe, my whole body was electrified, and tingled as I tried to absorb every word of Havel's powerful speech. That night, after the protest was over, I turned on my Sony Walkman, a forbidden product, and listened to Metallica or Michael Jackson, forbidden artists. Forbidden fruit always tastes the best. I felt invincible on my way home.

At age twelve, I would frequently take trips with my fourteen-year-old stepbrother, Patrik, to my stepdad's summer house. On Friday afternoons, we would persuade my mom to give us the house keys. Then we would get some money from Grandpa. "Grandpa, please give us some money for food. We are going to the cottage for the weekend." Cigarettes and beer would be the first items purchased at a train station in Prague. Then we would smoke, drink, and play loud punk and heavy metal music on the train. Most of the time the adults would not say anything because they knew what the answer would be: "Fuck off and return to the grave, you old man (or woman)." One particular trip stands out among all the others. As the train was departing, there was a young couple French kissing at the platform. I spilled a beer on their heads out of the slow-moving train. We then threw the empty beer bottles at cars waiting at a railroad crossing. For early teens, this was the zenith of the trip. I don't have to tell you what we did that weekend. Use your imagination.

It was normal in those days to see young people French kiss on the streets. This was before cell phones and beepers, so boys and girls would meet at squares, subways, or bus stations at a particular time. Often a girl would run and jump into a boy's arms. Then they would French kiss for a long period of time and not care that the street was full of strangers. "Love really is beautiful," I said to myself. At this early age (from about nine), I often daydreamed that sometime in the near future I would experience this with my girlfriend.

Oddly, the country was pretty open regarding sexuality, despite the Communist oppression. Semi-nude and fully nude beaches were widespread. I might have been about eight when I first ventured to a fully nude beach. I was shy and kept my swimsuit on. Even at that age, I really enjoyed the view as I was walking across the beach. ;-) Women and girls were sunbathing topless in their front and back yards, while being fully visible from main streets. Kids up to about age six did not wear any swimsuit at all while attending public pools and beaches. *Ronnee, I don't have to tell you any more details, just ask your husband.*

The summers were especially great. From early childhood, I spent most of the summers at the summer house. I was outside most of the day riding a bicycle (later motorcycle) and playing with friends. I loved going to the woods with my family early in the morning to pick wild mushrooms. I was taught at an early age to distinguish the poisonous ones from the edible ones. I enjoyed cleaning and cutting the mushrooms that I found. I eagerly watched them being cooked. The Czechs are well-known for picking wild mushrooms. I also enjoyed picking berries. My favorite place was the nearby flooded open-pit granite mine. My friends and I went there almost daily for a swim. I was about nine years old when I started to go there without adults. There were many cliffs of different sizes you could jump from. The highest was an incredibly tall flat wall of rock. I had respect for anyone who jumped from this particular cliff. During the next few years, I was slowly moving up and diving from higher and higher cliffs. At age twelve, I was standing at the top of the highest cliff, looking down and thinking for several hours and then, all of a sudden, I jumped. I flew flat like a bird and, just as I was approaching the water, I pressed my hands to a fist (to break the water, it hurts like hell if done with head only) and folded my body to a perfect dive. The cliff was twenty-six feet high. All my friends were cheering. It felt like I just conquered the world.

In 1998, I went to visit Europe for the first time since moving to the USA. I looked forward to swimming and to jumping a few times at the granite mine, but found the place completely destroyed. I fell apart, sat on the ground and cried for a while. This small piece of nature that I loved, the place that gave me so much, all the beautiful memories, had been destroyed forever. In the mid-1990s, a corporation had purchased the whole area and the mining had resumed.

My Family
Here are a few details about the members of my family…

Mom – I had a good relationship with my mom during childhood and early teen years. My stepdad was hardly around the house. I eventually figured out a way to brainwash her, to a certain degree. I was able to pretty much do whatever I wanted. She doesn't get along with adults, but she is perfect with small kids. Guys were always taking advantage of her. She was and still is a little crazy. One example: she bought me a motorcycle for my thirteenth birthday, but no helmet. In the USA, I had to help support her until 2005. She doesn't learn from her mistakes and keeps repeating the mistakes. She keeps calling me her Prince William. That comment pisses me off. I don't get along with her too well and talk with her for a few minutes a couple times a month.

Sister – I've always had a normal brother/sister relationship with her. Unwittingly, while living in the USA, we grew apart. I think this was due to me shielding her as much as possible from all the problems we had. I did not discuss anything with her. In the past few years, we've grown closer to each other than ever before. She is not as quiet as she was. She talks and smiles a lot. I think she finally got over the trauma she might have experienced during our early years in the USA.

Dad – I did not grow up with my biological dad. We didn't have any contact until 1998, when I went to visit him. He is more of a friend than a dad. I feel comfortable discussing any subject with him. He loves the outdoors and nature in general. At times he is sad that he was not able to raise me. Due to his obesity, he hasn't had a steady job since 2004. He spends most of the day recording interesting movies and TV documentaries regarding every possible subject you can think of. Dad has thousands of DVDs. I just found out that he wants me to inherit that knowledge. I was told the programs were always recorded for me.

Aunt – My aunt is only eleven years older than me. During my baby/toddler years, she played with me like I was her doll. She dressed me in female baby dresses and did all kinds of things with my perfectly white-blond curly hair. Dad freaked out: "I hope that she will not turn him into a gay," he said many times. She was more my sort of girlfriend than aunt. She took me around a lot, including on dates with her boyfriends. I often abused the situation; one time, I spat into her boyfriend's soup for no reason. I got a slap on the face from him. She sang to me and wanted me to sing with her. I started to sing, then all of a sudden sang bad words. I loved to provoke her and all adults. Oddly, she always had a lot of patience with me. She is the person who taught me camping, love for nature (especially frogs) and sports. We always played together at the summer house. She is the person who helped me to overcome fear while I was skiing my first black diamond slope. I saw her grow up from a teenager to a woman and a mother. What a pain these older girls are, I often thought. I held her long veil for hours as she was getting married, right next to the Astronomical Clock at the Old Town Square, a really magical place. She truly is an amazing person. I would not be the same person if she had not been around.

Stepdad – My stepdad is a great guy, always friendly, positive, and calm. Milan likes children, animals, and nature. He never mistreated any of us. I lived with him from age four to thirteen. He was not around much, but he always gave us whatever we wanted. We had a great life during that period.

Great-Grandmother and Great-Grandfather – She was born in 1899 and was the first of twelve children. Seven of her siblings died at an early age. She had to work from a young age to help her family. In her early teen years, she worked as a helper at a nearby sugar refinery. The lady of the household gave her meals on a regular basis. She often did not eat them, but brought the food home to help feed her brothers and sisters. The woman at the refinery noticed she was getting thinner and made her eat the meals in front of her eyes. From that point on, she was always giving her some extra food for the family. At age fourteen, she was sexually molested by a priest and has said nothing good about the Church ever since.

Great-Grandma was on the top of the pyramid in the 1930s, married to my great-granddad, who was a colonel in the army. She had servants and was forbidden to work (the norm at that time). Then WWII changed everything. Great-Granddad had to escape to England due to his anti-Nazi activities, consisting of the following. . . Early in the war, he worked as an accountant and was in charge of ordering food for the nearby concentration camp, Theresienstadt (Terezín). The food was ordered based on the inmate population; however, the calorie intake allowed per person was way below the survival level. He cooked the books and more food was smuggled in. The Nazis eventually found out and Great-Grandmother and her two kids were on their own. She was not a quitter and continued to smuggle food in much smaller amounts, by hiding the food in a stroller with Grandmother in it. When the guards were not looking, she passed the food to the inmates. One time a guard saw her and pistol-whipped her. I am 100% sure he would have killed her if my grandma had not been present. My grandmother said Great-Granddad was a patriot: "As we were walking through the town, the bells rang. My father told me this is to honor all the fallen soldiers. We than stood straight in silence for few minutes while he was saluting the whole time."

One more WWII story: there was a Hitler Youth training camp based at a castle close to the town where the family lived. These thirteen–seventeen-year-old kids were the worst of the worst. They were brainwashed by the regime from an early age and knew nothing other than Nazi Germany. One example: you could get stabbed for no reason if you walked by them and they didn't like you. They were frequently walking around the town and terrorizing the population. The regular German army personnel didn't do this. As the Russian army was approaching, these "kids" refused to leave their castle, even after the German army was long gone. I think they really thought they were invincible and the inferior Russians could not defeat them. They were, of course, all arrested. Great-Grandma worked as a nurse and the hospital had a severe shortage of nurses due to the large influx of the "walking skeletons" from the nearby camp. They were not allowed to enter the general population. They were only able to drink liquid food; any solid food would have killed them. In addition, most of them were diseased. She went to the prison to get a small group of the former Hitler Youth kids to help her to take care of the sick people. "I have six bullets in my pistol. If any one of you tries to run, I will kill all of you," she said, in a strong voice. Nobody ever ran. The kids were made to take care of the "walking skeletons." The US intelligence community knew the camps existed. I don't understand why the camps or the surrounding infrastructure were never bombed. I guess anything is possible in the name of the national security.

After the war, my great-granddad returned home, but died of cancer a few years later, at age forty-nine. This was sort of a "blessing" since the Communists persecuted anyone who'd served in the Western armies during the war, including their families. The authorities felt sorry for the widow and her small child and she was left alone. Her life turned for the worse when the Communists made the whole country poor by implementing two monetary reforms in the late 1940s and 1950s. Her older daughter, Grandma's sister, had to support the family for quite a while. Great-Grandma died a happy person, in 1983. I vaguely remember her; she was this sweet old lady that always kissed me, hugged me, and sang to me.

Grandmother and Grandfather – I always felt closer to my grandmother than my mom. As mentioned before, my mom has a certain personality. She was young and not ready to have a child when I was born. I always felt loved more by my grandmother than Mom to a certain age. Grandma is a strong woman and, to this day, is in charge of everything around the household. She kept Granddad under control, since he was a habitual drinker. He was not a drunk. On weekends, he just drank little by little to have a certain buzz. He was always fully functional. He was a sweet person who never yelled or mistreated anyone and eventually always gave in to my grandma's demands and did whatever she asked him to do. I remember that I kept stealing his empty beer bottles to buy sodas and cigarettes. He was not too happy about that. :-)

Grandma was an elementary school teacher all her life. She loves children. She was my teacher in third grade elementary and I took full advantage of the situation. I entertained the whole classroom on many occasions. They laughed like crazy, my grandma did not. I went to a different class the following year. In early February 2017, I spent a lot of time with her discussing the family's history. Every time I visit Europe, we have similar discussions. She will be eighty this year. Her physical abilities are in line with her age; however, mentally, she is as sharp as ever.

Great-Uncle and Great-Aunt – He was born in 1922, she in 1929. They dated from 1944 and stayed together until 2003, when my great-aunt died. He was her first and last. She was an even stronger woman than my grandmother. My great-uncle had it much worse at home than Granddad. They experienced the Nazis, Communists and the Velvet Revolution. Here are some stories:

My great-uncle was a chemistry college student in 1942. After the Heydrich assassination that year, the whole class next to his was taken to the Terezín concentration camp to build a swimming pool. The Nazis closed every single college and university in the country. I am not sure why the camp needed a swimming pool. This was probably the only concentration camp that had one. After the pool was completed, the whole class, guys and girls alike – his longtime friends – were killed. This story was known to me when I visited the camp a few years ago. When I saw that pool, my head began to spin, body started to shake a little and I started to have a stomachache. I had to leave the place as fast as possible. After the family recovered from the monetary reforms of the 1940s and 1950s, my great aunt and uncle had a great life. He was a biochemistry scientist and she was a director of a music school. They were allowed to travel to the West and had no shortage of money, including hard currencies. I loved spending time with them, especially at their cottage in the middle of the woods. As I am thinking about this, every generation had their summer house or a cottage. I have only great memories of them.

An Adult's Life in Communist Czechoslovakia
Life was drastically different for an adult when compared to a child's life. An adult, or anyone else for that matter, was not allowed to speak against the one-party government. You were not allowed to form an opposition group or to protest or complain at all. In the name of national security, people were being arrested and persecuted because a neighbor complained. This was very true in the 1950s, not so much in the 1980s. People were only allowed to travel to other communist countries. Only the Communist elite or important people were allowed to travel to Western countries. You were not allowed to bring back certain items across borders when returning back from both Western and Eastern countries. From East Germany, for example, all baby clothes were being confiscated and fines issued. Car interiors were totally disassembled upon the slightest suspicion that you might be smuggling forbidden items. It happened to my stepdad. This reminds me of *War on Drugs*, a National Geographic TV series filmed on the US–Mexico border. There were no choices and the advertisement industry was nonexistent. There was an abundance of most Eastern-made products, but everything was one brand. Department stores, food stores, electronics stores, and car dealerships were carrying exactly the same products.

If you wanted Western-made goods, you had to come to a special government store called Tuzex, where "bony" coupons, initially purchased with hard currency, were needed to buy goods, or you had to use the black market. The prices were ridiculous. Here are some examples: in the late 1980s, the average monthly pay per person was about 3,000 Czechoslovak crowns. Rent was about 400, a weekly grocery bill for a family of four about 300, shoes, 80, a nice dress, 200. New car – about 50,000. So, very similar to USD, in today's money. The prices, however, were for Eastern-made goods. All Western goods were smuggled across the border. A larger item meant a higher price, since it was more difficult to smuggle in, and you often had to bribe border guards. The risk of selling on the black market also increased prices, since stiff prison sentences were often imposed. Here are some examples: Sony VCR – 40,000–60,000 crowns, VHS tape: 500, original Metallica record: 700, cassette tape: 150, Levi's jeans: 1,500, used Mercedes C-Class: 200,000, skateboard: 1,000. So, when someone like my stepdad had a VCR with thirty VHS tapes, you were easily looking at 70,000 crowns' worth of stuff.

The worst was that people were not allowed to own businesses and differentiate in any way. The pay for each possible work task, regardless of performance, was written in tables. No matter how hard you worked, the pay was the same. As a result, a cab driver, butcher, produce store manager and black-market dealer were all making way more money due to stealing than a doctor, engineer, or teacher. Everyone of adult age had to work, otherwise a prison sentence would follow. A mandatory ID card was stamped by your employer. Random ID card checks were common on the streets and highways.

The TV had two channels, mostly consisting of Eastern-made programs. Only a few US shows/movies pertaining to certain subjects were allowed: anything related to the Civil War, KKK, blacks struggling in ghettos, racial inequality, poverty, natural and man-made disasters. In the 1980s, this no longer worked, the population was madly in love with Rockys and Rambos. It's a shame they don't make movies like this anymore.

My Last Years of Life in the Czech Republic
Mom secretly divorced my stepdad in 1991. As I found out later, he let her stay in the house after the divorce since she had two kids. My seven-year-old sister was his. This arrangement ended after her boyfriend moved in and started stealing and selling our household items. In January 1993, we moved with him to an apartment. They were, of course, unable to keep up with the rent so we moved to a weekend cottage my mom purchased after the divorce. The cottage was located in the secluded woods of Vltava River canyon, about one hour from Prague. The nature was gorgeous; however, the cottage did not have electricity or running water. It had a full bathroom (you had to manually bring in water from a nearby well) a septic system, kitchen, two bedrooms and central coal heating system. It was livable. The boyfriend happened to be a Czech/US citizen, so we moved to the USA in fall of 1993. It did not work out. We returned a of couple months later and lived in the cottage again. This time my stepdad got pissed (don't blame him) and took my sister away from Mom. She realized she could no longer live like this and dumped her boyfriend. We moved to a homeless shelter for single moms where we stayed until May 13 1994, then we moved permanently to the USA.

From 1992 to May 13 1994, it was strangely one of the best periods of my life. I was rarely home and spent most of the after-school time with friends. On weekends, I usually crashed at a girlfriend's house. The girls did not care that I lived at the homeless shelter. It was about us wanting to have fun and not about money. The girls liked me for who I was. It was about pure love. Parents of the seventeen–twenty-year-olds did not care, but I had to sneak in when a girl was fourteen–sixteen.

13

During this period, I always made and fully enjoyed money. A few friends and I were frequently hanging out in the Stardust slot-machine casino located in a subway station below the main Florenc bus terminal. I was involved in two scams. There was one particular slot machine, "Flash," among many roulette and video poker games, that was vulnerable to a scam. You were able to win in two ways: by rolling bars for an instant win or by accumulating chances/winnings that were later taken by pressing a button positioned at the far left of the machine. Adults at that time didn't speak much English. I (sometimes with a friend) would lure people to play the machine while at the same time covering the chances button with a hand. When the person walked away, I would than withdraw the accumulated winnings, usually between 200 to 1,000 crowns. Not bad for a middle school kid, since the average monthly pay was about 8,000. Of course, I had to pay off the bartender, usually 20%.

Second scam: my older friends, aged seventeen–thirty-five, were playing a street shell game at the subway station upper corridor near the Stardust casino, or on walkways above ground leading to the bus terminals. Multiple-player stands were strategically placed in the area. Rules of the game: a person (*skořápkář* in Czech) moves around a ball hidden in one of three cups and the player has to guess where the ball is in order to win. Nobody ever won. The guys hired undercover fake players (*volavky* in Czech), such as dirty construction workers and old retired women, to lure in unsuspecting real players. If a person ran out of cash, gold, in the form of wedding rings, necklaces, and other jewelry, was frequently used and accepted. On many occasions, I saw women crying after losing their wedding rings. I didn't give a shit, greed was good. It was a fucking gold mine, especially on Fridays when people returned home to all parts of the country with pockets full of cash after working in Prague for a week. The guys hired me and my peers to watch for police, paid about 500 crowns for four hours. A *skořápkář* would easily earn 20,000–30,000 per stand on a Friday afternoon. If police were approaching the subway corridors, I would yell a code word, "*Gajá*," and everyone would run away. I was questioned by cops on many occasions, but nothing ever happened since I was under fifteen and not legally responsible for my actions. The older friends always treated me with respect and took me in as their equal. It felt like I really belonged to their group.

We fully enjoyed the fruits of newly acquired capitalism. We blew money like crazy; we frequently drank at the casino, dined at the nearby Hilton Hotel, drove cabs around the city, bought fireworks, the older guys were buying hookers (perfectly legal in the Czech Republic), went to bowling bars and hotel pools. The city belonged to guys like us. The law changed in late 1993 and the shell game was no longer a ticketed offense, similar to a parking ticket, but became a criminal offense. After a massive undercover police operation, most adult friends went to prison and it was all over. At least I still had the "Flash" slot machine scam going on. I had to adjust my spending habits, since I was only making about 5,000 per month and my "prison" friends were no longer paying for most of the fun activities. I always tried to help my mom and gave her about 40% of what I made at any given time.

The early 1990s was a period of almost complete lawlessness in Eastern Europe. People were stealing as much as possible of what was left of the state-owned enterprises. The so-called privatization was only for certain people. The same people that stole under communism were allowed to legalize their hidden wealth overnight without any questions asked by the central tax department (IRS in the USA). My stepdad purchased a small hotel and three pubs at the same time. There were almost no consequences for this since so many people, including the politicians, were involved in it. It really was the Wild West.

Life in America – the Early Years (1994–2005)
Unfortunately, Mom started to date her crazy boyfriend again and they came up with a brilliant idea – kidnap my sister and escape to the USA. This was possible as many international treaties between the two countries had not yet been implemented. Mom, again, was not thinking rationally. It was a shame since we were a few months away from receiving a city-owned apartment reserved for single moms. The apartment was not in a ghetto, no different than any other apartments of that time. On May 13 1994, during her scheduled visitation granted by a court, we jumped on a plane and flew to the USA. Atlanta was chosen as the final destination since the plane tickets were the least expensive when compared to other cities. A cab driver took us to a cheap motel called Scottish Inn, on Delk Road in Marietta. Within a few months, my mom dumped her boyfriend and began dating the motel's manager. This actually worked out well. I was given a job as a maintenance person; I took out garbage, swept a parking lot and cut the grass. The position was paying $80 per week after rent for the room was deducted and Mom worked as a housekeeper a couple of days a week for an additional $80. We had just enough money to eat and buy some clothes once in a while. My mom was always a great and resourceful cook. To this day she can cook amazing meals from nothing.

I started attending Marietta High School in January 1995. It was a culture shock; for the first time I saw students being arrested, dogs searching for drugs and students were hanging out only in their cliques. Except for a couple friends, I kept to myself and tried to learn as much as possible. I frequently used a dictionary to translate the reading material before I was able to learn it. ESOL was the only different class I attended. In the summer of 1995, the motel opened a kitchen to accompany the existing bar. I was given a second job – flip burgers, fry wings, and make sandwiches. The place was successful and remained open after the summer was over. This was great news, since I didn't have to take out the garbage anymore. Nevertheless, the weekdays were long. I got up at 6.30 a.m. and went to school, then slept for an hour after returning home and worked from 5–11 p.m. I did my homework between 11 p.m. and 1 a.m. On weekends, I mostly slept. I couldn't date girls at all because we didn't have a car. The school bus was great, but it was unable to take me to a potential girlfriend. The city had no practical public transportation network. I felt most girls would not want to date me because I was so poor. I didn't have the time or energy for it, anyway. "What a fucked-up life, what a fucked-up country; a way different country than I knew from my beloved movies," I often thought to myself. I missed my life and everyone in the Czech Republic. I wanted to go back so badly, but knew I could not. If I did, my sister would have been taken away from Mom. There is no way my mom would have made it in the USA alone. I was always positive and believed our lives would change once we received a green card. I am proud of myself. To this day, I never drank, did drugs (except weed on few occasions) or took prescription medications, such as Xanax. This would probably have helped a lot. I've always believed my thinking has to remain "natural," free of drugs and alcohol, to overcome life's difficulties.

After two years, we still did not have the green cards. Our beloved African Americans at the Atlanta INS were really making our stay in the USA enjoyable. Not. They were rude, snappy, sarcastic, and were always coming up with additional paperwork demands after each visit. We were not able to defend ourselves in any way. We were treated as undocumented animals. Maybe they had been taught that this behavior could somehow make up for all the injustices that happened to their people in the past four hundred years.

The motel manager boyfriend dumped my mom and we were thrown out on the street. She was not able to comprehend what was happening and went back to see him. He called the cops and she was thrown in jail for trespassing. My sister, eleven years of age, and I were left penniless in a motel on Cobb Parkway. Fortunately, the ex-boyfriend prepaid the room for one week. Our grandfather flew in within a couple days, bailed Mom out of jail and took us down to Fort Lauderdale, FL.

Unfortunately, Grandpa, Grandma and two aunts, who moved from Switzerland to the USA in 1980, lived in a two-bedroom house. The three of us had to sleep in the living room. Mom was constantly arguing with all the relatives. Every day at the house was a hell on Earth. I stayed away as much as possible. One day, out of the blue and without any warnings, Mom disappeared from the house and went to Atlanta to see her boyfriend, and was arrested again. It was clear to me that her kindergarten schoolteacher career, that she hoped to restart, was over for the rest of her life. She was such a great teacher. It's a shame; once again she had made an irrational decision. My aunt found me a part-time job fixing shoes. The shop owner, Dave, was a retired oil man and had a great personality. He taught me a lot. For example: "After you get married, you'll have sex with your wife almost daily and it's great. But after a few years, it's like taking a shit. I know you don't believe me," he said on one occasion. I hung around the store as much as possible. We lived a couple miles from a beach and about a mile from my new high school. I often rollerbladed or skateboarded to the beach and the school. I had no friends, therefore mostly kept to myself, and was fascinated by Marilyn Manson, my favorite artist of that time. He is still one of my favorite artists to this day, especially his "Sweet Dreams (Are Made of This)" song. The video clip is great.

Fort Lauderdale High School was a real dump. The Whites were in the minority. I had not seen a real-life Black person until summer 1988. It was full of Haitians, other Blacks, Hispanics and, of course, security guards. Many kids behaved like animals. It felt more like a prison than a school. I missed my old high school in Marietta. I was pissed off, but at the same time felt sorry for the kids. Why not put them out of their misery? I constantly reminded myself of the perfect childhood I had in the communist Czechoslovakia. One day I borrowed *Mein Kampf* from the school library. The book provided many answers to my confused mind and I felt really excited as I was reading it. I seriously thought about devoting the rest of my life to reinventing the Nazi Party and exterminating all the non-Whites, plus other undesirable elements, such as gays and handicapped people. My dream was to create the socialist paradise/private ownership hybrid totalitarian state for the beautiful Aryan race in the USA and eventually in the rest of the world. I would simply finish what Hitler started. I am not proud of this. I was eighteen, confused, lost and hopeless, without any guidance and hope for the future. This was the answer to my American Dream. I cried a lot in private, was depressed and sexually unsatisfied. At that age, you can only jerk off so many times. The last time I had a girlfriend was in the Czech Republic. My life in the USA started to take its toll on me.

In spring of 1997, we finally received our green cards. The INS in Miami was controlled by Cubans and we were finally treated like human beings. We forgot to submit another green card application because I had reached the age of eighteen. The immigration officer said, "Don't worry about it," genuinely smiled and approved my green card application immediately. What a difference, I didn't think those kinds of people lived in America. I only knew them from the movies. I was hired as a security guard, Mom as a hotel housekeeper, and we moved out of the house at last. After a couple months, we moved back to Atlanta without jobs lined up, but Mom for some reason wanted to go back to Florida. Granddad did not take us into the house, so we drove back to Atlanta the same day. Our car, a 1985 Cadillac Coupe Deville, broke down in Valdosta. It was a real piece of shit, a "grandpa must-have mobile." I wanted a Honda Civic and, of course, my grandpa said NO. We arrived in Atlanta with about $800 and no jobs. Fortunately, it was the middle of summer. I told my mom in secret, "Let's go to Walmart and buy a $30-dollar tent and stay in a campground at Lake Allatoona. Let's not say anything to sister, she is only thirteen. We can bullshit her that we want to camp for a while, since it is such nice weather. As soon as one of us gets a job, we get a motel room." Within a week, I found a waiter position at Cracker Barrel in Marietta and we moved to the Super 8 on Delk Road. I went back to my old high school to finish my senior year. Mom found another housekeeping job. She was unable to find a teacher's position due to her criminal record. Mom was unable to comprehend this since, in her mind, she was arrested unjustly. The Super 8 was not much better than the Scottish Inn, next door. I saw in the news that someone was murdered a few doors from mine. There was police tape all over the door. My car was constantly broken into, so I left it open with the windows down.

At age nineteen, I found a waiter job at Houston's Restaurant on Powers Ferry Road, and finally started to make decent money (average $150 cash per night) and purchased a house. I dated a few girls, but it was always the same story. They cared mostly about themselves and money. One of them was crazy and abusive. I was not able to find a normal girl. I did not feel loved, like I did by the Czech girls. I stopped dating again.

Ronnee, I was getting tired, tired of all this bullshit.

My life was not satisfying me at all. So, I did the following for a few years: I got up at 9 a.m. and went to the gym. I had lunch at 12 p.m. and rode my bicycle by Chattahoochee River. Then I went to the pool to get some tan. And lastly, at 4.30 p.m., I went to work. This is what kept me going. I also travelled to Europe about four times a year and partied like crazy. Every time I went to Europe, it felt exactly like the early 1990s. I slipped into a depression after returning from each trip. It got to the point where I was unable to handle any seemingly miniscule tasks, such as finding a plumber to fix a toilet. I had chest pains, sweat on my face and breathed faster. I had to stop and let someone else do it. I was not going to school or doing anything with my life at all. I had two good friends and that was it.

The only exception was the gym and the outdoors. The place felt like home and the people were great. In 1998, I joined Main Event Fitness on Powers Ferry Road, owned by wrestling legend Lex Luger. Within a few years, I met many interesting people, such as Diamond Dallas Page, Kevin Nash, Disco Inferno, and Scott Steiner. I did not have a people's personality anymore, so I didn't hang out with them and pursued other opportunities. The only person that was more of a friend was Lex Luger. He had a great business model. The strippers from nearby clubs were given free memberships if they attended so many hours per week. This was brilliant, since it attracted a lot of guys. You could walk in there on Monday morning at 10 a.m. and the place was full of good-looking women. In addition, he had the wrestlers and nitro girls coming in. I felt small among all the meatheads and considered taking a few cycles of steroids to beef up. The good news was that I already had a "drug free" mindset and personally knew several people that had died due to steroid usage. At my peak, I benched 335 pounds, two repetitions, squatted 395 pounds, 10 times, and curled 60-pound dumbbells 12 times in each hand. I started to feel good about myself again. In 2001, Ted Turner sold WCW to WWE, Luger got into legal trouble (girlfriend overdosed, steroid dealer) and almost went to prison. Fortunately, he was able to find a "good" lawyer and there was no prison time. He was completely paralyzed from a nerve impingement, but fully recovered. He is currently an old, broken man. The gym eventually closed.

My dream at the time was to move back to the Czech Republic. Again, I couldn't do it because my sister was in college. I wanted her to have a stable home and concentrate on studies. She qualified for the HOPE Scholarship, therefore graduated debt-free. It was such a pleasure to see her graduate. Everything bad that ever happened to us was so worth it.

My life was not bad either. I lived in a decent house, was traveling a lot, worked at the restaurant and sold art on the side. I was selling framed posters of wild animals, scenery, rappers, black Jesuses, Scarfaces, Sopranos and other ethnic art at a gas station (on the street) on Windy Hill Road to our brothers and sisters. For a short period of time, I also sold fake Gucci, Prada, and Ferragamo purses for $30 a pop. I had a fake business license. It worked on the cops, but not on the code enforcement. It lasted for a couple years and it was great. The most I ever made was $1,800 cash one Saturday in 2003, when Atlanta hosted the All-Star basketball game. I sold every single large picture that day. On the street, I met many interesting personalities and started to understand the Atlanta Black community.

I always loved music, all kinds of music. It kept me relaxed and I was always able to escape reality. Anything from classical to heavy metal would do the job. These are my favorite artists, albums and songs:

Metallica's *...And Justice For All* album is a masterpiece. There are two songs on this album that stand out: "To Live Is To Die" and "Blackened." It feels great listening to those two songs. The first thirty-five seconds of "Blackened" is the most amazing musical segment (including classical) I have heard in my entire life. It feels like I am in a different dimension, especially when it's played loud. I have my eyes closed, can barely breathe and my whole body slightly shakes and tingles. I highly recommend watching the 1989 Seattle "Live Shit: Binge & Purge" concert. This is the raw, pure, young, crazy and uncorrupted Metallica at its finest. It is a couple years before the commercial success of the *Black* album. After that, the band gave in to the music industry's demands to appease the mainstream public. The core fans were sold out and the band was never the same. Other great bands of this era are: Slayer – the *Reign In Blood* album, and especially the "Angel of Death" song – Kreator, Sodom, Sepultura, Megadeth, and Helloween.

And then, for no reason at all, with the flip of a switch, while listening to the above bands, I started listening to the following music: Roxette's *Joyride* album; Bonnie Tyler, "Total Eclipse of the Heart;" Belinda Carlisle's songs, "Heaven is a Place on Earth" and "I Get Weak;" Bryan Adams' songs, "(Everything I Do) I Do It For You" and "All For One;" Bon Jovi, "Always;" Guns N' Roses, "Don't Cry;" Enigma, "Return to Innocence;" Cindy Lauper; Meatloaf; Cinderella; Scorpions, "Send me an Angel" and "Still Loving You;" Def Leppard; Aerosmith; Queen; and, of course, Michael Jackson. Michael is the perfect by-product of capitalism. He was at the right place at the right time. He is the artist for all people. I have the utmost respect for him. He changed the world.

After listening to the above musical combination, I am in a perfect emotional harmony and can sleep like a baby. I have sweet dreams on many nights.

And there is one exception to the above. It is The Smashing Pumpkins band, with *Siamese Dream*, *Mellon Collie and the Infinite Sadness*, and *Gish* albums. Filter and Bush are two other bands. These are the only three bands that have the perfect combination of soft and hard music. I can listen to these songs over and over again, almost endlessly.

Later Years – 2005 to the present
I met my wife in the fall of 2005. She was already packed and ready to go back home to the Czech Republic. It was love at first sight and we got

married in July 2006. I knew my life had to change in order to keep her. I constantly reminded myself of what she would expect Mr. Perfect to do. I was hiding my cycles of depression very well and was not saying much about my past life. I pretended to be this outgoing, friendly, and social person. Inside of me however, it was extremely difficult to meet new people and start relationships. I hated to network. I did not want to know people that I knew were never going to be my real friends. I resisted social media for as long as I could without becoming known as "weird." This is the main reason I chose to study accounting over professional sales. What a mistake, as I later discovered.

I went to Kennesaw State in 2009 and graduated in 2011 with a 3.6 GPA. I had to work full time. My first daughter, Teresa, was born in 2009. My wife got a job as a flight attendant. Life was great, the two and later three of us frequently travelled to Europe for free.

Shortly after graduation in May 2011, I found a job in indirect tax at Thomson Reuters. The tax division was purchased by KPMG two months later. The Big Four accounting firms are a classic pyramid scheme. The bottom 90% of the employees are just numbers, expendable and replaceable at any given time. Those employees are worked to death without the slightest consideration regarding their health and general well-being. During the tax season, sixteen-hour days are the norm. It is all about deadlines and the mighty dollar. Not all was bad. I learned a lot and met many interesting people. Most of my co-workers were hard-working people willing to step up and help others on their own, when needed. I liked the people but hated the work culture.

In late summer of 2014, I received two simultaneous offers through a local placement agency specializing in finance. I chose to work for a company called Immucor, a medium-size medical manufacturer. I was hired by a very attractive lady named Leah. She was in her late forties, had been married for twenty years and had two daughters. I am not sure about the marriage. Her husband never took her on vacation without her in-laws. I started to like her at the initial interview. There was longer than normal eye contact between us on several occasions. It did not feel like an interview at all. It felt like a nice conversation with a sweet lady.

I remember my first day at the office like it was yesterday. I was waiting in front of the finance section of the building. And there she was, opening the glass front door, wearing a certain dress. She looked absolutely stunning. *Ronnee, the dress was the same length as the white skirt you wore on many occasions at lunch.* The dress was not long, but not too short, either. She knew exactly what she could get away with. In my mind, it was a welcome party exceeding my wildest expectations. At first, I tried not to get distracted too much. She was still my boss and I wanted to do my duties as best I could. I had to learn the processes as fast as possible since the temporary person was leaving soon. Therefore, I kept to myself and focused on the work. Leah approached me and wanted to flirt on many occasions. I liked it, I liked it so much that I was unable to react in the way she would have expected me to. I mostly kept silent. I'd never experienced flirting in my life (way different from when you are fifteen years old). It was so new to me. It was gorgeous, electrifying, an indescribable feeling.

On a daily basis she smiled at me, was relaxed and made me feel great about myself. She eventually stopped the verbal flirting. We never discussed job performance. It was always understood that I would do my part. She did not have to supervise me. In her office, I really enjoyed us having prolonged eye contact accompanied by silence. It was perfect, since she kept the window blinds mostly closed. On one occasion, I was sitting there across her desk. I started to undress her using my eyes only. I moved very slowly from her waist until our eyes met. I had a feeling that being any closer, something magical would have happened between us. I've always felt there is a deeper connection once you look through the eyes of a person. This was the longest eye contact I had experienced to that day. It felt so good, until I was unable to take it any longer. I was the first to move my head. She did the same and smiled a little in a very satisfied way. This only happened one time.

In May, a few weeks before my vacation, I asked Leah to have lunch with me. Oddly, the two of us had never had lunch alone. Her face froze and eyes widened. "I can't today," she replied, in a surprised way.

"Let me know of a good time," I said to her in a non-caring way. She never brought it up again.

I returned from the European vacation in early June 2015 and wanted to see Leah to tell her about my trip. I missed her since we hadn't talked for almost two weeks. As soon as I entered her office, I noticed the pictures of her daughters were no longer there. "Hi, Joseph, how was your trip? My last day at Immucor is in two weeks, sorry," she said, without any kind of emotion.

All of a sudden, I felt a huge weight on my shoulders, I could hardly keep my eyes focused. The world collapsed around me. I was in a twilight zone. Of course, I pulled myself together fairly quickly, then asked her a few questions, wished her good luck and left the office. I knew in the back of my mind this might happen someday. "Why so soon, why this soon? She promised a few weeks ago to teach me corporate income tax," I thought to myself. In those two weeks, I had difficulty concentrating and completing everyday work-related tasks. At home, my mind was somewhere else until my wife and aunt, who was visiting from the EU, asked me what was wrong. I kept waking up several times a night. During this period, I realized that I had fallen in love with Leah a

22

long time ago. My mind was in a great dilemma; should I tell her about my true feelings or should I continue to maintain our professional relationship? I chose to maintain the current relationship and asked her the next day, "Leah, I would like to work for you again. Once you settle in, please let me know if there is an open position on your team." She smiled a little and explained the circumstances of her new company, PulteGroup. Due to the corporate headquarter relocation from Michigan to Atlanta, a brand-new tax team was currently being built. "Director of Federal Tax and Audit" was her new title. She was a manager in her present position. Leah had already hired her tax manager, Corey. "He is great," she said, and smiled again.

In early July 2015, about a week into her new job, I received an email from Leah asking if I would like to interview at PulteGroup and work for her again. I could not believe this and read the email several times. The answer was, "Yes."

On the day of the initial interview, Leah greeted me at the lobby reception area. I had not seen her for several months prior to this moment. Our eyes met at full stare for several seconds at close distance of about a foot. We did not blink at all. It was hot, lustful, and exciting. We were so in tune with each other. "Was this the interview?" I thought to myself. The interview process was a joke. Everyone was really friendly and I was not asked any technical questions. It didn't feel like an interview at all. Everyone knew I wasn't qualified for the position. Corporate income tax is way different from sales/use and property tax.

My first day at PulteGroup was on October 19 2015. I was hired as a tax specialist and had an exciting career ahead of me. My mentor/teacher was the person I was in love with. "Perfect, nothing can go wrong." Those and similar thoughts were constantly racing in my head. I was really excited, but nervous at the same time. I was looking forward to having a nice conversation with Leah. Oh, it was so long since the two of us had spoken in private. I had a brilliant plan. I was going to thank her for hiring me and offer to buy her lunch. We were finally going to have a private moment together, away from the office. I was so sure the answer would be "yes" since she indirectly already promised me shortly before departing Immucor.

All this went to shit; during our conversation in her office she wanted to flirt verbally. Again, my responses were the "silence." After several attempts, she was irritated and gave up. I proceeded with my plan and asked the question. She gave me the "What the fuck are you thinking?" look and I left her office shortly after, disappointed and embarrassed. "I failed my teacher again. She was probably looking forward to finally flirting with me verbally. What a disappointment. I fucked up so badly. Why was I so preoccupied with that stupid lunch?"

These were my confused thoughts. From that point on, we hardly ever spoke.

Manager, Corey, was in Leah's office daily. They spoke for hours and had a great time. Unfortunately for me, my cubicle was close by and I was forced to listen to the conversations. I was not jealous of Corey. He was a great person with an amazing personality. I was more disappointed in Leah; she was the director and able to set her own rules. To this day, I can't figure out how she was able to get me the job. It was a great job and I was not qualified at all. She knew that I enjoyed talking with her. She never invited me to come to her office and talk for at least a few minutes on some sort of regular basis. I understood that I was not working for her directly and things were not going to be the same as before.

I was four levels below her and, of course, was not able to "hang out" in her office. The VPs, other directors, and managers surrounded her office. At Immucor, it had just been the two of us. I missed that setting so much.

The position involved substantial travel to Michigan until March 2016, the deadline for legacy to current tax team transition. I felt bad for the Michigan team, especially after I met everyone in person, because they all were losing their jobs. This was due to the following reason. Also, here is some background info on the company.

Bill Pulte founded the company from nothing in the 1950s. He built the first Pulte house and sold it for $10,000. The company grew to become the largest residential builder in the USA, with over $6 billion annual revenue in 2015. Bill always placed strong emphasis on his employees. It was not unusual for someone to work at the company for thirty years. Pulte was always a Michigan company, a great company to work for. It answered the "American Dream" question for many people. Bill retired from active operations in 2010. A couple years after his retirement, Richard Dugas Jr, CEO since 2003, announced behind Bill's back that the company would be moving to Atlanta. He made the announcement in the Michigan office, in front of all the corporate employees. It was a short announcement and he and his security guard left abruptly. According to rumors, Richard wanted to live in Atlanta to pursue a career in politics. Some of the employees were offered jobs in Atlanta. Who would want to move? Especially if all their relatives lived close by. None of the eighteen tax department employees, including the VP, accepted offers. *Ronnee, after the facts became known to me, I wanted this guy to disappear from Pulte as fast as possible.* It appeared Richard didn't care about his Michigan employees. They all were just numbers to him. He cared about himself and apparently only loved himself. In Atlanta, he hired a custom builder and not PulteGroup to build his mansion. That is like Ford's CEO driving a Ferrari to work. It was an insult to everyone at Pulte. It makes me sick. In my opinion, Richard was the worst of the worst.

By January 2016, everyone in Atlanta was hired. The group was getting along really well and everyone had a great personality, an unusual feature for a tax accountant. The last trip to Michigan was in January 2016. This was the best trip to date. Apart from work, it looked like Leah and I would finally open up to each other again. Flirting aside, it was necessary, so we would be able to work together going forward. About eight of us went to a karaoke bar. Leah tried to verbally flirt with me for the last time. I blew it again. She spent the rest of the evening around Corey. I played pool with a manager named Rick. The next day, an even smaller group went skiing. Leah and I finally spoke in a friendly and relaxed way on ski lifts and in the cafeteria. This was the best day at Pulte so far.

The first day after we returned from Michigan, I went to see Leah in her office. "Can you please consider mentoring me? I know we talked about it before," was the initial question.

"Yes, like I will everyone else. You need to get with the managers and do a good job if you want to score some points with me," she replied. We had never had a performance-related discussion before. This threw me off, but I kept pushing my luck.

"We had a great relationship at Immucor and I miss it."

She smiled to herself and said, "So you're not getting it, right?" I could not believe my ears. We talked about a few more things and I left her office.

At that point I realized she may have actually enjoyed having me around. She knew I needed her and couldn't do anything about it. Every day at that office was emotional torture. She had to know I heard most of her conversations. There is only so much a person can take. Everyone has a breaking point. "Maybe if I tell her how I feel about her, she would figure out a way of not hurting me anymore," I said to myself, many times.

On Wednesday, January 23 2016, first thing in the morning, I remember the following conversation word by word, like it happened yesterday: "Leah, I need a few minutes of your time."

"OK," she said. I closed the door and we sat down.

"I started to have feelings for you in January, a year ago," I said.

"Really, you did?" was her initial response as she smiled a little.

"Yes, I did, and I was hiding those feelings as much as I could. You are married, I am married, that sort of thing. Then you left and just the thought that I would not be able to see you and talk to you was overwhelming. I actually thought more about you than the job. What a

25

mistake! When you hired me for the second time, I was not able to handle the situation and look what happened. I am not sure when the last time was that this happened to you, but you can't even think clearly. The last time it happened to me was with Romana, ten years ago, and I ended up marrying her. With you, it was never about promotions, scoring points, and money."

"Well, thank you for telling me this. I have to think about what to do next," she said, as her body started to shake a little bit. She then reached into her drawer, took and opened a bottle of pills, and shoved the bottle into her mouth. She then ran outside, probably to a restroom.

Not knowing what to do, I went back to my desk. In a few minutes, I realized I had said a little too much. I wanted to see if she was OK and went back to her office. She was resting her head on a desk so I was unable to see her face. "Please don't do anything. I'll get together with the managers and stay out of your way as much as possible. I am over this," I said. She then slowly raised her head up and down in agreement and was crying silently. I tried to keep cool as much as possible and continued with daily tasks. I periodically glanced into her office to make sure she was not overdosing on those pills. I hoped she didn't swallow any.

The next morning the VP of tax, Kim, called me into her office. She calmly and in almost a friendly way asked about the incident. I truthfully explained the situation with as little detail as possible about the feelings I had for Leah when she left Immucor.

"But you don't have those feelings for her anymore, right?" Kim asked.

"That is correct, I don't," I replied.

"Good, because she does not have those feelings for you and even if she did, you would both be fired. She can't manage you anymore. Rick will be your new manager, effective immediately. Nobody will know the details and we will move forward."

I could not believe I wasn't fired. That outcome was expected 100%.

After this conversation, I kept to myself and concentrated on work. Leah, however, was walking around the office in a fast, almost irritable manner. You could tell she was not doing too well. I hoped she would not fall apart. On Friday afternoon, at 3 p.m., she had a meeting with Corey and my new manager, Rick. I am not sure what was discussed, but nobody returned to their desks and it was already way past 5 p.m.

On the following Monday, Corey and Leah walked in at the same time. Leah took a much longer route around half of the floor so she did not have to pass my cubicle. (This continued almost every day.) I knew she had broken down and told the details to Corey and Rick. I could see it in their eyes, the way they were looking at me. I was able to see the fear in their eyes. At that point I knew my days at Pulte were numbered.

It was a fucked-up situation; a director was accommodating an entry-level employee four levels below hers by taking a longer route around the floor to her office on a daily basis. All communication, verbal and written, went indirectly via managers. I was not allowed to enter her office under any circumstances. It felt like she had an office restraining order against me. I was really sad and felt awful that things had turned out this way. From that point on, I was in pure survival mode. I tried to maintain an image of an outgoing employee fully devoted to his work. I went out with some members of the tax team to lunch almost every Friday. I helped everyone as much as possible. This lasted until the middle of March.

On March 17 2016, the whole tax department was scheduled to have a working lunch with the CEO, Richard Dugas. The whole team, especially the VP, Kim, was excited, but nervous at the same time. It is unusual for the CEO of such a large company to devote two hours of his or her time to such a small group. The meeting was held at the main conference room next to the CEO's office. The meeting was a lunch/PowerPoint presentation hosted by Richard and, lastly, questions asked by employees directly to the CEO on any subject.

I had one question prepared: "As a leader, are you still continuing to learn and develop or are you reaching, or have you reached, a certain point where you can say to yourself, 'I've seen it all, there is nothing that can surprise me anymore.'" To this day, I don't know why I prepared such a long question.

My turn came and I asked the question. "As a leader, are you still continuing to learn and develop or are you reaching, or have you reached, a certain point where you can say to yourself—"

Richard abruptly interrupted me and made the following comment, "I am one foot in the grave."

I immediately began to laugh. It was a genuine laugh but I laughed loudly. Out of the eighteen-person tax department, I was the only one who laughed.

I was fired the next day. They were not able to fire me for that reason, therefore a couple of reasons were made up: 1) I described in detail what my wife and I were doing in a Jacuzzi while vacationing in the mountains. Not true. I only said to Corey and Rick that we were playing in the Jacuzzi and to use their imagination for the rest. Anybody can play in a Jacuzzi. This was clearly a gray area. 2) I showed a picture of my naked wife to a manager named Phil. Untrue, I showed him a picture of my wife dressed in lingerie. This was a Victoria's Secret picture mailed frequently via catalogs. I knew I was being fired, but maintained my position in a meeting with the HR Director. When I left the building, it felt like a heavy boulder just fell off my shoulders. I felt so light and free. I was so happy this bullshit was finally over. When I arrived home, I broke down and cried loudly. I realized that I would never speak with and see Leah again. It is extremely difficult to get rid of those feelings, no matter how hard you try.

On Monday, March 21 2016, Pulte's board director, James Grosfeld, Bill Pulte and his grandson had a private meeting with Richard Dugas to tell him to step down by the end of May 2016 or "There would be a war!" It was all over the news. It gave me such pleasure to see this person go one business day after he fired me. All the legacy Michigan employees finally got their revenge. Bill Pulte lost a few battles, but ultimately won the war.

The next few weeks were not easy. I was unemployed, unable to focus, and thought about Leah on many occasions.

One day, I received a call from the same recruiting agency that arranged the 2014 interview at Immucor. I was told that a company named Argos was looking for someone to be hired immediately with no interview. The position was temp to perm. It was strange and I was skeptical at first. A woman named Sue would be my manager. "Great, I can't interview at this stage and can't focus on anything anyway. Maybe she'll give me a break, she is a woman," I thought to myself. I called back the agency and accepted the position. Going back to normal was proving increasingly difficult. I was thinking about Leah on a daily basis. I managed, however, to pull myself together. Sue was a great manager. She was fair, helpful and had a great personality. I really enjoyed working for her. We spoke almost every morning about subjects not related to work. This helped me to stay focused and to think positively.

Argos is a Colombian company with a slightly different work culture than your typical American corporation. The employees were a mix of US-born and legacy Colombian-born people. The people, especially the Colombians, were more relaxed and friendly. The place was full of good-looking women. The Colombian employees were taking turns working in the USA, you always saw new faces. Oh, the women were so hot. I wished I was working in Colombia, where the labor laws were so different compared to the USA. "It would be so easy to get in their panties." I questioned myself liked this several times. I loved the place. It almost felt like being in Europe. One odd thing was the cafeteria. It was located on the main floor (out of two) and was the only place that had a microwave. If you brought a lunch from home, as I did most of the time, you had to go there to warm it up. I went there almost every day and noticed that between 12 p.m. and 1 p.m., pretty much the same twelve people were there on any given day. Among the group, there were four women. They all looked different and beautiful in their own way. One of them looked like she was in her late thirties to early forties and had a distinct European look. The kind of look I was used to when living in the Czech Republic. She was very attractive. It later turned out that she was the company's attorney.

I went to the cafeteria almost daily but never introduced myself to the four women. I kept to myself, as I was trying to get over Leah. Until one day, about two months later, Sue was at the cafeteria and introduced me to the group. We talked ever since. At first, we would say "Hi" to each other and say a few sentences. In a few weeks, the European lady, named Ronnee, pulled her chair away from the group and sat with me at a table right next to the two other women. From that point on, the conversations intensified. Gradually, we spoke about anything, you name it. I was having lunch with one or more of the women three times a week. It was like a lottery. I never knew who was going to be there. I felt nervous. I loved feeling nervous, excited, and unprepared for the conversations with any of the women. Here is some background on my female friends.

Ronnee – Attorney, forty-eight years old, married with three kids, and husband from Denmark. She is very intelligent, always positive and smiling. She looks absolutely gorgeous. She is the sweetest person I've met in my life. I can't even describe the feelings I had every time I saw her. We have a lot in common, since her husband has the exact same views as I have on social aspects of life. He is skinny and blond, just like me. I loved talking with her. The conversations were sweet and spicy when we were alone. I felt comfortable discussing any subject with her; anything from everyday problems to giving birth and to love. I was never this comfortable with anyone in my life. I enjoyed the many occasions when she teased me with her short skirt. She always looked directly into my eyes.

Jessica – Branding and Communications Manager, thirty-two years old, married with no kids, has three dogs, husband is an IT professional. She is extremely smart with instant reactions and opinions on any subject discussed. Many times, I had difficulty keeping up with the conversations. We flirted a few times; however, I always had a hard time getting to know her better. I was unable to see through her eyes as she wore glasses. It's a shame since her face is so sweet. She has nice soft reddish hair. She was always friendly, happy, and forthcoming. I really felt comfortable being around her. She is one of those rare people you could trust with your life.

Christine – Credit Manager, forty-one years old, married with two kids. Many times, it appeared that she was the "leader" of the group. She talked a lot and had many great stories. I feel sorry for her because she had a rough childhood. I never found out the details, but I have a feeling it was pretty bad. She has nice dark and curly hair, thick eyelashes and beautiful large brown eyes. I loved when our eyes met at full stare, multiple times. On one occasion, the stare lasted more than five seconds, probably more like ten seconds. I started to feel excited and nervous. She, however, was the first to look elsewhere. She genuinely smiled after this happened. I always loved to see her smile and being happy.

Antonia – Over forty, married with two kids, if I remember correctly. I only had lunch with her a few times before she left the company. It was always fun when the two of us talked. We have a lot in common, since both of us grew up in Eastern Europe. She definitely was the icebreaker regarding sexual conversations. She came from a similar culture and I knew exactly what I could get away with. On one occasion, we spoke like this in front of the group and everyone else warmed up.

By September 2016, I was having so much fun that I was able to not think about Leah anymore. I was a happy person again, enjoying everyday life. I really liked the lunches and a lot of times thought about what might happen at the next lunch.

In early December 2016, it was the Thursday lunch that stood above all the others. For the past two lunches prior to this one, Ronnee's boss Mark showed up at the cafeteria. He saw me and Ronnee sitting close to each other twice in a row. Mark rarely ever went to the cafeteria; consequently, I thought Ronnee and I could eventually get into some sort of trouble. This preceded the following event that happened on the Friday the prior week: Christine and I had a long conversation with Ronnee at her desk. Towards the end, Mark walked by, didn't say anything, but he was clearly pissed off.

Back to the Thursday lunch; strangely enough, I had a conference call scheduled with external auditors, PWC (our corporate return preparers) and everyone, starting at the bottom with me all the way to the Colombian bosses. The meeting was scheduled from 12 p.m. to 1 p.m. I needed to disappear for a few minutes and talk to Ronnee regarding my opinion about Mark and the situation. At about 12.30 p.m., I placed the phone on silent and went to Sue to excuse myself. "I need to go to the bathroom. I don't feel so good." I arrived at the cafeteria and saw Christine, Jessica, and Ronnee sitting at one small table. I pulled a chair from an adjacent table and sat next to Ronnee. "Ronnee," I said in a moderate tone of voice.

"Yes, Joseph," she replied and turned her head so we were able to see each other. At this point, we were about a foot from one another and our eyes locked in full stare. We kept looking into each other's eyes and did not blink for the remainder of the conversation.

"Yesterday, I took some papers that needed to be signed and went to his office," I said.

"Mark's?" she asked.

"Yes," I replied, and continued, "We had a great conversation," (she smiled a little) "and I don't think there will be any problems going forward with—"

"Mark," Ronnee completed the sentence. She looked away and continued to speak, saying, "If you think so," then looked back into my eyes. And then it happened. We were locked in, our eyes were teasing each other in an indescribable, sexual, and lustful way. We were the only two people left in the entire Universe. We were so in tune with one another. It was an immense tease that left my mind and body completely weak, begging for more. I had never experienced anything close to this in my entire life. We were having eye sex in the cafeteria with Jessica and Christine witnessing the whole event. This made it so much hotter since it happened in public. I saw Ronnee was enjoying the moment as she then looked away.

I continued my sentence. "On Friday he was pissed, right, Christine?" She confirmed by slowly moving her head up and down, avoiding any sort of eye contact with me. I think she was scared to death. I therefore continued, "And then he showed up here twice in a row. That is so unusual." Shortly after, I excused myself since I had to get back on the conference call. This was the last time all three of us had lunch together.

The next week, Jessica left for Ireland and Christine refused to talk to me. I had one more lunch with Ronnee. We only discussed everyday things. The next day, I gave her a Christmas card and a teddy bear, and suggested we go out for lunch to a restaurant. I scared her a little bit since she returned the teddy bear to me stating "legal reasons." After the holidays, I saw the three girls at lunch for the last time. They actually blew me off by ignoring me and chatting about female-related items. I think they enjoyed this very much since I was sitting right next to them, alone, for the most part "high and dry." After this lunch I began to get sick. I cannot describe how I felt at certain points. I don't remember much from this period. I later found out indirectly from my wife that I cussed a few people out and walked out of the building. I was fired from Argos and eventually ended up in jail and a hospital. I don't remember almost anything from that period, either.

Final Thoughts

Where to begin? What happened? What will happen next? I guess I should start from the beginning. As a young child, I had everything that a child could possibly have. I was raised by four women of different generations. Each gave me something different. They all loved me and wanted to spend every second of their free time with me. I was hugged, sang to and cared for. In other words, I was loved beyond imagination. I was raised to be part of "nature." *Ronnee, who has this? How many people in the world are raised like this anymore?* You can't put babies and toddlers in front of a television. Their undeveloped brains can't process the fast-paced, choppy images of TV light. The images damage their little brains. A baby/toddler that is raised in front of a TV played even in the background doesn't fully develop emotionally. The emotions such as empathy, love, and love for nature, caring/enjoying simple things and feelings for music will never develop to their full potential. The final nail in the coffin is a babysitter. Every child has the right to be with Mom. Babies have to be nurtured and loved by their mothers. It is impossible to replace a mother's love. Who else than a mother can love a child at an early age? Babysitters only watch the kids, they don't love them. Sadly, to my knowledge, the Czech Republic is the only country in the world where women are paid to be at home with their children for two to four years. The same amount of money (equal to about 60% of the average yearly pay) is divided between the chosen years. Why doesn't the richest country in the world have this benefit for its people? Is our military more important to us than our youngest citizens? Let's not even discuss the health care system. That's another story.

I experienced the worst and the best of humanity. I indirectly experienced Nazi Germany via real stories that happened to my family during WWII. Grandmother told me most of the stories. I fully experienced the events of the 1989 Velvet Revolution. Everyone came together to make a real change. The government will never do it for you. It has to come from the bottom, from within the people.

I experienced the best and the worst of socialism. I could not ask for a better childhood. It was a carefree, safe and beautiful childhood. The whole country belonged to the children. The parents and the government took really good care of all children. The adults had it bad. They became slaves to the totalitarian regime. They were not allowed to think freely. This eventually killed their spirits, and many drank themselves to death. This is still a widespread problem in today's Russia.

I experienced the worst and the best of capitalism. From the age of fifteen to nineteen, I lived in poverty and was destined for failure. I've seen it all around me. Lives being destroyed due to drugs, poverty, and lack of education. The penal system is designed to destroy a person, not to correct that person. Higher education is mostly for the chosen ones. Yes, anyone can graduate from college, but a poor person will have to acquire massive student debts. With strong emphasis on materialism and to live the so-called "American Dream," most people will work to pay interest for the rest of their lives, so they can buy things they mostly don't need. In fact, becoming slaves to the system and unable to make any real changes in their lives. I was on the top of the pyramid (at least in my mind) when I was hired to work at PulteGroup. The job that I knew nothing about paid really well. I was treated like gold by the whole tax department and especially by Kim. She was a sweetheart, I could see it in her eyes. At least now I can feel for the poor and understand the rich. A person will only become human if he or she experiences having nothing.

At the end of January 2017, I was in jail and hospital. I can't remember much. I am sad because I missed the first week of Trump's presidency. I think he will either be the greatest or one of the worst presidents this country ever had. The more I hear him talk and act, the more I like him. He is not a career politician, therefore doesn't owe anybody any favors. People from both parties hate him. That is a great sign. A real change has already happened. Pictures of his naked wife are all over the internet. ;-) That will be great reading material for future generations.

I was never a material person. Sure, I want to make enough money to provide for my family. I want my kids to grow up in a good area and go to good schools. I want my family to take vacations and enjoy life in general. But those are necessities. I never enjoyed acquiring and hoarding wealth for my personal benefit. Most of the time, I enjoy giving more than receiving. I totally agree that individuals should be able to enjoy the fruits of their labor. There is nothing wrong with being rich and living like a rich person should live. Greed is good. Greed is good to a certain point. When the top 1% of the population controls 90% of the world's resources, something is wrong. The super-rich are so busy maintaining and building wealth, they have no consideration for anybody or anything on this planet. For every person who lives like a king, there are millions more who are starving, suffering, and slowly dying. I guess the Holocaust was a walk in the park. At least it was quick. Most had no idea what was about to happen until the very end. At least the Nazis were "nice" enough to play them live classical music just before they entered the gas chambers. How ironic is this twisted marriage of beauty and the beast.

How can we take care of this world if we don't care for each other? I hope we have not yet passed the point of no return. Artificial intelligence (AI) can grow exponentially smart in the area it was designed to operate. It will never be as smart as the human brain.

Nevertheless, if bad people are in charge, it cannot be controlled and/or stopped in case of an emergency.

Before I continue, I would like to mention two things I strongly believe and have believed most of my life. I will never change my opinion on these two subjects for anything or anyone as long as I live.

1. True love is the most powerful force in this world.
2. Organized religion is the source of most human misery and suffering. It is a pyramid scheme that keeps the people on the top in power and most of the population poor and under control. It is a haven for pedophiles and other predators who love to prey on peoples' ignorance and naivety. They sell you bullshit stories for 10% of your gross income. Charitable events are just a cover-up to hide the true intentions. For example, in the USA, the Church doesn't pay any taxes at all. The clergy should live a simple life. In reality, they mostly deal in cash, live in million-dollar mansions and drive expensive sports cars. Look at the history; most deaths from unnatural causes are attributed to religion. Long story short – the world will never be free unless it gets rid of organized religion. Yes, I believe in a higher power that created this Universe; however, nobody on this planet has the right to influence my opinion on this subject.

It all comes down to one thing, the good vs the bad forces of nature. For every person that ever walked the face of this Earth, it comes down to a struggle between the good and the bad. It is always more or less the same story. This is the ultimate eternal power struggle. In the end, the good always has a slight edge over the bad. It may not always be as obvious, but it will happen at the end. *Ronnee, it has to, and I believe it 100%.* If it were not true, our civilization would not have got this far.

Here is the reason why the good force has a slight advantage over the bad force: The good can only love, but cannot hate. The bad can only hate, but cannot love.

I experienced the following. As long as you can see, hear, feel, and speak, it will get worse and worse and worse. . . and at a certain point, as long as you can see and feel but can never hear and speak, it will get better and better and better. . .

This is not a game for the weak. It is only for the strongest of the strongest. *Ronnee, you are a smart woman. I am sure you already figured this out.*

Ronnee, the very first time I saw you, I felt you were a special person. You always smiled in a friendly and comforting way that made me feel relaxed. I couldn't wait to see you and talk to you again. I always loved that you can appreciate the smallest details of natural beauty. Strong empathy, for other people, animals, and the world you live in, is your best feature. You are a loving mother who gave everything she had to raise her three children. What a terrific job you did.

You care for other people regardless of background. Leo, for example; he was fat and unattractive with obvious difficulty in finding a girlfriend. You flirted with him anyway. You knew he was a great person inside and flirting would make him feel good. I admire that. You liked me for who I was. You did not care that I drove a Nissan Leaf to work, a sign that a person is on a budget. You have an amazing ability to see past all the bullshit filters and images that a person may put in front of a face to hide their true identity. You can see the real, raw, pure human beings. In other words, you can see and feel the soul of each person in question. You are loving, a truly and genuinely loving person. I did not think people like you existed anymore. I was so wrong. Everything in my life had a purpose. Every single event that happened in my life led to the incredible, indescribable and out-of-this-world event that occurred when our eyes met at full stare that day in the cafeteria. At that moment, I felt we were in love with each other. We shared everything that was inside us. We are now connected with each other, because true love is eternal and cannot be destroyed. Your love kept me going through the difficult times. It will also keep me going in the future.

Ronnee, you are the love of my life. I realize that I cannot be with you. I would like to be your friend. We have a lot in common and many great subjects to talk about. Philosophy is the ultimate answer to everything. I am sure that together we will find many more answers and solutions. I feel optimistic about the future, especially with your presence in my life. So, how about lunch sometime? It will be my treat, the first time. I already promised you this. Invite Jessica, I miss her as well. How is Christine doing? I hope all three of you are doing well and everything went back to normal at Argos.

What are the next steps in my life? Well, I need to get a job or start a business (my preference) so my wife doesn't divorce me. Coincidently, my stepdad sold all his businesses and wired me some money about two weeks before the incident. In the worst-case scenario, I will be OK for a year. I want to raise my two daughters as best I can. I want them to enjoy operas, play sports, travel, and fully experience the world. I want them to see the "bad" aspects of humanity as well, so they will be able to make the right choices. With a little luck, they will be like you when they grow up. :-)

After I came home from the hospital, the first thing my wife of ten years asked were some questions about my life insurance. Then she wanted me to sign a document giving her an authorization to disconnect me from life support if needed. In the summer of 2014, we started going to swingers' clubs three to four times per year. Maybe she did not enjoy it as much as I thought she did. I enjoyed it, that's for sure. Maybe she did not feel loved anymore and did it because of me. I have to take a step back and really think about this. A coin always has two sides.

The most important thing I realized from all this; I am in love with the world and everything in it.

Here is my contact; Cell (474)552-5690   t.joseph78@yahoo.com
Take care.

Chapter 2
After the Life-Changing Event

After the indescribable and beautiful incident that happened between Ronnee and I at the lunch on December 15 2016, my life was not the same. I felt really good in the first few days. I was happy, energetic and my thinking was in supercharged mode. I was in love with Ronnee and felt she was in love with me. This truly is the most powerful feeling a person can have, far surpassing any feelings generated by material items. I would not trade this feeling for any amount of money, including winning the lottery. It felt like "winning the lottery" when our eyes met at full stare.

The next day, Argos corporate employees were invited to celebrate the second-ever Best Employee Award event, directed by Jessica, the company's branding and communications manager. When I entered the conference room about ten minutes before the start of the event, I saw Jessica and said, "Hi Jessica, how are you?"

She looked at me in a neutral but curious way and said, "OK," smiled a little and kept walking away.

"I think that you're busy," I said to her. She smiled a little and continued to walk away.

Jessica has amazing ability. She is a natural-born leader who never falls under pressure no matter how extreme the situation may be and always remains calm while she is trying to figure out the next steps. That is another reason why I had such a difficult time getting to know her better.

As the conference room was getting fuller, there was an empty seat next to Ronnee. I had not spoken with her since the incident. "Should I sit next to her?" After this thought, I noticed her boss, Mark, was standing at the end of the conference room. "I better not," I said to myself.

After the event ended, I waited at one of the exit doors just long enough for Ronnee to see me. I slowly exited the conference room. After a few steps, Ronnee was right behind me and our eyes locked at full stare again for a few seconds. We were alone, standing in the hallway. She said, "Hi," smiled, and looked at me in a certain way. I said, "Hi," to her and smiled in the sincerest way possible. She continued to smile in a happy and genuine way as she walked to her cubicle. I knew for sure she liked what had happened between us the previous day. I felt Ronnee wanted more of those feelings and was ready to give herself to me again. I was able to see it in her eyes. I was able to find her soul and read her mind. This was only possible because I truly loved her. At that point, I loved and cared for her more than I loved and cared for myself. This, again, proved my philosophical point of view; if you truly love someone, you are willing to give up your life for that person. Love truly is the strongest force in the Universe. For love you live, for love you die. Love created everything in every possible universe, time, and dimension. Without love, there would just be an empty space.

The upcoming weekend was unusual as the feelings created by the Thursday event were fully present. I kept thinking and replaying the event in my mind. I tried to figure out what happened and why. "Was Ronnee feeling the same? Was she questioning the event the same way I did? Had she ever experienced this before? Because I hadn't. Who initiated the event? Was it her, or me, or did this happen simultaneously? Does this happen to people who search their whole life for true love and finally find the perfect match?" These were among many questions I asked myself. I also noticed, the more I thought about the event, the more my eyes become dilated. I researched "dilated eye syndrome" on the internet and found the following: "it cannot be controlled at will, however, it can be influenced via recreational drugs such as LSD." "Weird, I don't do drugs," I thought.

I saw Ronnee again on Tuesday. She was really busy because a lawsuit "went south" and Mark gave her more than the usual amount of work. She was unable to meet for lunch, but later changed her mind and went to the cafeteria shortly after me. As mentioned earlier, we only talked about ordinary things. Neither of us had the courage to discuss the Thursday event. Maybe both of us thought the event was a once-in-a-lifetime occurrence, something that does not just happen randomly, and it was better to leave it alone to protect ourselves. Susana, with her IT co-workers, went to the cafeteria. They were laughing and looking at me and Ronnee. It appeared that someone had started to spread rumors regarding the situation. "Was it Ronnee or Jessica? No way," I thought. "Was it Christine, or the receptionist named Aggie?" Possibly, but I didn't know which one. I knew for sure Christine was scared to death as she witnessed the event. Religion was used as the abuse tool by her family when she was a child. How sad that the people she trusted the most could do something like that to control an innocent child. I totally understood she could break down at any time and talk. My feelings toward her did not change at all. I still viewed her as my friend and the person I genuinely cared for. "Is she going to see me as the Devil or the person that fell in love with Ronnee?" That was the million-dollar question. If she saw me as the Devil, my days at Argos were numbered.

I purposely did not go to the cafeteria until I knew whether Ronnee wanted to associate with me or not. After our latest lunch, she returned a teddy bear to me, stating "legal reasons." She became scared by the whole situation and was afraid of losing her job. This was understandable as she mentioned a few months ago, "Joseph, college is so expensive!" Christine didn't want to speak with me. I decided not to contact the two girls for a few weeks and let everything calm down. It would be best to feel them out, to have lunch with the three of them when Jessica returned from her vacation.

During the Christmas holidays, I took time to reflect on eye sex. I recalled a night in the Old Town of Prague.

It was 3 a.m. in late spring. I walked across the Charles Bridge and stopped to enjoy the night and the beautiful scenery the place offered. I'd had a few drinks at the nearby Karlovy Lázně nightclub, my body was warm with the right kind of buzz. Stress and endless hassle of the ever-busy work week was replaced by inner peace and overall relaxation. I didn't care anymore. I was just there, in my own little world, fully enjoying the moment. The weather didn't exist, as time stopped, and the wind was at a complete standstill. I was alone, but felt the enigmatic presence of some of the many people who had walked over the bridge in the past 600-plus years.

A female was approaching, wearing a dark navy blue outfit. Due to the misty darkness of the night, I couldn't see into her face, but her way of walking was so familiar. It was the walk that only a confident and classy woman could possess. In the silence of the night, I was able to hear her stepping in a playful, sexual way as her high heels clapped in a perfect, metronomic beat against the sidewalk bricks. She approached me and stood still, with her eyes looking directly into mine, not in an intrusive way. I met her stare and fully consented. She started to undress me using only her eyes. I liked it. In fact, I was loving every second of it. "This can't be happening! Is this just a dream?" I thought, but did not move at all. Without any warning, my vision became blurry and I was not able to recognize the surroundings. Everything was mute except for a slight buzzing generated by vibrations of static electricity. Then, I saw her barely recognizable face moving even closer. She tilted her head to my right side, slightly smiled as her delicate gaze penetrated mine, and the eyes played their silent melody consisting of heat, excitement, lust, and curiosity. I was breathless, completely paralyzed, unable to move an inch as we were seeing into each other's souls. Our thought process was synchronized and enormous amounts of information were exchanged. It was a reading of the mind. After a few seconds my vision returned to normal and the woman quickly stepped back, whispering, "Wow!" She then lowered her head, looking down with eyes almost closed, barely breathing. It was all over. Without saying a word, she resumed her walk and disappeared into the darkness of the hazy night.

This wasn't just an eye fuck, this was different. To get off, you can have sex with anybody, without any emotions. The eye foreplay lasted for a short time, but it was a priceless moment, one of a kind sexual satisfaction far surpassing any emotions generated by material items. The longer the eyes played their magic, the deeper was the emotional bond that formed and the two of us transported ourselves to a different dimension, to a world where anything was possible. Were our hearts pierced by an arrow, signaling the beginning of love? True love – where it doesn't matter what the other person owns on the outside and what does matter is the kind of person he or she is, inside.

This raw, pure, unconditional attachment created by full frontal eye contact is so rare in the third millennium. Are we so preoccupied with our lives that we've lost the ability to see the big picture of how the world really works? Have our minds become so clouded by specialized pursuits, with emphasis on material items, that we've lost the ability to defend ourselves against outside threats; against entities whose goal is to enslave our minds, to fully control us, to bribe us with material items of little or no value and to steer us away from personal contacts to cheap, emotionless substitutes such as the latest phones loaded with a bunch of social media applications? We don't look each other in the eyes, let alone engage in eye foreplay. Are we so collectively sexually unsatisfied and afraid to look each other in the eyes because of possible threats of sexual harassment lawsuits and loss of careers? Have our minds already become institutionalized? How can we freely express our personalities and develop real, deep, hot and passionate relationships when we are constantly preoccupied with the fear of punishment for actions that consist of the most pure forms of human contact?

Consensual eye contact is the beginning of seduction, leading to the most powerful form of foreplay. Full frontal eye contact strips away all the endless bullshit filters and images we put on to hide our true identity. When someone stares into your eyes, and you fearlessly stare back, you're allowing him or her into your precious, private little orbit. It's dangerous. You are willingly giving yourself over to someone. All of a sudden, they are in total control and there is nothing you can do about it.

This was the only experience in my life that came even close to what happened between Ronnee and I on that Thursday afternoon. "How often does this happen? Does it happen only to a certain group of people?" A mystery was born. The more questions I asked, the more lost I became.

I missed Ronnee and wanted to see her and talk to her as soon as possible. I could not wait for Jessica to return from Ireland. I wanted to see Jessica as well. I missed talking with her, was curious about her trip and wanted to see how she finally interpreted the December lunch event.

On Monday, January 9th, I checked Jabber intranet messenger to see if she was available. She was not. "Fuck," I thought, "I hope she didn't block me as her contact." If she had, Ronnee would block me from her life, as well. I didn't know what to do at that point so I stuck to my original plan – to stay away from Ronnee and the cafeteria until I got more info on where I stood with the girls.

Next day my boss, Sue, gave me a letter related to legal issues the company had. "What a coincidence, this is the perfect excuse to see Ronnee." I was first going to check out Steve, the HR Director, who sat a couple cubicles from Ronnee.

As I was walking to the third floor, I was going over my masterplan. Sure enough, Steve was at his desk and said to take this letter to "our wonderful Ronnee Pedersen." After he made this comment, I knew for sure people were talking about the incident.

Steve was on my side, since he'd flirted with Ronnee in front of me and Jessica a few months ago. Ronnee was talking about half-naked eighty-year-old women in Denmark's parks.

"Did you say 'naked'?" Steve asked her, in an excited way.

I jumped into the conversation. "Ronnee, maybe when you are eighty, you can dress up like that in public."

"I still have some American in me," she said, and smiled in a sleazy and excited way. Jessica, as usual, was not saying anything and avoided any sexual conversations in front of a third person. She was just listening. She truly is the smart one.

Jessica, sitting at the adjacent cubicle, heard the conversation between Steve and I, said something to Ronnee and quickly walked away. In the past, I noticed she walked away from her cubicle every time I started to talk with Ronnee at her desk. She possibly did this to give us some privacy. Ronnee did the same on one occasion when I began to talk with Jessica first. I don't know, maybe this was just a coincidence.

As I was approaching Ronnee, she was blushing with excitement. "Steve told me to come to your desk," I said, and gave her the letter. "How are you?" I continued to speak.

"I am OK, just busy," she replied.

"You better get back to it, I don't want to interrupt," I said. I smiled a little and started to walk away.

I turned around and noticed a smile on her face and then she gave me the wink. I knew I was golden. I cannot even describe how I felt when I returned to my desk. She was the love of my life. It was impossible to feel any better. I was on top of the world again. The lunches would continue as usual. ;-) I was so excited and wrote a Jabber message to Jessica: "I hope that Ireland met your expectations. Welcome back!"

In about a half hour, Jessica replied (most likely after a conversation with Ronnee) in a friendly way, like nothing had happened. I knew that I was golden with her, as well. One final obstacle remained. The million-dollar question remained unanswered. It was Christine.

The next morning, I went to see Christine to feel her out. She was sitting at her cubicle, smiled a little and said, "Hi," and then quickly looked away. I could see that she was afraid and my presence made her feel uncomfortable. I tried to loosen her up by discussing everyday events. She played along and continued the conversation. She felt safe, since her co-workers were present. Finally, I asked the question, "Are you gonna be at lunch today?"

"I don't know, probably not," she replied in a hesitant way.

"Really?" I asked her. I was sad and disappointed, said goodbye and went back to work.

My only hope was Jessica. I knew at some point she would be able to persuade Christine to believe that I am just an ordinary guy and not the Devil. "If this happened in the 1600s, the HR department would have already burned me and Ronnee at a stake, no questions asked. I am so lucky we live in the 21st century," were my relieved thoughts.

About an hour later, oddly enough, I saw Christine on the fourth floor having a conversation with my boss, who was two levels above me. I got nervous. She probably told Val that I sexually harassed her earlier in the day. Or, maybe, she just told her something related to accounting/credits. I was not sure, but was able to overcome my fears and went to the cafeteria to have lunch.

Sure enough, Jessica and Christine were at lunch together. I sat next to them at the adjacent table and had a "business as usual" conversation with Jessica. Christine loosened up a little bit and answered a few of my questions. However, she still looked scared. I could see the fear in her facial expression. Her family really fucked her up. No child deserves to live like that.

"I would probably gladly kill all the people that made her childhood a living hell, if that would make Christine feel better," I calmly thought to myself, as I was looking at her face. I wanted my old Christine back. The happy Christine, the Christine who was the leader of the group and always had a story. I wanted to hug and kiss her right there in the cafeteria to prove to her that I was not the Devil.

On Wednesday the 11th, I did not go to the cafeteria. I wanted to give the girls some privacy and allow them to decide together, as a group, what to do about me. I had a feeling that all three would be in the cafeteria on Thursday. It had been a month since the four of us had lunch. I wanted to look my best, therefore that evening I went to get a haircut and prepared some nice clothes for the upcoming day. ;-)

The next day, I could not wait to see the girls. The morning dragged really slowly as I kept looking at the clock. I could not wait until 12.10 p.m., my usual departure time for the cafeteria. I rarely left my desk before this time. I wanted the girls to be there first, so I could see which one of them was reserving her empty seat for me. If the occasion permitted, I would try to flirt with that particular girl on the same day to show her my appreciation.

The three women were at the cafeteria, dressed at their best. I was so happy Christine was there. She genuinely smiled at me after our eyes met for a split second. Christine was finally able to overcome her fears. I walked in there at just the right time to catch Ronnee in front of a microwave, warming up her lunch. We just said, "Hi," to each other.

Unknown to me, at that moment, the girls had conspired to "fuck with me" that day. In their minds, they were losing control of the situation and wanted to be in charge again. They did not want Joseph to be in charge. They wanted to decide when and how they would allow Joseph to enter their precious little private orbits again. I was totally ignored as the girls were discussing female-related items. It was amusing to them as there was no way to break into the conversation. "I would have to be a gay to keep up with that type of conversation," I thought to myself, in a sad way, as I was looking at the girls and listening to the conversation.

Then I understood what was going on. They were just messing with me to teach me a lesson. The girls would like to be the dominant ones. I decided to play along and thought about my favorite movie, *The Witches of Eastwick*. At that point, I wanted to be Daryl. I knew we had all experienced a not-so-ordinary event together, therefore I could steer the girls to play that game to a certain degree in the future. "If Jessica loses her glasses and Christine comes to her senses, maybe it would then be possible to have eye sex with them, as well." My mind was racing with this and similar thoughts as the girls were having fun.

I decided to acknowledge to the group that I had lost the battle that day. As I was leaving the cafeteria, I smiled at the girls and said, "You guys have a great day."

Ronnee and Jessica said, "Bye, Joseph," and gave me the victorious, "We got you fucker and there is nothing you can do about it" look.

"This cannot get any better," I said to myself as I was leaving the cafeteria, smiling and fully satisfied.

That afternoon I started to get sick. My eyes were slightly dilated and I felt uncomfortable looking at the computer screen. I was so happy my workday ended at 4 p.m.

The next day I felt dizzy and lightheaded again, I was barely able to stay focused on work-related items. I kept thinking about the fun lunch we had the day before. I was able to get away with this since Sue was on a business trip related to a major acquisition that expanded Argos' manufacturing activity in the Northeast. The weekend was strange. I started to notice that at certain times my kids were behaving in an unusual way. It was the classic scenario of "good and bad kid" with slight abnormality. The pattern did not change at all during the whole weekend.

On Monday, 16th of January, everything turned for the worse. That morning, I began to have facial pains; my eyes were hurting and my jaw was stiff. I had difficulty opening my mouth. The weirdest thing was the computer screen. It appeared that vibrating flashes of light were being emitted at certain intervals towards my face. I had a really difficult time completing any kind of work.

In the evening, I went to LA Fitness health club on Terrell Mill Road. My eyes were hurting especially badly when exposed to a bright light. I thought a little physical activity would make me feel better. I needed to be sharp and productive at work, because tomorrow Sue would be reviewing all the work assigned to me last week.

When I scanned my membership card, the receptionist was looking directly into my eyes in a very surprised way. I immediately went to the bathroom to check my face. I could not believe what I saw; my eyes were almost fully dilated. She must have thought I was on LSD. "What am I going to do? I need to come up with something to get my eyes back to normal."

I stood in front of the mirror at a distance of about an inch, and tried to focus my eyes to the tip of my nose. After a few minutes, the dilation slightly subsided. "Good, it appears this may work in the long run," I thought to myself. "I cannot be walking around in public looking like Satan. Sooner or later, the police will pick me up."

I calmed myself down, jumped on a treadmill, turned on Pandora Radio and concentrated on the workout. The lights appeared brighter than normal and I experienced severe, sharp pain in my eyes. I went to the bathroom again to check them. "Shit, they are fully dilated again. What am I going to do? How am I going to function in society with this kind of condition?" I was scared to death and decided that tomorrow was another day. "I better get some sleep. There is a good chance this will not be a problem tomorrow." I then thought of what to do next if the problem didn't go away. I covered my eyes and abruptly left the gym.

When I woke up on Tuesday, January 17th, my eyes were slightly dilated but nowhere near as bad as the previous evening. They were, however, still sensitive to light, but I decided to go to work.

After about an hour of work, the pain in both eyes increased dramatically. I went to the bathroom and, to my disappointment, my eyes were almost fully dilated. I hoped Sue would not call me to her cubicle to go over the assignment, since most of the work was not finished. :-(

Sure enough, I received the Jabber message to stop at her desk. I had no choice but to go over. I made all kinds of excuses why the work wasn't completed. Sue remained professional and gave me the benefit of the doubt. I had never before had any performance issues and always tried to go above and beyond. We began to review the work that I was able to complete. It was a basic spreadsheet reconciled on a monthly basis. The review turned out to be my worst nightmare. She found so many errors, so quickly. The worst was that I could not remember when and how I had completed the spreadsheet.

"Joseph, what is going on?" she asked, in a disappointed way. Sue was clearly upset as she saw my fully dilated eyes.

"It's all over, she thinks that I'm on drugs," I thought. I remained calm and promised to fix the errors quickly. It took me forever to correct the spreadsheet. After a great struggle, I was able to complete the task. She reviewed the work and did not find any errors.

"Good, because I am unable to remember if I fixed them all," I thought to myself in relief. Apparently, she was satisfied with the work and asked me what I wanted for lunch. We ordered gyros from a nearby Greek restaurant.

After the lunch, I began yet another reconciliation. My symptoms had significantly worsened. The colors in the spreadsheets started to change in an unpredictable manner. I didn't know what was real and what wasn't anymore. "Did the 'thing' really happen between me and Ronnee during that lunch in December? How about the eye foreplay in Prague? Do my three female friends even exist?" These were my confused thoughts. "If I sit here any longer, I am gonna end up in a mental institution. I need to find the truth, right now."

I ran out of the building as fast as I could. As I was looking at the trees adjacent to the parking lot, my breathing slowed to normal and my chest pains went away. I was able to calm myself down. I reached for the phone; what a relief when I was able to the find everything intact. This was enough proof to reassure myself that everything I had experienced in my life was real and, most importantly, I also realized my love for Ronnee was real. "In order to save my job, I need to get the fuck out of the office as soon as possible," I silently said, and came up with a brilliant plan.

"Sue, I am so sorry that I am unable to focus. My grandma, who basically raised me, is dying. She is more of a mother to me, since my real mom is a little crazy. I'll tell you the story later. I'm going to have to

45

go to Czech Republic very soon. Please, I need to go home right now and get some rest," I said to my boss, in the most believable way possible, after returning to the office. I didn't have to act at all, since I felt really sick anyway.

"I'm sorry to hear that, no problem, Joseph. Go home and come back when you can. I'll finish the reconciliation that is due today." As she was finishing the sentence, she raised her head and looked me in the face. Her eyes were almost fully dilated and a small orange coffin with a tombstone was displayed in the center of each eye.

"I don't want to think or see anything today anymore!" This raced through my head as I was running towards my car. At home, I immediately went to bed and slept for the rest of the afternoon. After waking up, I was so happy that I felt OK again and my eyes had gone back to normal.

Naturally, I needed to do something about this situation. I thought about and replayed the events in my head several times. The oddest thing, besides the dilated eyes and related hallucinations, was the computer screen. I assumed this was probably the source of my medical problems. "Why would someone try to shoot vibrating flashes of light into my face to cause hypnosis and hallucinations?"

When brainstorming, I came up with an explanation; people at work talked about the unusual event that happened between me and Ronnee. Somehow the intelligence agencies found out about this. This was entirely possible since, according to "The Snowden Report," all internet and telephone communication is recorded and stored on a massive server farm owned by the people in charge. Artificial intelligence systems scan the stored data for code words to identify potential enemies of the state. They got curious and tried to cause hallucinations and a nervous breakdown in me. A 911 would then be called to take me away for medical analysis/experimentation.

This was crazy, but the only explanation my mind was able to come up with at that time. I became nervous and was really afraid something similar had or would happen to Ronnee. I had to warn her as soon as possible and came up with a solution; go to the Microcenter store located a couple miles from home to buy a privacy screen protector to see if that would block the flashes of vibrating light. To my astonishment, the store wanted almost $200 for this piece of plastic. "That is a great sign. This may actually work, since it would deter most people from buying one," I thought. I bought one piece and would come for another one if this solved the problems.

The next morning, I was so happy my issues were solved. I felt great again and told Sue about my eye problems and the solution. "It would be a good idea to see an eye doctor," I added, at the end of the conversation, in case my eyes dilated again, so she would not think I did drugs. I also asked her when would I receive an offer for the permanent position. We had been discussing this for eight months.

"Look, Joseph, I will give you a piece of advice. Many employees on the third floor are not the nicest people. Try to associate yourself with the employees located on the fourth floor. But, even then, be careful what you say and what you write. All electronic communication, including Jabber, is closely monitored."

I could not believe what I was hearing and noticed Sue had a small image of a white cross displayed in the center of each eye. "Great, my problems are not solved," I thought, but I remained calm and asked, "So, you said that even some people on the fourth floor are not nice. Is someone like Tony bad?" Tony was a deeply religious person. I especially mentioned him after seeing the white crosses in my boss's eyes.

"Come on, Joseph, Tony is not bad. I am just telling you, if you want to be hired full time you are gonna have to become an office politician, to a certain degree. Just use your judgment."

I kept thinking about the incident as I was sitting at my desk. "This is BS and I don't care anymore. For all I know, Ronnee's life is in danger and I have to warn her asap." I sent a Jabber message to Jessica telling her about my medical issues. I also wrote that I felt much better now and would tell her the story at lunch.

I went to lunch at the usual 12.10 p.m. and, sure enough, Ronnee and Jessica were already sitting at one of the tables. They were, however, not sitting at their usual place and were having lunch at the table where Aggie, the receptionist, normally sat. There was one more person having lunch at the other end of the small cafeteria. It was Tony. I sat next to the ladies and began to talk about everyday events. I had to, since Tony, who I suspected was most likely spying on us, could hear everything. There were also a couple of HR employees, Becky and Debbie, going back and forth between the cafeteria and adjacent rooms, looking at us with each pass. I knew something was happening, but kept calm.

Ronnee was in a great mood and teased me with her short white skirt. I started to look at her naked legs, slowly moved my eyes up to her face and noticed that her pupils and corneas in both eyes were shining in bright crystal white color. It was the same crystal white color of the small crosses Sue had in her eyes. "At least nothing yet has happened to her, but I have to warn her anyway," I thought, while chitchatting with both girls. Tony finally got up, said goodbye and walked away. "So, yesterday, I was really sick but I feel much better today. I went to Microcenter to buy a privacy screen to decrease the amount of light emitted by a computer screen."

"You went where?" Ronnee asked.

Jessica jumped into the conversation, "Microcenter, they were in Texas."

We continued to be disturbed by the HR ladies, so I said, "My grandma is very sick and is dying, she is almost eighty. I will have to go to Czech Republic very soon."

Ronnee asked the following question: "How is she dying?"

"Well, slowly, you know, her physical abilities are decreasing."

I saw Ronnee was astounded and started to shake a little.

Jessica then said, "My grandma is also dying."

"Really?" I replied. "I am so sorry to hear that. I hope she gets well soon."

I then continued to speak. "Ronnee, the higher the percentage of brain you utilize, the more your eyes dilate. You are taking in too much light. A privacy screen is the most expensive piece of plastic, $200 a pop. So, you will spend $400. Get them now, they're worth every fucking penny."

Jessica said, "I wear glasses, so I don't have this problem."

"Well, Jessica," I replied, "you should lose your glasses. You would look great." I answered in this way because I still had the eye sex idea in my head and tried to prepare her for the future Witches of Eastwick game.

Both girls left the cafeteria shortly after, but at different intervals. Little did I know, this was my last lunch at Argos. As I was returning to the fourth floor, Val stopped me in front of the elevators and made the following comment in the nicest and most sincere way possible. It almost felt like she was hitting on me.

"Hey, Joseph, you have some work to do this afternoon. The PWC income tax deadline is today."

That afternoon my symptoms worsened again. The privacy protection screen no longer worked and I saw the flashes of vibrating light hitting my face at unpredictable intervals. I was fighting the fatigue and the facial pains in order to meet the PWC deadline. I would definitely be fired if I was unable to complete this task. "I really need to go home and jerk off." As soon as I imagined this thought, the accounts payable person sitting behind me loudly said, "That would definitely make him feel better."

Then I said to myself, "The flashes of light are really making me hallucinate. My hearing is now affected."

"He is strong, I cannot believe that he can withstand it for this long. He makes it look like a piece of cake," said the person sitting at the desk next to mine.

"The privacy filter will definitely keep me from getting sick," I thought, and again the woman next to me answered, "If he believes in it, maybe or maybe not."

This happened at least eight to ten times in a row. I thought of a question and someone in the AP department would immediately answer it in a loud tone of voice. I began to brainstorm. "What is this? No agency in the world has this kind of technology, at least I hope not. They are not able to read my thoughts, no way! Am I dead? Did I somehow die at Argos? Maybe, I am somewhere in a hospital and all this is the imagination of my dying brain."

Then, all of a sudden, I saw a ladybug fly in front of me and land in front of the monitor. I carefully placed her in the center of the palm of my right hand and for few seconds admired how simple and beautiful she was. I slightly turned right towards the window and gently blew her away. Right away, I turned back so I could see the monitor and there was another ladybug exactly in the same spot as the first one. I did the same thing again and thought to myself, "Oh no, I am probably dead." I didn't panic. "No matter what, I need to finish the reconciliations to meet the deadline. Hopefully, I can figure this out later." I kept thinking in a more and more frantic manner.

Luck was not on my side that day. The flashes of light and the weird communications from my AP neighbors steadily increased and it became increasingly difficult to work. The AP manager said, "Our job is done. I learned so much from him. This is the beginning of something great." He took a stack of papers to the recycle bin and threw them in. It was late in the afternoon and I could not take it anymore. I needed a cup of coffee.

In the break room, I saw an accounting manager named Lori. Her eyes were the same crystal white color as Ronnee's. She smiled, looked directly into my eyes and said in a sleazy way, "Hey, Joseph, how is your day going?"

At this point I had had enough. I went to my desk and closed my eyes for a few seconds to refocus. The AP team kept laughing and was talking about someone's great abilities. I decided to go home. Unfortunately, I really lost it this time and said "Fuck you," to every single person I passed by, including my boss. Strangely, nobody looked at me anymore and the whole room was quiet.

The ride home was even stranger. Every twenty to thirty seconds, cars that approached me in the opposite direction (except on Highway 400) honked the horn or flashed their lights. I wanted to get home as soon as possible and was speeding way over the legal limit. I was driving over 60 mph on Roswell Road towards Marietta and suddenly saw a parked police car. The officer was pointing a radar gun right at me. As I passed him, he continued pointing the radar and did not make a move. Cars kept honking and flashing their lights until I reached home.

At home, I noticed my computer was gone and there were about ten books perfectly lined up on the floor leading from the office towards the master bedroom. I quickly went to bed, hoping this was just a bad dream that would be over once I woke up.

When I woke up, I felt close to being normal and went downstairs to the living room where my wife, Romana, was playing with our two daughters. We have three-year-old Julia and seven-year-old Teresa. They talked to each other in a strange way. The sentences appeared normal, except they mixed a word or two into each sentence that made no sense. The words were totally irrelevant to the meaning of each sentence. I was unable to comprehend what was going on and kept quiet for a while.

I overcame my fears and joined the conversation. Judging by their facial expressions, they understood what I was telling them; however, all their replies had some irrelevant words mixed in the sentences. It became almost impossible to have a deeper conversation. The color of the children's eyes was the same as Ronnee's, crystal clear white. Another disturbing fact was that at certain times the kids were slowly moving their heads from left to right, totally avoiding direct eye contact with me during the conversation. At least Romana's eyes looked normal.

Based on the events I experienced that day, I knew there was nothing else to do except to play along and ignore all the abnormalities. The strategy worked. After dinner, I began to feel dizzy and disoriented, so I went to bed. I woke up around 10 p.m. and was unable to go back to sleep. I wanted to figure out what was going on and why this was happening to me. Three scenarios crossed my mind:

1. I am dead and on my way to either Heaven or Hell. This is just a transition scenario to get used to abnormalities until I reach the final destination.
2. I have lived my whole life in some sort of matrix and I am slowly being awakened by a resistance group to help them to save the real world; a dead planet where a few survivors live underground and most of humanity is enslaved by artificial intelligence. I would eventually be approached by somebody who would offer the blue or the red pill. I would have a choice; to continue to live in the Matrix or be awakened and help to save the world.
3. I am part of a multinational sick reality TV show similar to *The Truman Show* (1998), a movie that began on June 30 1978. My whole life is being broadcast live, 24 hours a day, 7 days a week, to the entire world. Everyone that I ever knew is a paid actor and

I live in some sort of a dome, hidden from the real world. My life was staged to such an extent, I would eventually have to a make a decision which political system is better. If I decide on my own that capitalism is the better system, the USA would win the Cold War and the Soviet Union would peacefully acknowledge defeat. The Soviets would change their system to mirror the United States' capitalism, including all US laws with the US Constitution. All nuclear weapons would be destroyed, all armies in the world would be dissolved and all borders in the whole world would no longer exist. Everyone in the world would unite to a peaceful coexistence. The same situation would happen if I were to decide on my own that socialism is the better system. The USA would become a socialist state, mirroring everything the Soviets would do, going forward. The producers would than disclose the true meaning of my life to me and I would be freed from the dome to live in the real world. The Reality TV show would then end.

The more I thought about this, the more I believed I was in the Reality TV show. This would explain the abnormalities. During the December 15 2016 lunch, I was somehow drugged so my eyes would dilate. Ronnee was a paid actress, she just acted her part once this happened. I was made to hallucinate and the producers were able to read my mind because the year in the real world was not the present year of 2017, but closer to the future year of 2117. The dome was a Hollywood studio set exactly mirroring the past year 2017 from all technical and social perspectives except for politics.

Everyone at Argos was a paid actor. The computer at work was programmed to make me sick. Everyone in a car that honked and flashed headlights at me while I was driving home was an actor. The cop was an actor. That is why I was not pulled over. All my family members were paid actors. That would explain the irrational conversations. I concluded the 2117 real-world politicians were getting impatient. They wanted me to make decision so the "ifs and maybes" regarding the future world order would be settled for good.

Multiple thoughts crossed my mind. If I am unable to make the decision, sooner or later the producers and actors would be forced to drive me insane and/or kill me. The game would end in a stalemate and both political systems would continue to exist, without any changes. The USA would remain a capitalist society and the Soviet Union would remain a socialist society. Maybe the Reality TV show would start all over again from the beginning, but with a different person.

I can't make a decision at this point because I like both systems. From a child's perspective, socialism is better. From an adult's perspective, capitalism is the better system. If the year is 2117 and the Soviet Union still exists, it means the 1989 Velvet Revolution never happened in the real world. It only happened in the "dome" to make me believe that capitalism won.

So Miloš Jakeš is also an actor? I can't believe this. That is why he is still alive, he is almost a hundred years old! Jakeš was the main political figure in communist Czechoslovakia in the late 1980s. He was the organizer of the most famous political meeting in the history of the country. At the Communist Party meeting that took place on July 19 1989 in the city of Červený Hrádeček, he made comments such as: "I feel like a piece of stick in a fence. The singer, Ms. Zagorová, is a nice girl but she made Kčs 600,000 per year, three years in a row! And the others, they don't make Kčs 600,000, they make a million, two million per year, such as Janda and the others!" He also mentioned the socialist state farms were raising boilers. (In the Czech language, "boiler" is a water heater, "broiler" is a chicken.) Someone had managed to steal the raw unedited video of the meeting and distributed it to the population via the black market. After this event, the Communists were publicly laughed at. They lost the last small piece of respect they had in front of the people. It was obvious to everybody, the regime's days were numbered.

As I realized this, I screamed, "No, this can't be happening!"

I continued to scream as loud as I could until my wife came down and asked in surprised but calm tone of voice, "What is going on, Joseph? Why are you screaming?"

I calmed myself down and said, "I'm sorry, I had a bad dream and cannot sleep, sorry."

She bought the answer and went to bed. It was 2 a.m. on January 19 2017. I did not feel tired at all. "I have to go for a ride and find any other abnormalities out there in the dome."

I took my 1995 Mercedes E320 for the ride because the electric Nissan Leaf would not get me too far. Once I left the house, I observed that incoming light from cars and street lamps was way sharper and brighter than usual. I loved it, especially when I saw the colorful billboards on I-75 and I-285. I felt relaxed, time significantly slowed down when looking at the billboards. On I-75, every single car I approached from behind moved to a different lane. "This is awesome and it definitely proves that everyone is an actor. Hell yeah, hallelujah! I need to start acting like I am the movie star. Everyone in the whole world is watching this."

I was so excited and wanted to see the gas station on Windy Hill Road, right next to I-75, where I was selling pictures in the early 2000s. The place had been completely renovated and looked way different than the Citgo gas station, fifteen years ago. The place also had a Bitcoin gambling slot machine. "Yeah right, this is definitely fake." I found out the owner sold the place a few years ago. The interior colors were amazing and the cashier had the crystal-clear white eyes! I was so happy to finally figure this out. "You know what, since I am technically invincible and the producers are adjusting the settings based on my behavior, I'll drive to the ghettos. I won't be robbed or killed because all the homeless Blacks are actors." I had made up my mind.

As I was driving on I-285 towards the Bankhead Highway exit (renamed Donald Lee Hollowell Parkway), an LCD billboard displayed a picture of my chiropractor friend, Mark, with the following message: *Hey, Joseph, come on over and get adjusted tomorrow!* "This cannot get any better and the world now belongs to me. I am the one!" Those were my very satisfying thoughts as I continued to drive the car. I was also sure that the "Fuck you" incident that happened at work earlier today would be forgiven and I would be able to continue to work at Argos. Most importantly, the lunches with the women would continue.

As I was fearlessly driving on Bankhead Highway towards Atlanta, there was a dirty Black homeless man standing at a bus station. "He won't get anywhere at 3 a.m.," I thought, and pulled over. "Hi there, where are you going? Would you like a lift?"

"Sure, I need to get to downtown, but first I need to pick up my medicine," he answered, in a friendly and polite way. The person's eyes were crystal clear white as well.

"No problem, we'll stop at the pharmacy, jump in," I replied in a euphoric way.

We drove for less than a mile and the man pointed to a small boarded-up building with graffiti all over the walls. "Hey, pull over, that's my pharmacy."

"Come on," I replied, "that's no pharmacy."

I pulled over anyway, but drove away immediately after the man exited the vehicle. The place was dark, dirty, and surrounded by trees. Even when I was 100% sure the producers would not allow anyone to harm me, I got scared. At that point it was pure instinct. A person cannot change behavior overnight. For the past thirty-eight years, I was told to abide by rules, like everyone else. "I am no Superman," I assured myself, while continuing to drive.

I had to pee, so I stopped at a gas station. The bathroom was locked for security reasons and I decided to take a piss behind the building. I was in shock and appalled when I saw how dirty and run down the surrounding area was. The rear of the gas station smelled like piss and shit. "People must use this area frequently as bathroom." I spotted a bunch of rundown "project" apartment buildings, went to the car and made up my mind to explore the area. It was horrible, there was garbage all over the streets. I saw a pink plastic battery-powered motorcycle for three–five-year-old girls. It was the same toy Romana and I had bought for our girls. "Oh no, a little girl like my daughter lives here. She will be psychologically damaged for life, will not have any meaningful future and her children will be unable to break the cycle, as well. I can't believe the richest country in the world would allow people to live worse than animals."

As silent tears were coming out of my eyes, I had to stop the car for a few moments. I realized the producers purposely placed the toy on the street for me to see it. As I continued to explore the area, there was a police car in front of a small rundown house. The officer spoke with some person, probably the tenant, who stood in front of the entrance door. I stopped and offered my assistance, "Hello, is everything OK here?"

Both the officer and the tenant looked at me simultaneously and genuinely smiled. The officer replied, "Thank you, everything is OK." Again, the people's eyes were crystal clear white. I kept driving deeper into the ghetto and pulled over when a person crossed the street in front of me. The person appeared to be a skinny woman dressed in dirty old clothes. I pulled down the passenger window and the woman said, "Hi there, I have something that I know you want. Do you want to play?"

The fear of death rushed through my body; there was no visible face and no eyes at all underneath the hoodie. There was just an empty black space. "This is a bad sign. I will probably get killed." I floored the car and kept driving frantically through the ghetto as fast as possible until I found my way back to Bankhead Highway.

I had had enough. This was one crazy day. I drove to downtown Atlanta, merged to I-75 north and was not able to recognize the city. The colors everywhere were so sharp and bright. It looked like my vision significantly improved as I was able to see in greater detail than normal. This truly was a beautiful and out-of-this-world experience. I calmly drove home and enjoyed the view of my new world to the fullest.

I only got a couple hours of sleep that night and had to go to work in the morning. I was rethinking the events from the previous day and began to have serious doubts about the situation. Maybe I am not in the Reality TV show but, instead, I am dying in a hospital. I have lived a good life and abided by the laws most of the time; I am no angel, however. I slowly influenced my wife to have sex with men and women, sometimes more than one at a time, in swingers' clubs and at private sex parties. We actively lived this lifestyle from June 30 2014 until the end of 2016. It was no easy task to convince Romana to attend the clubs. It took years of classy, indirect, and diplomatic conversations before she finally agreed.

"Maybe both God and Satan want me," I wondered. "They, however, cannot yet get me because the good and bad forces in me are in perfect balance."

I didn't have sex with Leah or Ronnee. They each represented an "agent" of Hell and Heaven.

Hell's Agent: Leah perfectly fits this profile. On several occasions, she appeared to be the classic narcissist and materialistic person who blindly agrees to everything the church throws in front of her face. She never loved me and only cared about herself and her career. No matter how much I loved her, she only wanted to flirt without any emotions involved. I refused to verbally flirt with her because she never loved me. She only wanted to flirt and possibly fuck.

Heaven's Agent: Ronnee perfectly fits this profile. She was the sweetest person I have ever met in my entire life, and always made me feel great when I talked to her. She was not afraid to show her affection for me in front of other people. I have never loved anyone this deeply. I would truly be in Heaven if she was my wife. Ronnee was not a materialistic person, she loved nature and everything in it. She cared for people of different backgrounds. I could talk to her for hours and hours as we were so tuned in with one another. Getting to know her truly was an amazing and beautiful experience. I will not forget about her for the rest of my life.

The Angel: The referee, Jessica, was always there in the middle of everything, listening and giving good advice to everybody. Jessica always remained neutral, appeared and disappeared without a trace, sort of like an angel. That's why she was never on any social media sites. Jess could either be the cockblocker or the key to a lustful night with Ronnee. It depends if you can get her on your side or not. ;-)

So, it could be than I am lying in a hospital, possibly suffering from complete paralysis due to severe injury to the brain. I was in a vegetative state. Both God and Satan were upset and impatient because they couldn't get me. I was stuck in a paradox, a no-man's land between Heaven and Hell. They both were playing mind games with me in order to lure me to their world. "Oh, shit, I definitely want to be with Ronnee, but what if this scenario is not true? Maybe I am still in the Reality TV show. This is just another episode, so I am forced to make a decision about socialism and capitalism." I answered myself in an unsure manner as I continued to think. "I need to equally play both sides in both games. The number one thing is to protect Ronnee and me from danger."

I did not want to go to Heaven, or Hell either, for these reasons. . . If I go to Hell, I will boil in a barrel of hot water for eternity. If I go to Heaven, I will end up crucified on a cross for eternity, like Jesus Christ. This was a no-win situation. It looked like no matter what I did, I couldn't win.

"Screw this," I said in a loud and defensive tone of voice. "All I want is to go to work and have a normal lunch with Ronnee, Jessica, and Christine."

To drive the Mercedes to work that morning was the only option because I forgot to charge the Leaf. As I was idling on the driveway, I called my ex-boss Leah for advice. I thought she might be able to help, because of two odd events that happened to me while working at PulteGroup.

1. About eight of us went to a Karaoke bar in Michigan. Leah was sitting at the bar and I was standing above her. We kept looking into each other's eyes during the conversation. As Leah tried to flirt with me, she looked down for a few seconds, raised her head up and looked into my eyes again. Her eyes at that point were fully dilated. I remained professional, did not ask her any questions and thought she somehow did it on purpose.
2. The PulteGroup office was located in Buckhead, about twenty minutes from my house. Just before the initial interview with the company, in August 2015, Leah met me at the lobby level of the high-rise building. Our eyes met at full stare, the color of her corneas was bright crystal blue and she wore thick make-up. I was surprised, but did not say anything. She might have worn colored contact lenses and the make-up to let me know we would "play" to a certain level again. After the interview, she said goodbye, the make-up was gone and eyes were of normal color. It was confusing and I chose not to react.

I called Leah around 7 a.m. from a hidden number and, luckily, she picked up the phone. I could not tell her directly what was going on, so I came up with an indirect statement. "I like to ride the NY subway at 7 a.m. and like vodka tonic, I need your help!" She hung up the phone.

I called again and left a message. "First time this happened to me was about a month ago. I need your advice. Please call me back."

During the drive to work, I kept thinking about the events and realized that by contacting Leah I was closer to being admitted to Hell than ever before. I started to get nauseous and had facial pains. I was about a mile from the city of Roswell and then it happened. My whole body, from head to toe, started to vibrate. The vibrations were increasing at a slow but steady rate and I thought, and almost yelled, "Thanks to Leah, I finally figured this out. I am the Antichrist, this is it! I am the new Hitler! That's why I am driving the Mercedes to work today, to commemorate him."

The vibrations increased to an unbearable point and I was not in control of my body anymore. I raised my head towards the ceiling, deeply exhaled and continued to look upwards and resumed the thought. "Yes, I will get rid of all the undesirable elements and create the paradise on Earth for the Aryan master race! Ronnee, it's all her fault anyway. That bitch was fucking Mark on a regular basis in the hotel right across the street from the office. She fucked him there right after the Argos' Christmas party was over. She disappeared from the conference area and went upstairs to meet him in a room!! She then fucked with my head in the cafeteria. I'll get my revenge!! Leah pointed me to the dark side and finally won. Screw Heaven!!"

Just before I had to make the turn to Oxbo Road, the vibrations finally started to go away. I pulled into a small park adjacent to the road and parked close to a creek. "Why did I say these horrible things? I don't hate anybody and I like all kinds of different people. I love Ronnee and would never do anything to harm her. I don't understand what is happening. Why did I lose the ability to control my mind and body?" I was asking myself this while walking along the creek.

The weather was gorgeous that morning. It was warm, the sky was completely blue and birds were singing around me. The air was refreshing, all the trees and bushes were so green. This was very unusual weather for the middle of January. I walked across a metal pipe to the other side of the creek, where there was a small trail leading deeper into the woods. I managed to calm myself down completely and continued to think. The vibrations felt unlike anything I'd felt in my entire life. It appeared that every piece of nerve in my body was played like a guitar. I did not have seizures or difficulty breathing. These were extremely strong vibrations, but they felt like tingling at the same time. I stopped walking, as I was in complete shock, and realized. . . I was mostly looking at the ceiling of the car while this was happening. Who drove the car through downtown Roswell during rush hour? Because it was not me.

I was unable to remember how I got to the Oxbo Road/Roswell Road intersection. I was not in charge at all while this was happening. The remaining drive to work was fairly normal. I kept replaying the events, but was not able to come up with any explanation and ended my thinking with these sentences, "I'll figure it out later. The priority is to arrive at work as quickly as possible and finish the PWC assignment that was due yesterday."

I parked the car and promised myself not to look directly into anyone's face and not to react to any conversations that did not make sense. From the building's lobby, I walked upstairs to the fourth floor. The access card no longer worked, therefore I went to the third floor to see receptionist Aggie. There was nobody in the area except for her, sitting behind the reception desk. I told her about the incident.

She answered in a very surprised tone of voice. "Really? Sorry honey, I will make you another card."

Again, I walked up to the fourth floor, but the card did not work. I walked downstairs to the lobby and entered the first available elevator. There was a person who resembled my neighbor. He looked and smiled at me. I looked down and pressed the third floor button and totally ignored the person for the duration of the elevator ride. After exiting the elevator, the reception area was full of people and I told Aggie about the déjà vu, but Becky, the HR lady, who was standing next to me, answered the question instead of Aggie.

"Joseph, go home. We'll let you know when you can come back to work." She smiled, looked directly into my face, and her eyes were crystal clear white. Becky was a cute girl in her twenties, but way too skinny for my taste. At that point I knew the weirdness was continuing.

I did not want to create a scene and said, "Becky, please let Sue know she needs to finish the PWC work today. It's imperative the information is available to the firm as soon as possible for them to prepare the 2016 Income Tax return for us."

"OK, I'll let her know. Please give me your access card. It's not working anyway," Becky said.

I said, "Goodbye," and began to walk towards the elevators, purposely looking down to avoid eye contact with anyone.

At the elevators, I looked up and saw Steve smiling at me and, of course, his eyes were crystal clear white. Steve, who worked in the mailroom, and Aggie, were the two employees who won the "Best Employee Award" in December of last year. I ignored him, took the elevator to the lobby and exited the building, unable to comprehend what was happening. "To drive home" was my only wish.

Chapter 3
Life after Argos

I arrived home at 9.30 a.m. and told my wife the office had an emergency power outage last night and everyone would have to work from home until further notice. I still hoped Becky would call by Monday to let me know I could return to work the next day. I wasn't feeling good and didn't do much that day except for lying around and sleeping. Coincidently, my stepdad, Milan, sold his businesses and wired me some money a few weeks ago. I told Romana about the money and said that I would like to go to the Czech Republic to personally thank him. She did not believe me and accused me of making the whole thing up.

"Joseph, stop telling me this story over and over again. Calm down! Are you on drugs?"

"Weird, this is the first time I am telling her about this. I don't remember ever mentioning this to her before and I am calm. What is she talking about?" I wondered, then went back to bed and tried to find an explanation to what she just said.

In the afternoon, I received a text message from 6 Degrees Group, the employment agency that found the indirect tax position at Argos: "Hello, Joseph. You can no longer work at Argos. Please call me when you can to discuss further opportunities."

At the back of my mind this situation became a real possibility after the way I acted the previous day. "I better be honest with Romana and tell her what happened," I thought. "Hopefully, she will give me a break and will let me go to Czech Republic for a few days."

I was little too optimistic, but had to tell her anyway. "Romana, honey, I have to tell you something. I just found out that I was fired, but don't worry, I'll quickly find something else. This job was temp to perm anyway and I never received the offer. So, who cares, right?"

"What just happened?" my wife asked. "Didn't you just get fired about eight months ago from the other job? What's wrong with you? So, I should be the only one that held a stable job for the past ten years? Do you think it is easy to be a flight attendant? You think it is, right? You just use my flight benefits to fly around the world first class for free. That's over with."

I did not try to stop her because she was clearly very upset and needed to vent her anger.

"You better find something quick, otherwise I will find somebody else; someone more dependable than you!!"

I tried to calm her down as much as possible. "Romana, I am truly sorry. Don't worry, I will find something else and I promise you, the job is going to be even better than the one before. We'll get through this and you know why? Because I love you. We were always able to get through tough times together because we love each other."

She interrupted me and said, "I don't love you anymore. You are just making my life miserable."

Romana almost started to cry and I wanted to comfort her, so I hugged and kissed her. "Don't worry about it, your life and our kids' lives will not change at all. I'll make it happen and just need one small favor. Please book me a flight to Prague. I would like to thank my stepdad and will be back in a few days."

"Are you crazy?" she replied in a surprised way. "You just lost your job and you want to go on a vacation? You're not going anywhere, because you're going to find work as soon as possible."

I didn't want to argue with her anymore and agreed to start looking for work shortly. Again, I did not feel good, I had a headache, my eyes started to hurt, I had chest pains and difficulty concentrating. I had to go back to bed.

When I woke up, it was just the right time to eat dinner. I felt better and my wife and the kids and I had dinner together.

After the kids fell asleep, Romana wanted to know why I was fired. "I need to know what happened at work. Why did you get fired?"

I didn't know what to say, no excuse was prepared. Maybe it would be best if I told her the truth. "Well, Romana, I don't know how to say this, but at work, I was having lunch with three women for the past eight months on a fairly consistent basis. We started to flirt a little bit."

"You did what? You started to flirt with them? Did you also sexually harass them?"

"No, I would never do anything like that. You know me, come on, Romana. We have been married for ten years, now."

I realized too much had been said. Regardless, I tried to talk my way out of this mess, but Romana began to speak in an angry way again.

"Because we are swingers doesn't mean you will disrespect me like this behind my back. You know I don't really care if you flirt with women or not, but at work they can easily sue you and your career would be over. Don't you know how the women are in this country?"

I quickly replied, "I am sorry, but the women flirted with me and especially this woman of Russian descent. She was wearing a short skirt and kept pointing her naked legs towards me on numerous occasions. I screwed up because one time she asked me what I like about Russian women. At that time, I didn't know she was Russian, and joked with her that many Russian women are great strippers. I think her boss, Mark, got upset because he saw me and her having lunch many times."

Romana was looking at me with her mouth and eyes wide open. She said, "You are an idiot. Even if the woman was sitting there naked, you should have never looked at her. Do you get it now? Do you get it?"

"Oh really?" I replied. "Find me a guy who would not look at a naked woman that was having lunch with him. You know what you are? You are a hypocrite, because something like this would never happen. If Ronnee was sitting there naked, every guy that walked by would stop, stare at her and get an instant hard-on! Listen to yourself, you don't make any sense at all. I feel like shit and I'm going to bed. Have a great rest of the evening."

Romana did not try to stop me. I didn't see her until the next day.

I wanted to figure out what was actually going on. Was it the "Reality TV" or the "Matrix" or the "Heaven vs Hell" scenario?

Another idea entered my mind again; the original idea I'd thought of while getting sick at Argos. The NSA somehow found out about the unusual event that happened between me and Ronnee during the lunch on December 12 2016. The agency somehow drugged me with some sort of truth serum to make me hallucinate. I came to the conclusion my whole house and all electronic gadgets, including cars, were bugged with surveillance equipment. The agency also forced Romana, my kids, the rest of my family and my friends to cooperate with them. My family was instructed to drive me mad. On certain occasions, they had to mix words into sentences that did not make any sense at all. I realized that I couldn't do anything out of the ordinary; like trying to complain to the authorities or debug the house and cars. If I did anything crazy like that, I would be locked up for good in a mental institution. I would then be subjected to all kinds of medical experiments. I therefore kept calm and came up with the following plan: to slowly destroy all cell phones and anything that has a screen, such as the TV and iPad. We would buy new gadgets free of any bugs. I had to make the destruction look like an accident and promised myself not to give the agency any excuse to take me away from my wife and kids. It was close to midnight and I was finally able to fall asleep.

The next morning, on January 20 2017, I tried to put the plan into action, but didn't know where to begin. Should I first destroy the cell phones? If yes, then how? For some odd reason Romana was constantly on her phone, even during our conversation. "She's definitely reporting all my activities to the agency. What am I going to do? No matter what, the key is to remain calm! I'll pretend a TV remote control is lost. I'll then be 'forced' to pull up a small chair in front of the TV so I can reach the shelves mounted close to the ceiling. I'll find the remote, accidentally slip and catch the TV with my hand. This will definitely look like an accident," I thought, and I did just that as my wife was in the kitchen, able to witness the event. I grabbed the TV as I was falling towards the floor and it fell on my right foot. I seized the moment and started to scream. "Great," I thought to myself. "I'll pretend I'm injured, so Romana will take me to the hospital and there will be more witnesses to the accident."

I kept screaming and telling Romana my foot hurt. She didn't see anything wrong, as the foot was not swollen or bruised.

"I have to make this believable or my life as I know it is over," I said to myself, then thought about the worst possible pain imaginable. As I was looking at my toe and replaying in my head the worst possible "pain" images of the Holocaust and the concentration camp victims, the toe started to get blue.

"You see, I am injured. Take me to the hospital now!!" I screamed at my wife. I was so happy this had happened. I continued to act; I grabbed my cell phone and broke it in half, all while screaming in pain. Romana realized this was serious, called Delta, and took the weekend off. We drove to the WellStar clinic, about two miles from our house.

When we parked in front of the clinic, I told Romana I was unable to walk. A nurse brought a wheelchair and wheeled me inside. I frantically breathed and my head was hurting; this was not an act, this was for real. Oddly enough, there was always one good and one bad nurse. The "good" nurse was communicative, sympathetic to my injuries and sporadically smiled at me. The "bad" nurse was the exact opposite. She didn't look at me, was not smiling and was not communicative at all. She only said one sentence: "If you don't get well soon, we will have to transfer you somewhere else."

When she said this, I knew something was wrong. "I have to slowly improve, so Romana can take me home. If I simulate the injury too much, I will not be believed and the doctors will think I am crazy," I thought, and proceeded with next steps.

I asked for a water and slowly went to a bathroom, then came back and told Romana I felt much better. The foot wasn't injured, but I was diagnosed with a panic attack episode. My wife and I waited in the lobby for the discharge papers. It was close to noon. Trump's inauguration was being broadcast live on the TV hanging above the seats. A Black woman next to me was watching the broadcast and I thought she probably was not happy with the winner. "Why not make her feel better about the defeat?" I thought. I told her the following: "You know it doesn't matter who wins. They're the same crooks, Trump and Hillary, and nothing will change. They are both liars." My wife told me to be quiet and we left the hospital shortly after.

62

Upon arrival at our house, Romana and I had a few disagreements regarding my work situation and the plane tickets to Prague. I kept to myself for the rest of the day.

On Saturday morning, January 21, I went with my wife and kids to Sam's Club on Cobb Parkway to buy a new TV. I also had a plan to see an eye doctor to buy some colored contact lenses to hide pupil dilation. The eye problem was worsening and I didn't want to let anyone know about it. At the store, I could not concentrate at all and picked the cheapest 42-inch TV with built-in Roku internet entertainment. My vision had greatly improved, the colors and people at the store looked different than normal. I was able to see the individual skin pores of every person that passed by me. The brightness of the TV screens on display were out of this world. My vision was similar to the other night, when I drove through the ghetto. I was not able to take it anymore and sat down on a couch close to the cash registers. "This is astonishing. It looks like everybody is walking slower than normal and people at cash registers are removing items from carts at a slower rate, as well," I said to myself, then saw a drop of water falling from the ceiling. All details of the water drop were visible as it was falling in front of me. The drop fell on the floor and made a splash. Falling drops of water are truly magnificent when watched at slower speed. My visual abilities were amazing, but scary at the same time. "The agency can't find out about this." I reminded myself to keep cool, to be myself, no matter what. It was too late to see the eye doctor, but we bought the TV, had pizza, then left the store.

After lunch, I went to Sope Creek Park by myself. My visual abilities remained enhanced, and so I thought, "Why not do a few tests?" I drove to the park, which is about two miles from the house. This particular area is great as it is a protected natural reserve. There are the ruins of an old mill, way over a hundred years old. It is fun to explore the banks of Sope Creek. In the early 2000s, I almost followed the creek all the way to the Chattahoochee River. The terrain at the shores became unpassable to continue without getting wet.

The woods looked more beautiful than I could have ever imagined. I was able to see the individual cones on pine trees a few hundred yards away from me. The branches at the top of the trees in front of me were the same sharpness as branches located several hundred feet behind the first row of the trees. The bark looked like it was under a microscope. Each tree looked alive. Each pine straw, cone, and tree crown itself was moving slowly in perfect harmony as the wind played its magic. I was in a fairy tale and couldn't get enough of the view. The water of the pond was crystal clear, with small rainbows appearing right above the waterline at different times. I placed an empty coffee cup on the ground and walked to the other side of the pond, then focused on the cup from a distance of about 150–200 feet. The longer I looked, the closer and sharper the cup appeared. As the cup was moving closer, at a certain point I had to stop focusing because of the pain in my eyes. I was able to repeat this experiment several times with the same results. Never in my life had I had this zooming ability and I wished the pain would disappear for me to zoom even further. Unfortunately, I was no hawk and the pain remained. Nevertheless, I was plenty happy with the newly discovered ability. The eye pain was getting worse, so I focused on small objects such as leaves, grass, and my wedding ring, with eyes almost closed. This helped to lower the pain and my vision returned close to normal.

After my playtime at the park was over, I drove to the T-Mobile store on Roswell Road/Highway 120. The health symptoms I'd experienced through the week at different intervals appeared again. I was dizzy, tired, and couldn't concentrate anymore. My eyes started to hurt again. Shopping for a new phone became a nightmare. Since my eyes were so light-sensitive, I wanted a phone with an OLED display. That stands for Organic Light Emitting Diode and is much healthier for your eyes than LCD, especially at a close distance. There was a slight problem; I couldn't remember the specifications of more than one phone at a time. I must have been there for way more than an hour and kept going back and forth among the available phones. The employees were looking at me funny. "I better make a decision quick. They're thinking I am high," I thought, and quickly settled on ZTE; an unknown Chinese model that was less than $200.00.

The cashier looked almost exactly like my stepbrother, Patrik, who lives in the Czech Republic. "Interesting, I never saw anyone with such a resemblance. Could this be an agent? They are probably trying to trick me so an ambulance is called. There would be enough witnesses to tell my wife I acted weird. I am not going to say anything unusual to that person," I thought.

The cashier, "Patrik", was very helpful and way friendlier than a normal cashier. "You picked a great phone. It has the same features as your 700-dollar phone, including a fingerprint technology. I don't understand why more people don't buy it," he said.

I wanted to make him laugh, so I pulled out an empty wallet and made a joke. "If I had a five-dollar and a hundred-dollar bill in here, which one do you think I would give you?"

He smiled and replied, "The five-dollar one."

"You're wrong," I continued, "I would give you the hundred-dollar bill, because you saved me a hell of a lot of money today. Push this phone and it will happen with the next customer."

We both laughed and I left the store feeling happy.

After lunch, Romana took a nap. The girls wanted to rollerblade and ride their bicycles in front of the house. It was a cloudy day and the temperature was unusually warm for January. We wore short-sleeved shirts, and shorts. My mind began to race with ideas. "Who can control the weather like this? Who is able to input unusual items and experiences directly into my mind?"

I remembered the weather was unusually cold about two weeks ago. In Maggie Valley, North Carolina, I experienced the coldest weather in the Southeast in the past twenty-three years. As we were approaching the ski slopes, the car's thermometer displayed one degree Fahrenheit.

"What if I am in the Matrix?" I kept thinking and looking at the cloudy sky. The rainclouds were moving at faster than normal pace and it was so warm. The birds were flying and singing all around us. "Oh no, I am really in the Matrix, and about to be awoken to help the surviving people living underground to fight the AI machines. On second thought, I would rather stay in the Matrix and live quietly with my family. I don't care if the world is real or not. I like my life here. Why should I help to save the world that no longer exists?" I was brainstorming at faster and faster speed. "But what about the 'real' people that need my help? I can't say no to them." With tears in my eyes, I realized I had no choice but to be awoken from the Matrix. "To wake up out of the Matrix I have to fall asleep next to my wife, knowing I will awake in a filthy underground refugee camp. My family will no longer exist at that place. They were just part of a software package uploaded into my brain to keep my real body functioning."

As the thoughts were racing in my head, Teresa looked at me and said, "Daddy, go back to the house and fall asleep next to Mommy."

This confirmed my worst nightmare was the reality. I slowly went to the house. Teresa and Julia wanted to stay downstairs and play, so I hugged and kissed them for the last time to say my final goodbye. My body was shaking, a few silent tears dropped. I opened the bedroom door and turned around to see the kids for the last time. Romana was fully asleep and I screamed as loud as possible.

Romana quickly woke up. "What is wrong with you? Why are you screaming? Go to bed and get some rest!!"

She walked out of the bedroom, upset she had been abruptly awakened. I calmed myself down and thought, "The rule was to fall asleep next to my wife. Well, my wife is now gone and maybe the real people realized I am not yet ready to leave the Matrix. Additional training will be needed before the awakening." I was falling asleep while comforting myself in this manner.

I awoke in the real world or the Matrix or whatever you want to call it at this point, as my body and mind were present in the bedroom and the surroundings had not changed.

That evening, Teresa and I went to a father/daughter dance held at East Valley Elementary School. "Cool, at least I'll be able to take some pictures and videos with the new phone." I felt OK but still was not able to concentrate very well. "I better stay close to Teresa and focus on taking pictures, so nobody notices anything unusual about me."

I did just that, danced with Teresa, and took a lot of pictures and videos. My vision remained enhanced and I had no problem focusing on the phone screen while taking the videos. It appeared that my brain was able to process more information at the same time than ever before. I was able to focus on and process not only information from the phone screen, but on all the people who were dancing around me. "Do I now have the ability to slow time? Can I comprehend time differently than everybody else?" This reminded me of the falling drop of water I experienced earlier in the day. This was so cool, because I saw events at a slower pace, but was able to react to them at the same speed as everybody else. "Unbelievable, that's what I call competitive advantage! What is this? How did this happen? Who is doing this to me?" I was amazed but again scared at the same time. "What is really going on? Is this 'Reality TV,' 'Heaven vs Hell,' the 'Matrix,' or the 'Paranoid NSA'? Which one is it?" I thought in greater and greater speed.

Due to the uncertainty, my breathing increased, I had chest pains and was fatigued. I talked to Teresa and my friend Zack who also attended this event with his older daughter. His kids were the same age as mine and our families became good friends.

At home, I was relieved the event had ended as I wanted to forget about everything and go to bed as fast as possible. It became impossible to solve the riddles that night. "It would feel really good to close my eyes," I thought. I heard a loud noise and my younger daughter, Julia, began to cry. I ran downstairs as fast as I could.

Romana was comforting Julia, but she kept crying.

"I hope this is just an accident and the agency did not force Romana to do this, to make me angry," I thought. I wanted to find out the truth and calmly asked my wife, "Romana, what happened and what was the noise? Look at her, she keeps frantically crying."

"She fell from a stool and hit her back," was her answer.

I wanted to make sure she was OK and hadn't broken any bones. There was large blue mark in the middle of her back. "We better take her to the hospital. This doesn't look good," I said in disbelief.

Romana turned her head towards me and said, "Let's wait a few minutes. I think she will be OK."

"This doesn't look good, but let's see if she is able to walk." I finished the conversation.

To my relief, Julia was able to walk and didn't lose any ability to move whatsoever. I seriously believed the agency had something to do with this and within a few minutes became tired again. The unusual events that happened this week started to mix in together. "I have to fall asleep as soon as possible to protect myself and the family. Nobody, regardless of the scenarios, will be able to mess with me anymore," I thought, as I was falling asleep.

On Sunday, January 22nd, my wife and kids wanted to go to Woodruff Arts Center in the afternoon. My sister, her husband, and my nephew would be there as well.

Conversation during breakfast was unusual. Again, Romana and the kids started to mix words that didn't make much sense into sentences. Both kids were looking away while speaking with me. I therefore kept to myself as much as possible.

After breakfast, I needed a few minutes of quiet time and drove to Town Center mall to buy some new shirts. I hoped eventually my wife would let me fly to Prague.

The ride to the mall was unusual. I sat at an intersection waiting for the light to turn green and saw that people waiting in front of me were changing their minds on where to go, one by one. There might have been about eight cars, but I ended up third in line by the time the light turned green. This happened again at the next intersection. A black SUV followed me at close distance. Once the car turned and drove away another black SUV pulled right behind me. I heard planes and helicopters flying above me at close distance. "This better not be the agency," I said, and hoped the cars were just coincidences and the unusually high flight activity was perhaps an exercise in progress at the Dobbins Air Force base, located about five miles from my house.

I parked close to the mall's entrance doors as it had just opened. It was a rainy Sunday and most people were in church or had slept in. The lights, TV screens, surrounding objects, and people looked way sharper than normal; the enhanced vision had come back. Products didn't interest me because I was unable to concentrate. I kept walking around the corridors, food court, and different stores observing what people were doing. The eyes of each passing person were larger than normal and I was able to see much deeper and in greater detail into their eyes than ever before. Everyone who looked directly into my face was smiling. "I am definitely in a different world, way different from anything I ever experienced before. I was fired because I reacted to unusual events in an unusual way; everyone was told to go fuck themselves. This action produced the associated reaction."

I concluded, no matter what the circumstances are, I cannot react to them in an unusual way. The perspective of the world I lived in was changing to more extremes with each passing day. I was experiencing the following symptoms daily at different intervals; enhanced vision, conversations that at certain times did not make much sense, change in time perception, difficulty concentrating, short-term memory gaps, unusual surveillance and traffic activities.

Déjà vu happened during the drive home; the airplane and especially helicopter noises were louder than before, black cars and SUVs were following me at close distance. Cars at the intersections were going elsewhere one by one. I almost panicked and wanted to drive home as fast as possible. At the last minute, I realized this would not solve anything at all. It would only worsen the problems since my actions would create reactions. Little I knew of any upcoming surprises and figured out I have to abide by this rule going forward: No matter what I do, I cannot win. My only chance of survival is to play this "game" and act like an actor until I figure out what is really going on.

I struggled to stay positive and joked to myself as my thoughts switched to a friend of mine, Rob Rosen, who in the early 2000s moved from Atlanta to Los Angeles to become a movie star. He was a dreamer who never had a steady job. The last time we saw each other was in Los Angeles in 2007. At that time my construction business was falling apart and I had massive debt of almost 80,000 dollars. With little income, bankruptcy was inevitable. At least my wife had a steady job working for the airlines. During the trip we had a lot of fun; went to a gym daily, ate good food and talked about our lives and girls. It was the classic "locker room" talk. He took me to Gold's Gym in Venice where Arnold Schwarzenegger began his bodybuilding career and the *Pumping Iron* (1977) movie was filmed. I was not able to concentrate and breathe regularly during that workout. I had tremendous respect for the place and every piece of equipment that I touched, as strange feelings overwhelmed my body. I knew it would not get any better than this, because I was on sacred ground. Arnold and Sylvester were my role models when I lived in Czechoslovakia and were the main reason why I got into bodybuilding in the mid-1990s. I worked out at Marietta High School during the week and at the Scottish Inn motel on weekends. The motel manager, who was my mom's boyfriend at the time, had a small private gym in one of the rooms. My life had meaning and I was able to stay away from drugs and alcohol during the difficult times. Both Arnold and Sylvester indirectly saved my life.

During this trip Rob came up with a crazy and at the same time brilliant idea.

"Joseph, I have a great idea where we can make some extra money. I know you love pussy. How would you like to act in a porn movie? Come on, it'll be fun," Rob said, and I looked at him like he was insane.

"Act where?" I asked. This idea had also entered my mind in the past, but I'd never acted on it. I kind of liked what I was hearing and kept quiet.

"Yeah, in a porno. I always wanted to do it but I'm too shy and don't wanna go to the place by myself. There is an agency not too far from my house. Come on, Joseph, let's go there and see what happens," he said.

I knew this was not going to work out anyway. "The porn industry is looking for girls. They already have plenty of guys that are willing to do anything to be in the porn business. Also, the size of my dick is average, nobody wants to see average," I thought to myself, but decided not to spoil the fun moment. I said to Rob, "Why not? It'll be fun and I need the cash anyway."

Rob was ecstatic and we immediately drove to the agency's office. I was not surprised when a beautiful woman told us that the agency was not looking for males at this time. She smiled to herself. It appeared she was clearly amused and entertained by how courageous we were to follow our dreams.

As we walked out of the office, Rob was clearly disappointed and said, "That's bullshit. I thought at least they would invite us for an audition. My dick is the right size and I can fuck."

"Rob, don't worry about it. It will definitely happen next time. Just don't give up," I said, to comfort him.

I continued driving home while obeying all traffic laws. When I finished replaying the memories of the California trip in my head, I said to myself, "If I see something unusual, why not call myself 'The Hollywood Rob.' This will definitely remind me not to do anything stupid and to stay calm, no matter what."

I was happy there were no more surprises waiting for me at home. The kids, however, were behaving strangely. They both religiously adhered to the "good kid vs bad kid" scenario and were not looking at me during a conversation. This continued until the whole family was ready to go to Woodruff Arts Center. We entered the car and the kids started to provoke me again. I turned around and said in a strong voice, "Be quiet, I've had enough of this today!"

My wife looked at me like she had no idea why I'd said this. "Why are you yelling at them? Who do you think you are?"

"What am I?" I said. I paused for a while and continued, "I am their father. They have been driving me nuts for the past several days!"

"Get out of the car right now. You were driving me nuts for the past week. On top of that, you had the balls to tell me that you were flirting with women at work and that you were fired because of that. Get out now!!!" she said.

I exited the car, greatly disappointed, and realized I broke the number one rule; I have to stay calm, no matter what. "I am 'The Hollywood Rob' who should act to win the Academy Award and not react to unusual circumstances. The house and cars are most likely under surveillance and the agency is waiting for an excuse to take me away against my will." As soon as I finished the sentence, Romana drove back to pick me up. Everyone in the car was silent. I entered the car and kept quiet until we reached the Woodruff Arts Center in downtown Atlanta.

Once we met with my sister Milli, her husband Jonathan, and their son, Asa, some of the symptoms reappeared again. I had the enhanced vision, was sensitive to light, accompanied by light eye pain, and had difficulties concentrating. I was in a good mood because the kids and Romana behaved normally. They were no longer mixing unusual words into sentences.

The arts center organized an interactive event for small children and their parents. A woman in her mid-thirties played a flute and a man of similar age played a bass instrument. They would stop at certain intervals to ask the children questions related to the instruments. There were about ten children ranging from two years to roughly eight years old, accompanied by their parents. My family and I were sitting on the floor in the second row. As I was looking at the woman, interesting thoughts occupied my mind. "She reminds me of the movie, *American Pie*. It's like, one time in band camp, I stuck a flute. . . She is good-looking. I wouldn't mind having a 'play day' with her. She certainly wouldn't mind if I offered my assistance to insert the instrument somewhere else besides her mouth."

At that moment, my time perception changed as time slowed down again. The flutist slightly jumped up and down from her chair then closed her eyes, looked down and slightly opened her mouth to exhale. "Wow, she is getting excited. Maybe I have something to do with this. Somehow, I am able to influence her bodily functions :-) because I am in the Matrix and the real people who will awake me in the near future would like to have some fun. Great, no harm done. Nobody in the room will know what I am doing," I thought, and continued to think while looking at the woman, my eyes did not blink at all. "This is my The Witches of Eastwick game. You are slowly getting wetter and warmer down there. The sensations are increasing until you will not be able to take it anymore."

Both the woman and the man continued to play until intermission. He presented his questions to the children and the woman breathed heavily and was looking down to her right away from the audience. She kept slightly moving her legs from one side to the other. It looked like she was trying to find a comfortable sitting position because something down there bothered her. I noticed two older men in black suits were approaching the musicians simultaneously, one from each side. I did not completely rule out the NSA scenario, even after I was pretty sure my mind and body were in the Matrix. I reminded myself of the "The Hollywood Rob" rule. "I better stop it right now! If she reaches climax, the agents may take me away for questioning." I was well aware what happened to Ronnee at the lunch on December 15 2016. She was pretty loud and obvious when this happened to her. I did not want to raise any suspicions and spoke with my family for the rest of the event. I periodically glanced at the woman, who was doing just fine, and her "symptoms" went away completely. Oddly enough, right after I started to socialize with my family, the "agents" went back to the other end of the room and my time perception went back to normal.

I had so much fun with the female musician that I did not bother to figure out the right scenario. My brother-in-law, Jonathan, had a great time as well. We talked about work, camping, and smoking weed. He was in a good mood and it appeared he had smoked something before the event. He had slow reactions and laughed at everything I told him. I joked about being fired a few days ago and how women in general make my life difficult.

"I can't live with them and can't live without them. Let's go camping to Ellaville since I have all this free time. Let's make it a guys' trip so we can have some real fun shooting guns," I said.

"That sounds like a lot of fun, let's do it," he said, and smiled.

I always liked going camping to South Georgia. Jonathan's dad owns about 200 acres of land, consisting of field, surrounded by forest for three-quarters of the perimeter. There is a pond and the ruins of an old house located in the middle of the forest. My favorite activity, besides camping, is "drive by shooting"; all kinds of targets such as paper figurines are placed around the outer perimeter of the field. One person drives a pick-up truck and the others sit on a flatbed trying to do as much damage as possible. In the past few years, we hadn't done much shooting at all. We started to bring our small children with us and didn't want to endanger or bother them with loud noises.

I was in a good mood and didn't experience any unusual symptoms. As we were walking downstairs from the first floor to exit the building, I noticed one "agent" continued to stare at me.

71

I overcame my fears and asked him a question: "It is a beautiful day today, isn't it?"

"It sure is," he answered, in a dry and suspicious tone of voice.

It sounded like he was trying to get more information out of me. I did not say anything else and just kept walking toward the exit. I played with the kids as much as possible at a playground located in front of the building. I went to all the slides and attractions where an adult person could fit.

"Guys, come on over," I yelled at the adult members of my family, but nobody came.

After the fun with the kids, I tried to loosen up my wife to help her forget I was fired a few days ago. It would be nice to see her smile. "Come on, have some fun! I will fix everything up. You know women, they're giving me a hard time at work and at home." Romana smiled a little but kept quiet, so I talked with Milli and Jonathan until we drove home.

When we parked the car and entered the house, Romana asked me to come to the kitchen so the kids were not able to hear us. "Why did you disrespect me in front of everybody like that? Why did you keep asking about the same things over and over again?"

I stopped her and said, "What things? How were you disrespected? I just asked Jonathan about camping and possible employment at his company. I tried to make you smile and joked about women a little bit."

I could not recall anything close to what she was saying. I did make a few jokes about how some women in general treat men, classy jokes and comments, nothing sleazy. I reminded myself of "The Hollywood Rob" rule and wanted to normalize the situation.

"I'm sorry if I said something unusual. I'm really tired and need some rest. This week has been crazy so far," I said, and went to the office upstairs to be alone, to recap the unusual events.

"What if I am not the only one experiencing this?" I wondered. "Since the December 15 2016 lunch, things were never the same between the girls and me. The next day, on the 16th, Ronnee felt really good and excited about what happened on the previous day. When our eyes met at the hallway, I was sure we both felt the same way about each other. When Jessica returned from Ireland, I began to get sick. I love and care for Ronnee and have to warn her, no matter what, without raising suspicions. I really don't know what is going on and hope she isn't experiencing the same abnormalities. It is all just speculation at this point, any scenario could be the new reality." Many thoughts were racing through my head. For some reason the women and I never exchanged phone numbers. I had no way to communicate with them. Ronnee indirectly asked me for a phone number during our last private lunch on

December 21 2016, but I didn't have a chance to give her the information.

"Joseph, I would like to have the number for your car mechanic."

Our eyes met at full stare during and after she finished the sentence. We both enjoyed the moment. I continued to think and hoped to solve some or all the riddles: "All the women, including Leah, and the unusual events I am experiencing are somehow connected. With Leah, it was always an emotional roller coaster ride. With Ronnee, Jessica, and Christine, it was nothing but an emotional roller coaster ride. The women are different, but beautiful in their own way. All four have a different set of skills; Leah is a tax accountant, Ronnee is a lawyer, Jessica is a communications manager and Christine is a finance person. They have a couple very important qualities in common; none of them are the typical 'gold-diggers' and all have down-to-earth personalities. I could spend hours and hours talking with any one of them. The four made me feel comfortable and good about myself. The more I was around them, the more I liked them. It is rare to find such a great group of friends. This has to have a purpose, especially when all the circumstances are factored in."

I began to get lost in my thoughts and was unable to figure anything out. I proceeded with the plan to warn Ronnee, to send her a LinkedIn message. I didn't want to send it directly to her since the NSA agents would definitely pick her up for "questioning." If the "Heaven vs Hell" situation was real, she would be crucified on the cross. If the "Matrix" was the reality, the artificial intelligence or the real people could kill her. If the "Reality TV" show was real, then the politicians could remove her from the show to expedite my decision-making regarding socialism vs capitalism. "No matter what the scenario, nobody can know that I love her. I can't act on these feelings and need to bury the feelings as fast as possible in the place called 'mind'." This was my final decision before starting up the computer. I reminded myself of Leah and looked at her LinkedIn profile picture. "She is definitely the agent of Hell, with black hair and slightly blue eyes. I would expect her eyes to be a different color, perhaps brown like Christine's. Yes, let me look at Christine's profile picture," I said to myself, and kept thinking on how to pull this off.

At that point, I felt really tired and unable to concentrate and focus my eyes. As I was looking at Christine's picture, the time slowed down again. She was becoming more beautiful with each passing second and her eyes appeared larger than normal. It almost looked like the photograph attempted to communicate with me as the following thoughts appeared in my mind: "Yes, this is it. I will send the message to Christine, who will than show the message to the rest of the group. I will describe some of the symptoms that happened at the park yesterday. On top of that, I will be nasty to Ronnee to protect her. Ronnee's life is more important to me than my love for her. She needs to forget about me, anyway, or at least to a point when I realize what is really going on. I also care for Christine, who needs to learn a lesson; be able to overcome her deepest fears and realize Joseph is no Devil. What about Jessica? Well, I also care for her very much, but don't think she is experiencing any symptoms. At the December 15 2016 lunch, she was there just to watch, kind of like a sweet angel. Jessica was not abused as a child so why would she fear the Devil?" These thoughts were pouring in, one after another, until I opened LinkedIn and wrote this message:

Hi Christine, I apologize to you and everyone at Argos for what happened. It felt like I was losing my mind. I went to a park and focused on my wedding ring and faraway objects with my eyes almost closed. I feel much better but still would love to have a joint! :-) Contact me anytime you would like to have a cup of coffee ;-)
You know what that means.
You always said I am your little Devil ;-)
Say hi to the asshole Mark and the cunt Ronnee :-(
They really fucked everything for both of us.
I always believe what I see and not always what I hear! We will see each other again when the time is right!
Love, Joseph

"This is perfect. Nobody will have any idea about my true feelings for Ronnee, who will surely get the message if she has similar symptoms. Maybe I'll be contacted in future for additional help. Christine will get the message as well. She will probably be scared to death at first, but will become a stronger person once she realizes that Hell or Satan Joseph is not waiting for her around the corner."

After reassuring myself and reading the message several times over, I pressed the "send" button. After dinner, I began to feel good again. It was like someone just gave me an extra shot of adrenaline. I wanted to tell Romana about my work-related plans to continue to flip stocks on the side and get back to construction. "Let's sell the house and make 150k. We live in a country club and the houses around us sell for about 400k to 450k. We can use the money to buy a fixer-upper to flip. We can rent a house somewhere close by until the cash flow increases. It will be perfect, so what do you say? You have a steady job and are gone three to four days per week. I can do whatever on the side and finally be able to spend more time with you and the kids. Who cares about money? I just want to be with the kids as much as possible before they grow up. I don't want them to grow up with a babysitter and in front of a TV. Those kids are like zombies, unable to think for themselves."

I presented the case with as much enthusiasm as possible. Unfortunately, Romana was not happy at all and kept making negative comments.

"You did not go to college to become a construction worker. Are you gonna throw your career away just like that?"

At that point, my reactions to her comments were too fast. I had to concentrate really hard to not answer before she finished her sentence.

After the fruitless conversation, I went upstairs to check out the new phone. The brightness and sharpness of the screen was incredible. I read several news articles and noticed the screen was emitting vibrations of light, the same flashes of light emitted by the computer screen at work! The phone's shape was not straight, it was slightly curved. I panicked and threw the phone on the floor. "Shit, what am I gonna do? I can't act suspicious and complain about this to Romana, to T-Mobile, or the manufacturer. I'll continue to look at the screen as long as I can take it. The screen is not large, hopefully it will not be too bad."

I calmed myself down and resumed reading the news articles. The flashes of light were shooting into my eyes at unpredictable intervals, creating extreme difficulty when I tried to concentrate, as my eyes were hurting. Also, I felt pressure in both cheeks and temporal bones. It felt like my face was about to collapse into itself as I was losing consciousness. "I have to stop right now before I collapse," I thought. I turned the phone off, lay on the floor and closed my eyes.

I was feeling better after a few minutes and started to think. "How am I going to function in society, like this? I need to be able to look into a computer screen for a minimum of eight to ten hours a day to work in my field. Will the abnormalities ever disappear or am I going to live like this or worse for the rest of my life? If I restart the construction business, I will not have to worry about computer, phone, or TV screens too often. I can manage this, I just have to believe in myself." I was unhappy how the day ended. That evening, it felt so good lying in bed with my eyes closed.

On Monday January 23rd, I woke up with facial pains. The pain was not as severe as the previous evening, but it was annoying. I couldn't read much news on my cell phone because the light flashes reappeared. "I am screwed, the NSA know I broke my phone on Friday. The agents contacted my current provider, T-Mobile, and hacked my future phone. They drugged me so I would not be able to concentrate while making the purchase. The agents are not stupid and by this time know more about me than I know about myself. They knew I would purchase a cheap model. I never buy the latest gadgets and why should I? Most electronics will be worthless within a couple of years." I tried to hide my fears and read a few more articles.

Romana planned to buy a new couch today. She left the house shortly after breakfast to run a few errands. I was supposed to meet her at 11 a.m. on Barret Parkway, at Rooms To Go. Again, I experienced the unusual surveillance activity on my way to the store. I heard helicopters and airplanes flying above the car most of the time and different vehicles followed me at close distance. One new situation experienced before appeared again: as I was approaching vehicles from behind on I-75, each car moved away to a different lane. "That is nice. I have the whole highway for myself, but I shouldn't abuse the situation by speeding, it is not worth it. I remember very well what happens if I react to any event in unusual way."

The Rooms To Go store was located somewhere on Barret Parkway. I called my wife for directions, but the phone did not work properly. I tried several more times, but the calls kept getting disconnected. There was a "beep" signal shortly after the beginning of each call. I gave up on trying to reach her and continued to drive on Barret Parkway, towards Kennesaw. In less than a minute, the store was on my right side, but I was unable to cross over the right lane quickly enough and missed the turn. I parked my car at a Chevrolet car dealership positioned right next to the furniture store, found a nice parking spot in front of the main entrance and walked to the adjacent store. "Nobody will care if I leave the car here for a few minutes. Why would they bother their future customer? The new Corvette looks good, but I wouldn't buy it. The electric Bolt is the car of my interest." I kept thinking about cars until I saw Romana at the store talking with a salesman.

"Hi, Romana, so show me what you like," I said.

"Hi, OK, come on over. You will like this one in the dark maroon color," she replied, in an excited way. It was a modern-looking leather sofa with a forward-facing flatbed extension. The sofa was really comfortable and looked great, so I gave her the "OK" to purchase it, despite its price. A few days ago, I tried to convince her to postpone the purchase until the business I had in mind started to produce a stable income. I didn't push her too hard because she hated the current living room set. It was a used two-piece white Italian leather sofa given to us by my ex-boss and good friend, Jeff Mathis.

Jeff Mathis story
Jeff was an interesting individual whom I met at Main Event Fitness, back in 2003. He was cool, relaxed, and always had a great story. Jeff was the classic salesman who would talk to anyone about anything for hours. I lost my people's personality a long time ago and was the exact

opposite. I kept to myself and did not initiate conversations with strangers, either men or women. He was the one who approached me, and we talked more and more with each passing day. Jeff was married to a good-looking Russian lady in her mid-thirties, named Regina, and had three daughters: four-year-old Brooke from the current marriage, another small girl from his second marriage and sixteen-year-old Jacqueline, from his first marriage. This was his third marriage.

In the summer of 2004, Jeff hired me to manage day-to-day operations at his company, Georgia Credit Systems, a small collection agency of four people. I didn't know at the time that Jeff had already run the company into the ground. His largest customer, a Natural Gas company, stopped forwarding collection work several months before I started, and Jeff didn't even know it. The person he trusted with everything was lying to him about what was going on at the business. Jeff made the terrible mistake of not watching and verifying what his employees were doing. He was not checking the numbers either, as his main hobbies were the women, traveling to Europe, and partying all the time, like there was no end in sight. He almost never worked, therefore became totally dependent on James, the person I was replacing. Jeff realized something was wrong when one of his employees, a young woman, accidently caught James watching porn in his office. There was one small problem. The porn was not just the regular porn that most males ranging from about ten to ninety years old watch on daily basis. The porn consisted of women having sex with dogs. :-o The young lady was traumatized by the scenery (who wouldn't be, right girls?) and reported the incident straight to the owner. Jeff started to dig into what was really going on at the business and decided to replace Mr. James. :-)

I did my best, even after finding out the company would eventually go out of business. Jeff was spending most of the cash on partying, with no intention of reinvesting some of the money to grow the business. I truthfully reported my concerns and what was going on at the business, but he didn't care anymore. I was frequently told to leave work early or not to work at all (especially on Fridays and Mondays), and to meet him at a bar. I would then drink a little and drive him around until late at night. It was a lot of fun at first and the pay of $800 per week wasn't bad either. He paid for all the entertainment and was letting me drive his 2002 convertible black-on-black Porsche 911, with six-speed manual clutch, for weeks at a time. I had so much fun driving this vehicle around Atlanta. This was the perfect company car! Jeff was color-blind and loved black. His favorite clothes were black workout attire, which he wore almost daily.

After a while, I knew this lifestyle wasn't for me. "There is no future in this. Life becomes meaningless, as a person doesn't develop and only lives to survive. This is a path to self-destruction and I need to find a way to get out of this." I kept analyzing the situation more frequently as time went by. Jeff's attention-deficit disorder kept getting worse. He had countless Botox injections, all his teeth were replaced by perfectly white implants. He was checking his face and hair in a car's rearview mirror all the time. I liked Jeff, but didn't want to be around him anymore because I was unable to help him turn his life around. Deep down, Jeff was a great person with too big a heart. He wanted everyone around him to be happy and would do anything for his family and friends, regardless of money. He was one of those rare people you could trust with your life and not some two-faced fake who could backstab you any minute.

One party event stood above the others. After the usual drinking at a bar, Jeff decided to pick up one of his girlfriends and take her to the Four Seasons hotel in downtown Atlanta. The Presidential Suite was chosen as the appropriate room and Jeff gladly submitted the company's credit card. The rate of the room was $3,500 per night. We looked around the reception area and the three of us sat in a saloon close to the lobby. Everything in the hotel was immaculately and beautifully decorated. There were plenty of small trees and flowers in the saloon to keep a person feeling comfortable.

"Hey, Joseph," Jeff said in a curious tone of voice, "I'm here with my girlfriend and I don't think it's fair you're sitting here alone. How would you like some female company?"

I stopped admiring the scenery and replied, "It would be nice, but you know I am not dating anybody right now."

"That's not a problem," he said, and continued to speak in a slow tone of voice. "We can arrange that. You know I would do anything for my best friend. I'll tell the concierge to order you a young beautiful blonde."

I was so surprised by the offer, but instantly became worried because prostitution is illegal in this country. "Come on, Jeff, this is not Europe. They'll call the cops on us. It's not worth it!"

He refused to listen and instructed the concierge to call over a young blonde woman. The person politely declined and stated the hotel doesn't offer these kinds of services. Jeff asked for the hotel's manager to come over immediately. Within a few minutes, a woman in her late-forties to low-fifties, dressed in a professional business suit, came over.

"Gentlemen, what can I do for you this evening?" she said in a friendly, slow, and polite tone of voice.

You were able to tell the woman had class. The lady wore "secretary glasses" and looked and acted like a CEO.

"Well, my friend here," said Jeff, then pointed his hand towards me, "would like a young blonde girl to escort him to our room. You know what that means. Would you be so kind as to arrange this for us?"

I felt horrible and unable to look into the woman's face anymore, so I looked down.

"I am so sorry, we always try to accommodate our guests as best we can. This, however, is beyond the services offered by the hotel."

I glanced at her and noticed she was looking directly at me while speaking. I raised my arm upwards by a few inches away from my body and pointed towards Jeff like I was giving her a signal to let her know I had given up on my friend this evening. This was all his fault not mine.

"Please do it for us. We stay at the Presidential Suite and are one of your best customers." Jeff was not giving up.

Again, she politely answered, "I appreciate the business. We will do anything we possibly can to make your stay enjoyable. I would like to help you in this area, but cannot do it because of legal issues. I would suggest calling someone from the Yellow Pages."

Jeff eventually realized the hotel would not fulfil this request, no matter what. I was impressed with how professional the woman and the staff remained. I thought for sure the manager would call the cops and we would be arrested or, if lucky, we would be kicked out of the hotel. This proved to me money really talks.

I was astonished how large the Presidential Suite was. The main conference room had a table for about fifteen people and the view of the city out of the large window was amazing. There were two separate bedrooms and each had a private bathroom. The furniture, fixtures, and art were beautiful. Each room had a large LCD TV, an unusual hotel feature for mid-2000s. "What a difference from the Scottish Inn motel." I remembered how dumpy the place was compared to this room.

Jeff told his girlfriend, Kimbo, to pick up the Yellow Pages and order the hot blonde. I don't know why he insisted on a blonde girl. I knew he liked blondes, but he didn't ask me what I liked. My preference would have been a brunette. At that point, I gave up on trying to stop Jeff and took it as a quarterly employee bonus for my hard work. By the way, I started to get a hard-on anyway, there was no point in resisting this any longer. "Whatever, I need to have some fun. I will not have sex with the girl. A massage with a happy ending should do the trick." I promised myself not to fuck her since she probably already had a few guys before me.

When the escort girl entered the room, Kimbo welcomed her and talked with her like they were best friends. The four of us ordered steak dinners and chatted for a while. After the dinner, Kimbo looked at me and the girl, then smiled and said, "This gentleman is the lucky one. Go take care of him. You go, girl." I went to my room and helped the girl undress. We entered a bath tub together, where she gently washed me and I washed her. Then we returned to the bedroom.

"So, Joseph, what do you like?" she said.

"I don't know," I replied.

"You don't know? But I know exactly what you want. Why don't you lie over there on the bed and let me be in charge from now on," said the girl, named Stella.

She was almost thirty, but looked like she was in her early twenties. Stella spoke in a soft, comforting tone of voice. She touched and looked at me like she really liked me. I probably was not one of her usual customers. She massaged and kissed me all over my body. I wanted to return the favor and did the same for her. I did not want to make her feel like a paid hooker, but wanted her to feel more like a person that I cared for; my girlfriend I fell in love with. She was enjoying herself, our eyes met at full stare and she began to French kiss me. I was surprised but did not try to stop her. "She really knows how to kiss," I thought, as we continued to kiss and touch each other all over our bodies for several minutes. I went down on her and within a few minutes Stella climaxed. She was not faking it because her body was slightly shaking, then she moved her head backwards, opened her eyes and deeply exhaled. Her tone of voice was not loud at all. She made an orgasmic sound and squeezed her lips in full satisfaction.

"Did you like it?" I asked her.

"Every second of it. Joseph, nobody ever ate my pussy the way you did. Lie down and I'll do the same for you, just let me know when you are ready to put on a condom and go inside me," she said.

"That's so sweet, Stella, but I would just like head. Please don't take it personally, it has nothing to do with you. I just promised myself not to do this, no matter what," I said.

"No problem, I will do whatever you like," she answered.

I lay on my back and tried to relax. Stella genuinely smiled and again was kissing me all over my body and went down on me. It felt incredible. She really knew what she was doing by taking her time and not rushing it. I had a strange thought: "I am in the Presidential Suite, so I should try to make it as memorable as possible."

I said to my lover, "Stella, can you do me a favor? Please put on your blouse and let me cum on it. Sit in front of the bed and I will stand while we are doing this."

She smiled and replied, "Whatever you like, Joseph."

She put on her white blouse and resumed the blowjob. I purposely came all over her right shoulder, breast and said the following sentence to myself, "I did not have sexual relations with that woman!"

I smiled in full satisfaction and said, "This could not get any better than this!"

After the endless fun, we continued to talk for a couple hours. She gave me her real phone number and address. Strangely enough, Stella lived in the apartment complex right next to where my mom lived. I never called her again because I could not date her. I knew I wouldn't be able to get over one important factor in her life, her place of employment.

Back at the furniture store
"I really like the sofa. It's very comfortable and will fit great into our living room. If you like it, then let's buy it," I said, and Romana smiled in satisfaction that I shared her taste.

"Let's get some discount. Please don't say anything or you are going to ruin my negotiations," I said, and approached the salesman, who was waiting for us behind a computer located in the center of the store.

He was an older gentleman who knew for sure the sofa was sold. My wife, like most people, is unable to hide emotions while shopping.

"How are you? I am Joseph and I am this young lady's husband." I shook his hand and continued to speak. "We may be interested to purchase the sofa that is placed over there, but the price isn't right. It is a substantial purchase. Can you help us with the price so we can reach a deal?"

The person looked directly at my face and answered politely but firmly, "I am sorry sir, we don't give discounts. It's against the company's policy."

"Are you sure? Because everything is negotiable," I answered, while looking directly into his eyes.

"Believe me, I would like to help you, but unfortunately I can't do anything." He maintained his position.

I looked at Romana and firmly said, "Let's go, we can get a better deal somewhere else, maybe from an online store."

I was walking away towards the exit, but Romana kept standing next to the salesman and would not move. I tried several times to make her leave, but was unsuccessful. Given the circumstances of what was going on in my life, I didn't want to push my luck. I could not concentrate and kept answering or asking questions faster than anyone else. I had to continuously remind myself to let the other people finish talking before entering the conversation. At least these were the only symptoms I was experiencing.

"OK, you're the boss. Do whatever you want," I said, and gave up.

Once the salesperson entered the order, he asked me how I was going to pay for it.

"Don't ask me," I replied. I pretended to be surprised and pointed my arm towards my wife. "She made the decision and she will pay for it. I just stand here."

Romana looked at me like I'd lost my mind, but made the first payment anyway and financed the rest at 0% for twenty-four months. The salesman was happy and walked us out.

Just before we exited the building, I asked him a question. "You're a pretty good salesman with a lot of experience. I'm sure you can sell anything at this point."

He looked at my face and replied with a smile, "That's right, I can sell anything. I've been in the business for years."

"Good for you. Can I borrow your pen?" He then gave me his pen and I said, "If I tell you to sell me this pen, you can't do it, can you?" I gave him the pen back and he abruptly walked away, without saying goodbye.

Romana wanted to do some more shopping and we agreed to meet for lunch at the nearby all-you-can-eat sushi buffet, Ru San's. I was curious about the upcoming electric Chevy Bolt and walked into the Chevy dealership to look at cars.

A salesman introduced himself. "How are you today? Can I help you with anything?"

I smiled back at him and calmly responded, "Good, is the Chevy Bolt on sale yet? Can I get a brochure?" The car was not on sale and the dealership had no idea when the model would become available.

"Why wait for the Bolt when we have the Volt on sale right now? Let's sit down at that table over there and discuss your options," the salesman said.

For no reason, I started to feel dizzy and time slowed down. Everybody spoke and moved around at a slower pace. My vision increased and everything looked sharper and brighter than normal. I gave up and answered, "Why not. The Volt is an electric/gas hybrid with forty miles range on the battery alone. I can get the best of both worlds."

We sat down and a second salesperson joined us for the conversation. They both tried really hard to make a sale that day. The more questions I asked, the cheesier the answers became. I'd had enough and wanted to end the conversation, and said, "I have about a year and half worth of lease payments on my Leaf. Does it make sense to break the lease?"

"Sure, go ahead and break your lease. We'll give you a great deal today."

I didn't expect that kind of answer and abruptly stood up from the chair. "Gentlemen, you think I was born yesterday? You're telling me that breaking a lease makes economic sense? I'll never come into this building again." Both men were stunned by the answer and didn't say a word. I was leaving the dealership and, just before the exit, I turned around and said to everyone, "Next time, try to rip off someone else, you phonies!"

I drove to the Ru San's restaurant, located about a mile away on the other side of I-75. I sat at a bar and tried unsuccessfully to call my wife. The pictures on several TVs that were hanging from the ceiling above the bar were moving up and down. It was the same movement of the TVs made in the 1960s. Back in those days, the sets had to be manually adjusted with the "turn" button positioned at the back of a TV. A young server in his early twenties came by and asked if I needed anything. I asked for a glass of water. We then spoke about nature and traveling. He was a free-spirited individual. The type of individual who would one day decide to walk the Appalachian Trail, quit his job and pack the next day, then leave for six months to complete the journey.

I became worried about what was going on. The NSA situation seemed the most realistic. The TVs and the cell phones had to be replaced.

"Where can I get a nice used phone with a customized operating system? You know what I mean?" I asked the server.

"There's a small store right next to the restaurant. They'll be able to help you," he calmly replied, smiled, and went back to work.

The TVs continued to have the issues with picture, but oddly nobody noticed or said anything to the restaurant employees. I made a decision to leave the restaurant and go to the cell phone store next door. As soon as I exited the restaurant the phone rang.

"Hello Joseph, this is Tim from 6 Degrees Group, how're you?"

"So-so; how're you?" I answered.

Tim continued, "You cannot contact anyone at Argos."

"In that case I also can't send anymore LinkedIn requests," I replied.

Debbie, the human resource employee at Argos, abruptly entered the conversation. "That is correct, Joseph, you can't contact anybody in any way. What you did to Christine—"

I interrupted her. "Please say 'I am sorry' to everyone at Argos, especially to Christine. I apologize to Ronnee and Mark, goodbye."

"Wait, Joseph!" Debbie wanted to get more information, but I hung up the phone. I felt awful and hoped Christine didn't end up in a psychiatric institution. Religion was used, among many tools, to abuse her, the Devil was one of her genuine fears. During one of our conversations, she mentioned the Devil and Angel are not real and organized religion is a scam to keep the people under control. I knew she would eventually be able to pull herself together.

I was in a bad mood due to the phone call and scrapped the lunch and the phone purchase. To go home as soon as possible was the number one wish.

The ride home was accompanied by the usual weirdness: loud aviation noises, cars following at close distance and unpredictable behaviors by other drivers at intersections. I didn't care anymore as this was becoming my new reality. I was beginning to accept the idea of unpredictable "weirdness" and thought this might have been orchestrated by the intelligence agency. "They are wasting millions of dollars to monitor a person just because of a 'he said, she said' story. I will not give them the pleasure of driving me insane and will play this game as long as I have to. It has to end someday because even the NSA has limited resources," I thought, but wasn't too sure about the last sentence and remembered the circumstances surrounding Edward Snowden.

At home, while eating lunch, I wanted to read the news on my cell phone. When alone, I liked to read the news while eating breakfast, snack, lunch, and dinner. I read most news while eating lunch, or at least I did until I met the four women at Argos. :-) Besides being unable to focus, the phone kept giving me the same problems. The flashes of vibrating light were intensifying and the touch screen behaved oddly. The picture moved up and down at irregular intervals and the finger touch command function was off, as well. I had to press the screen several times for the phone to work. I received a text message from Tim at 6 Degrees: "Joseph, come to our office to pick up the screen privacy protector and a sweater."

I wrote back, "I will not come. I am too ashamed."

After the message was sent, I resumed reading the news and saw a picture of on old stroller with a microphone hanging from the top down. The tip of the microphone was a few inches above a baby. The article mentioned that someone had been recorded since birth. "This can't be happening. There is no way the 'Reality TV' scenario is real, as the circumstances of my present life point to the 'NSA' scenario." I became so confused, turned the phone off and went upstairs to take a nap.

After not being able to fall asleep for at least an hour, I walked downstairs to the kitchen/living room area. There was a large suitcase standing next to the main entry door.

"What is going on, Romana? Why is the suitcase here?" I asked, in shock.

"You need to leave the house. I just about had enough of you."

I did not want to cause a scene and said, "Let's talk about it—"

She abruptly interrupted, saying, "There is nothing to talk about. Leave, leave right now." She maintained her ground.

"This is ridiculous. You know what, I'll go to my sister's house. Have a nice life." I packed a few more items, grabbed the suitcase and took the Leaf instead of the Mercedes. During the drive, it became difficult to keep my eyes on the road. I had a headache, my whole face felt like it would collapse in itself at any moment. Luck was on my side; the house was only fifteen minutes away.

Chapter 4
It's Showtime!

My sister Milli was understanding and took me in after I explained the situation.

"Milli, I am so tired and have to take a nap."

"OK, Joseph, go to the master bedroom. I hope you will not mind the mess," she said, and pointed her hand toward the bedroom.

"I don't care about anything anymore," I thought. I said "Hi," to my little nephew, Asa, and went to bed. I fell asleep several times but kept waking up in less than twenty minutes. The weather was strange. It rained on and off and the Sun was hitting my face at different intervals. I began to analyze the situation again and went over all the possible scenarios. "I don't know anymore. I just need to be patient as there are too many unknowns at this time. My symptoms and the surrounding effects keep changing at an unpredictable rate."

I looked out the window and was amazed by the scenery. It was right after the rain ended, the sky was crystal blue, the Sun's rays were entering the bedroom and everything looked so peaceful. "Maybe I am in front of the gates to Heaven. This will all be over soon." I thought of this as I was learning to accept the "Heaven vs Hell" reality. I also reminded myself of "The Hollywood Rob" rule and went to the living room to talk with Milli and Jonathan.

We spoke for a while about my situation. I was told to stay at the house until I found a job and a place to live. I hoped this would blow over soon and I would be able to return home.

Jonathan and I went to the backyard and the conversation continued. "This week has been rough. I lost my wife, my job, and I don't feel too good. I need a joint! Do you have any?" I asked Jonathan.

"Joseph, you need to calm down and relax, then I'll give you something."

I knew Jonathan always had a little bit of weed lying around somewhere. I kept asking for the joint but the answer was always evasive. He finally gave in when we entered his workshop; a wooden structure with two separate rooms that could easily be converted to a man cave. He picked up a small smoke pipe that was lying around among the countless number of individual tools.

"Here it is, Joseph, enjoy it. I need to find a lighter."

I was really excited as I was holding the pipe with both hands. "It sure will make me feel good and help to forget about all this shit that's happening in my life." My thoughts were interrupted when I realized that I don't really care for drugs. "I don't do drugs and hardly ever drink. I am a gym freak and this goes against my religion." The last time I'd smoked weed was about six years ago while camping in South Georgia. Weed and alcohol never had any effects on me, besides making me feel euphoric at first and sick later. I wouldn't be able to work out the way I did if I was a party person. There are exceptions to every rule. There were two occasions in my life when I enjoyed getting drunk and high.

A couple short memories. . .
In 1994, a few weeks before permanently moving to the USA, my buddy Honza and I went to my mom's cottage for the weekend. The cottage is located in the wooded Vltava River canyon, about an hour from Prague. It was a great trip. We did all the fun stuff fifteen-year-old kids would do when left alone. We explored the area by inflatable kayak, cooked our own meals, talked about everything, drank beer, and listened to our favorite bands of that time; Tři Sestry, Vysací Zámek, and Orlík. In late afternoon, it was time to visit the pub located in the nearest village, Krňany, about a forty-five-minute walk through the woods. In those times, nobody checked IDs. If you looked old enough you were able to drink as much as you wanted. A restaurant or pub could not be sued if you drove drunk and killed a person. That evening, I had ten half-liters of a lager beer, one Bavarian beer; a mixed drink consisting of Fernet and tonic and, of course, one "Zelená," (peppermint liqueur), a favorite drink of the Tři Sestry band. I felt OK until I started to walk across the pub toward the exit; I opened the entrance door and immediately fell on the sidewalk. Both Honza and I had the same amount of drinks, but he didn't appear to be drunk at all. I don't remember how we returned to the cottage. He was holding me as much as he could, but it didn't help, as I fell on a bunch of rocks more than once. The next day, I was really sick and vomited several times. This was the first and last time in my life being this drunk.

The first time I visited the Czech Republic as an adult was in 1998. In Prague, Honza, his friends and I went to a bar for a few drinks. There were about ten of us, so we sat around one large circular table. Honza's girlfriend, Hana, who was very cute, wore a short dress and had a small purse. Everybody wanted to smoke a joint, so Hana pulled big rock of hashish out of her purse and broke it into many small pieces. The rock must have taken most of the space in the purse. "How nice the bartender doesn't care, and we don't have to worry about police," I said to everyone, in great relief. This was the first time in my life I saw people using drugs in public without the fear of being persecuted. The weed and hash mix was amazing. An instant high rushed through my body after just a couple of inhalations.

87

At my sister's. . .
Jonathan was searching for the lighter, but after several minutes could not find it.

"Come on, Jonathan, what's wrong with you? I need to get high as fast as possible, to forget about everything." I kept asking this and similar questions over and over again. He gave me answers totally unrelated to my questions. I instantly thought about my wife and kids mixing irrelevant words into sentences. On certain occasions, Jonathan was moving his head from left to right and not looking at me at all when answering the questions. My kids behaved the same way over the weekend.

"It's starting again! The NSA or the Hell/Heaven or the TV producers or the Matrix people instructed another person I trust and like to drive me insane. What am I going to do? Don't panic, remember 'The Hollywood Rob' rule."

My thought process accelerated at a faster and faster rate. I began to have severe chest pains, breathed heavily, was scared and frantically asked for the lighter.

"Joseph, relax, I have the lighter but it doesn't work. Here, take it and calm down."

I took the lighter and tried it several times. I was feeling worse and worse but finally, the lighter worked. I lit up the joint and inhaled multiple times, as hard as I could.

"Thanks, Jonathan, this is exactly what I need. I'm fucked up, you know women, they give me a hard time everywhere I go. I can't win with them. I got to tell you all these stories. . . in Prague, my buddy Rob fucked all these hookers. . ." As I was saying this sentence, I lost control of my body. From that point on, I only remember a few memories and circumstances surrounding those flashbacks. Probably due to the drug, I began to think faster and faster until all the possible scenarios blended together into one new reality. I tried to adjust my behavior to stay calm and at the same time to appease all four scenarios at once. As a result, it became impossible to control my own body regarding all actions/reactions and the ability to communicate in a rational matter. I was not able to control my voice, and all questions and answers. The following pages have the most detailed recollection of the events that I am able to remember. I wouldn't wish this on my worst enemy.

"The NSA will come soon to take me away. They will be able to do it because I am high. I better break the aquarium and fake an injury. An ambulance will come to take me away before the NSA." I frantically broke the aquarium. Milli and Asa ran away from the house. Jonathan tried to hold me down, but I easily broke free. It felt like I had supernatural strength and physically could do anything.

I continued to think. "The aquarium will not be enough. I need to break something else, like the computer sitting over there. . ." I folded my hand into a fist and smashed it into the screen as hard as I could. I wanted to get more people to witness the injuries, so I ran outside to contact some neighbors.

"I am in Reality TV so I better give them a good show."

I danced on the street, yelled that I love Michael Jackson and even attempted to moonwalk. For no reason, I realized that I couldn't become too happy because I didn't want to go to Hell or Heaven. I had to become neutral and not be positive or negative. I then lost the ability to control my thoughts altogether; thinking and saying one positive sentence followed by thinking and saying one negative sentence in order for my mind to stay neutral.

"I love Michael Jackson but I hate niggers, no I love Black people. I hate Jews, no I love Jews, I hate Asians, no I love Asians. . .

"I like Gorbachev, no I hate Gorbachev, I like Reagan, no, I don't like Reagan, because he made everybody miserable. No, wait, Gorbachev made everybody miserable. I like capitalism and hate communism. No, I like both socialism and capitalism. . ."

My uncontrolled thoughts and speech, similar to the above, occurred at a faster and faster rate until I decided to run back to the house. For some reason the "Heaven vs Hell", the "Paranoid NSA", and the "Matrix" scenarios now became part of the Reality TV show. The show, however, was not about deciding between socialism and capitalism anymore. It was a sadistic reality show with these rules:

The game was a Reality TV show broadcast live, 24/7, all over the Earth in the year 2117. Due to severe overpopulation, there were frequent wars over raw materials, land, food, and water. Everything tangible became scarce and the world's governments, consisting exclusively of religious fundamentalists and related sects, had no choice but to ration everything. The middle class no longer existed. People were either poor or rich, nothing in between. All media, including internet communication, was strictly censored and monitored. The freedom of speech and assembly was nonexistent. Democracy no longer existed. The government struggled to keep the people from protesting, therefore, a show was developed where live suffering of human beings became the zenith of the program. The people loved the show since it somehow relieved them of the misery they were experiencing in their everyday lives. The game was a joint venture between the US government and a major media company. A political prisoner, usually an atheist, was taken to a hospital where his memories were erased. New memories were implanted in his or her brain to mirror a fake life between June 30 1978 to December 15 2016. After the memory implant, the person was released to a "dome" where everyone was an actor and the settings mirrored the year 2017 to the smallest possible detail. The person's brain was wirelessly hacked by the producers. The sickness and hallucinations that I was experiencing were periodically uploaded into the brain. At the same time, all the actors, including fake family members, were instructed to drive the person crazy until he or she would be killed or driven to complete insanity. There was always a lucky person in the audience who had a chance to decide and direct the killing of this person. All methods of killing, including torture, were permitted.

I ran toward my sister's house, realizing what was going on. I was stopped by a police officer a few feet from the house. He said the most unusual and frightening sentences I had heard from any of the actors so far: "So, you met your friends, the aliens from Pleiades, right? This is how it's gonna go from now on. . . as long as you can hear, see, feel, and touch, you are not saving the world and everything will get worse."

He then touched my right shoulder. I quickly began to think about the meaning of the message. "Any normal person would be more than happy to give his or her life to save the world. I can still see," I said to myself and closed my eyes. "I can't see any more, but I can still feel, hear everything and my shoes touch the ground. What am I going to do?" I woke up lying in an ambulance, turned to my left and there was a nurse sitting next to me. She asked what happened. I continued to think again at a faster and faster rate. "The actress is trying to trick me. This is all part of the TV game. I was told not to see, hear, feel, and touch. She is asking questions to get me to talk. If I continue to break the rules of the game everything will get worse. The ambulance will take me to a hospital where I will be tortured. I won't say anything, but I can still see, feel, and touch."

I ran out of the ambulance but was stopped by two Cobb County police officers, a Black male and White female. The officers attempted to arrest me. I was approached and touched by one of the officers. Immediately after I was touched, I woke up lying in the police car. "No," I said, and continued to think. "I keep breaking the rules of the game. I can still see, hear, feel, and touch. Instead of going to the hospital, I'll go to prison, where I'll be subject to torture according to the viewer's wishes. I need to come up with something really quickly to reverse this. As long as I can get back to my sister's house, I'll be able to stay in the game unharmed."

I closed my eyes and the ability to hear went away. I was lying on the back seat of the car and my body started to get cold. The areas of my body that were touching the car seat became numb. "Good, at this point I can't see, hear, and touch anything. Let's see if I can feel something." The surrounding air was becoming colder and colder and the only thing I was able to feel was the beating of my heart. I focused my thoughts. I didn't want to feel my heart anymore. I continued to think with my eyes closed and noticed it was beating at a slower and slower rate until I couldn't feel a single beat. I was relieved, since I would wake up in Milli's house in a few minutes.

I woke up unable to concentrate and focus my eyes. I looked out the window and the scenery was changing. "Where are we going?" I was taken out of the car, but was unable to walk on my own. The officers searched me inside of the police station. I was in handcuffs and tried to run away. The officers were holding me and as I fought harder, they also fought harder.

I woke up in a small holding cell. The walls and the flat bed made out of concrete were a white color. There was no pillow or blanket. The metal toilet with a sink was right next to the bed. The ceiling was high and there was a camera above my head. I was cold, nauseous, and dizzy. My face and eyes were hurting. I did not know what was going to happen next; I reminded myself of "The Hollywood Rob" rule and became afraid again. "My life was fairly normal from June 30 1978 until December 15 2016, when I had the lunch where the first weirdness appeared. My eyes became dilated, Ronnee the actress reacted according to a prewritten script and so did the other actresses, Jessica and Christine. Therefore, everything in my life that happened from June 30 1978 to December 14 2016 was a fake memory implant. The live Reality TV show with real people started on December 15 2016. Everything from the point of awakening that morning in my house was real. Now the show was coming to an end and I would be tortured in the most brutal way imaginable, similar to the Inquisitions directed by the Catholic Church in medieval times," I thought, and I had no choice but to lie down and wait for the executioners.

I closed my eyes and heard noises coming from inmates in the surrounding cells. I also heard Milli, Jonathan, and my chiropractor friend, Mark, calling me to wake up.

"What is going on? I could also be at the gates of Hell. My body is lifeless, somewhere in a hospital, and my dying brain is generating the voices of relatives and friends who are standing next to me."

As I continued to lie in the cell with my eyes closed, everything around me was quickly getting colder. I was not able to feel anything except a small tingling in different parts of my body. The tingling feeling first appeared in my right arm. It felt like someone was cutting the nerves, until I lost movement in the arm. The exact same scenario happened in my left arm and in both legs, one after the other. I lost the ability to move my limbs. "Maybe I am already being tortured, but was given a mercy. Some nice person in the audience decided to cut my limbs, however, an alternate reality was being uploaded into my brain simultaneously, so I would not feel the pain." This thought made me feel better as I was falling asleep.

My body was lying lifeless, almost asleep, in a small cell without the presence of any other human being. Suddenly, there was a bright white light that felt like sun all around me and I was gently touched on my right shoulder by some person's hand. As the brightness of the light intensified, I realized how to overcome my difficulties. "Act normally, but change your patterns from time to time. As long as you can feel and see, but can never hear and speak again, it will get better and better and better. . . love will provide the ultimate answers in the most difficult situations and, eventually, you will help to save the world. If you break the rules, everything will reverse and you will continue to sink deeper and deeper into the abyss. . . to a certain point, or when you figure it out, the game will reverse in your favor again."

The light disappeared and I was in the holding cell again. "I feel refreshed and can move my limbs again. Great, this is the next chapter of the TV show. If I abide by the rules, I will eventually get out of the jail."

My fingers felt cold and numb. I massaged them and noticed the wedding ring was still on my finger. "Interesting, why wasn't the ring taken away when I was booked?" I normally did not wear my wedding ring because it interfered with gym workouts. The gold ring would easily scratch after prolonged contact with metal dumbbells. I also liked to keep a potential flirting buddy in suspense about my marital status as long as possible. This was also useful during a job interview. I kept Leah in suspense about my marital status until several days after I started to work at Immucor. About a week before I was fired from Argos, Romana handed me the ring and said, "Take the ring and wear it from now on. You will need it." This was a strange comment. I listened to her and wore the ring continuously, going forward.

There was nothing to do in the cell but wait. I kept hearing the voices of relatives and fellow prisoners. There was a small rectangular window by the entrance. The glass was blurry to a certain height, a person would not be able to see outside while sitting on the stone bed. I jumped on the bed to glance into the adjacent room. This was the main area, where detainees waited to be booked. There were ten rows of blue chairs in the middle of the room where people waited for paperwork to be finalized. There were other holding cells (probably similar to mine) at the edge of the room, where my cell was located. The officers were sitting at their desks, across the room, directly facing my cell. I saw Jonathan and his friend, Mike, sitting in the chairs.

"They helped me and fought the police. Now they are being booked in for assault on a police officer. What should I do? Should I scream and bang on the window for help? No, I can't do this. I don't know what is going on. These are most likely just paid actors trying to trick me into breaking the rules of the game. Remember, I am allowed to see and feel, but not to hear and speak."

I thought of another strange rule of the game. "If you look at and concentrate on a person sitting in front of you, it will go faster or slower." This was unusual, but I gave it a try anyway. There was a man sitting directly in front of me, wearing a hoodie. I was not able to see this person's face. Within a few minutes, he looked at me directly, but there was no visible face. There was just an empty black space inside of the hoodie. "This already happened, on the night I was driving through the ghetto. This could be a sign. I will only look and concentrate on this person and ignore everyone else." The more I looked at the man, the more he began to lean back, as if he were falling asleep. Everyone around the person started to move at slower and slower pace until everything came to almost a complete standstill.

"This is not good. The time is coming to a standstill. If I continue to look at this person then my mind will be stuck in this place forever." I was able to move my body at normal pace and continued to think. "If my body functions according to regular time flow, I will starve to death. There will not be enough time for a guard to bring me a meal."

I stopped concentrating on the person and focused on Jonathan. He was sitting at one of the chairs, looking down, not moving at all. He wore a bright red shirt. The longer I looked at him, the faster everyone in the entire room moved until they were all running around. "This is too much. I need to get some sleep right now." I experienced the same symptoms again while trying to fall asleep. My body was cold, shivering and numb, until I did not feel the bed anymore. I took the wedding ring off my finger and inserted the front part of my tongue inside the circle, then closed my mouth. The ring felt real. "At least I still have some feelings left." At that point, it was the only thing I was able to feel. "I need to remain as calm as possible for the game to continue. There is a camera right above my head so I'll give them a good show." I repeated the following scenario several times, but made sure it was slightly different from the prior one, so the guards would not think I was crazy:

1. Sat on the bed and played with the wedding ring for a few minutes.
2. Used the toilet, washed my hands and face.
3. Lay on the bed pretending to be asleep, then played with the wedding ring.

I did this until I was so tired, I fell asleep on the floor. I had wild dreams and as soon as the white bright light appeared again, a guard looking exactly like my friend Kamil, who moved back to the Czech Republic a couple years ago, walked in, woke me up and asked, "Are you OK?"

"Yes, I am fine," I answered. As soon as he walked away, I realized one of the rules was broken. I can never speak again. "Kamil came here to help me get out of the jail and I fucked up by answering his question. I'll never get out of this cell. Hopefully, there will be another chance to get out of here." I fell asleep on the bed and as I was having wild dreams consisting of all kinds of craziness related to the possible scenarios, two guards walked in and woke me up.

"You there, are you ready to walk out of this cell? Are you going to behave?" One guard asked the question while I was sitting on the bed.

I reminded myself of the "don't talk, no matter what" rule, so I kept quiet.

"He is playing hard. We will keep him here as long as we want to. Let's teach him a lesson," the second guard said, while I kept looking down, ignoring both of them.

"OK, let's go, then, he had his chance." They both walked out.

"Should I have talked to them? No, it would not do any good anyway. Best I just remained silent." At this point, everything seemed like an eternity. I looked out of the small window and all the people waiting to be booked were gone. The officers were also different. "The shifts must have changed. Maybe I will get out of here soon." There was a TV set hanging from the ceiling on my right-hand side, playing the current news. I watched the TV for a few minutes and observed the program was steadily speeding up to higher speeds. The TV program was speeding up faster and faster, but everyone in the room moved at normal pace. The longer I continued to watch, the faster the program was playing. The guards did not notice there was anything wrong with the TV. "This is another trick played by the producers. I will not give them the pleasure of driving me insane this quickly." I stopped watching the TV and sat on the bed and thought about what to do next. "There is another possibility how to end this. I will indirectly tell the guards that I don't want to play the game here anymore. There are three possibilities for what could happen next:

1. The game will end and I will be tortured before I die.
2. I will be taken to a hospital for a new memory implant and the game will resume in the jail or somewhere else.
3. The audience and the producers will be impressed I figured everything out. A full pardon will be awarded and I will be

released out of the dome to the year 2117 to live a normal life. My original memories of my real life in the 21st/22nd centuries will be re-implanted into my brain."

I made the decision to end the game there. I didn't like the holding cell at all. There was nothing to do but wait and look out of the small window. After staring out of the window for a while, two female guards were walking around the perimeter, checking on the prisoners restrained in cells similar to mine. "Good, that's perfect. I am sure they will be able to help me. I better sit down on the bed, so they won't be scared."

The guards entered the cell and one of them asked, "Are you ready to walk out of here?"

"I'm not saving the world because I can't hear and speak, but I can only feel and touch," I replied in relief, hoping to walk out of the jail in a few minutes.

Both guards looked directly into my eyes trying to figure out what was going on. They looked at each other and walked back to the booking room, leaving me in the cell by myself.

"Am I doing something wrong? Maybe the person in the audience is patient with me because he or she doesn't want to end the game this soon. You know what? Next time a guard asks if I want to walk out of here, I'll just say 'Yes.' I'll probably remain here but it's worth a shot to try all the options. I have nothing to lose anyway."

I wasn't able to keep up with the time anymore. Sometime later, one of the female guards entered my cell. I told her I didn't want to be in the cell anymore. She took me to the main room, where I was told to sit down on a blue chair so the booking process could resume.

It felt great to be out of the small holding cell. The claustrophobic cell was designed for a person to lose time perception. The cell had a video camera, but did not have a clock, magazines, or anything at all to keep a person occupied. The cell was designed to drive a normal person insane. I realized once a person is at the mercy of any institution, the employees of the institution can treat anybody as they please. If, somehow, the person gets injured or dies, the evidence can be manipulated to such an extent the entity is not at fault. A reason for natural or accidental death could easily be fabricated. The blame is placed on the person or fellow inmates, and the video showing the actual evidence is somehow lost or damaged.

I was ecstatic and positive until I realized the game would continue in the jail for the foreseeable future. The room looked bigger than if viewed from the holding cell. There was a round black clock mounted on the right-hand side wall. It was a mechanical clock with small and large pointers for hours and minutes. This type of clock was frequently used in schools, hospitals, and train stations. "I am going to look at the clock to kill some time." I didn't know the day, but the clock showed a few minutes after nine. It was probably morning, since I was arrested at night. As I was watching the clock, the large pointer was moving faster and faster. Everyone except me, including the TV program, was moving faster as well. I was frightened so I stopped looking at the clock and shifted my eyes towards the floor. "I don't want to become part of some invisible dimension where time moves way faster than normal. The flow of time would continue to accelerate to a point of no return. I would simply just sit here for centuries or until the surrounding area became completely blurry. At the end, the seconds, minutes, and hours of the time would move close to the speed of light. A point of singularity would be created, where time would separate from the fabric of space-time. Time would no longer exist, and I would be sucked in and 'spaghettified' by a black hole, where atoms of my body would flow for eternity." This was really scary, and I had no idea where all this information was coming from. The producers must have uploaded more data into my brain to keep the show interesting. Anyway, I was so happy when the flow of time returned to normal after a few minutes. I did not dare to look at the TV or the clock again.

A female officer called me over to her desk and explained the situation. I was advised to call someone to bail me out. It was very difficult to concentrate, to dial the number to reach my wife. After several tries, she answered the phone and I said, "Hi, Romana, I am in jail. I don't know where I am or what is going on. Can you find out and bail me out?"

My wife then answered, "Why did you act like that at your sister's house? What's wrong with you? I am sorry, but I will not bail you out. Go see the judge."

The phone disconnected and I was standing there speechless, looking at the wall in front of me.

"I have two children with Romana. She is the last person on Earth I thought would let me die here. I have to remain calm, no matter what. She isn't really my wife, she's an actress acting according to the instructions. This is Hollywood."

I hung up the phone and walked back to the female officer sitting at her desk. "I cannot reach anybody. What should I do?" I asked the officer. I gave up on trying to figure out what to do next.

Everything, including my family, was directed by the producers.

"Please go back and sit over there. Someone will call you to take a picture and your fingerprints," she said.

I went back to the same chair where I sat before. Several men sitting behind me were having a conversation. The discussion seemed normal until the participants started to mix unrelated words into sentences. To ignore the abnormalities, to sit and wait, were the only options left for me to move to the next level of the game.

A male officer called my name for me to come over for the picture-taking and fingerprinting. I fully cooperated with the requests. There was nothing unusual about the procedures. The officer pointed to a small room and advised me to change into a prison uniform. The officer who looked like Kamil came by to see if I'd changed into the uniform.

"What should I do with my clothes?" I asked.

"Just throw them in that bin and come over here. We'll take the elevator to the basement," he said, and the two of us went to a nearby elevator. "We'll wait here for the rest of the group," the officer Kamil said.

Shortly after, another guard and a prisoner approached us. The four of us entered the elevator and the other guard said, "You'll like it down there, we have showers and nice beds ready just for you ladies."

As soon as he finished the sentence, I began to have chest pains and my body felt cold. "I messed up," I said to myself. "I broke the rules again. Why did I open my mouth? I am going deeper into Hell, where I will be raped and tortured by fellow inmates. The member of the audience chose this type of death for me."

We exited the elevator and one of the guards said, "OK, ladies, go over to that room."

There were several rows of chairs, and a TV hung from the ceiling. We were told to sit down and watch the TV. The other inmate was a rough-looking Hispanic guy. I looked at him several times and hoped he would make it painless and quick. He must have noticed that I was staring at him.

"What are you looking at? Do you want some, hah?"

I looked away and did not say anything. My body began to shake uncontrollably, I was unable to control the seizures. I woke up in a room that looked like a cafeteria. There was a small window located near the ceiling displaying perfectly blue sky. Another idea was imagined by my mind: "You have to keep the good and bad forces of nature in perfect balance. Due to love, the good force will always have a slight advantage over the bad force in the end. You have to save yourself before saving the world." I realized this as I was looking directly out of the small window, admiring the perfectly blue sky. Prior to this moment, there was a real possibility of never seeing daylight again. "You quickly learn to appreciate simple things in life if you know they're lost forever. What is Ronnee doing? I hope she is not going through something similar. I miss Ronnee so much and would do anything for her to hug me. The next stop may be Heaven."

I gave up again, I didn't care what was going to happen next. I lay on the floor and covered myself with a blanket. As I was falling asleep, the time kept speeding up again. The prisoners were running in and out of the room until someone attempted to pick me up.

"Are you OK? What is going on?" I felt that a guard and an inmate were dragging my body out of the cafeteria. "Maybe I will enter the next stage of the game."

I couldn't move my limbs at all and was placed in a wheelchair. The uncontrollable seizures returned. The officers and nurses were holding my body to the wheelchair. For no apparent reason, the facial pains went away and I was able to focus my eyes and move my limbs again. I grabbed a hand of the officer standing behind me. He was scared and immediately pulled his hand back.

"No, wait," I said to him. "Please, put the hand on my shoulder."

He gently placed his hand on my shoulder.

"It feels so good to be touched by another human being, thanks."

My breathing went to normal and I was able to understand the conversation among the officers and medical staff. Time perception also returned to normal. I finally regained control of my body and mind again.

"Is it over? What is going to happen next?" I kept asking myself, over and over again.

There is no question that if I had not resumed control of my body, I would have been sedated. I was feeling close to normal and assessed the situation. "All this is really strange, but anything can happen when you are on TV. I better get used to the craziness if I want to live a little longer. What if this is the 'Heaven vs Hell' or the 'Matrix'? How do I really know what is happening? Every situation that made me believe I am on TV is purely circumstantial."

I was able to walk on my own and a guard took me to a larger cell with a window and shower. "This is definitely a good sign. I am reversing the situation by moving from the underground gates of Hell back to the surface, to the real world. I need to interact with everyone like nothing unusual has happened."

The water flowing out of the shower was cold. I dressed again and lay on a mattress that was on the floor. This was the first time since the arrest that my body and mind felt normal. My brain was able to process information at normal pace. The time appeared to be flowing at normal speed, as well. My head, face, and eyes were not hurting anymore. I was able to relax and concentrate again. "Maybe I've been given a chance to relax a little and to plan my next move." I just lay there, not tired, and kept looking out of the window at the perfectly blue sky.

A female guard opened the main door and I was told to follow her to the adjacent room, resembling a larger hallway. There was a nurse waiting for us not too far from the holding cell.

"I need to ask you a few questions before your release," she said.

I froze my face to hide emotions. "The game has probably resumed and this could be another trick for the audience to see my reactions. I better remain emotionless no matter what." I thought to myself, as the woman was speaking.

"Are you having any thoughts of suicide or harming yourself in any way?"

"No," was my instant reply.

"Do you have history of mental illness? Are you on any prescription medication?"

She asked several more questions related to health and lifestyle and I always answered "No."

At the end, I sat down on one of the empty chairs and waited for a guard. About twenty minutes later, a guard and the same rough-looking Hispanic inmate I met earlier in the day approached me.

"OK, let's go, follow us," the guard said.

The three of us were walking through empty, grey, windowless hallways and the inmate started to talk. "I will have my way with you. You're gonna be my bitch. We're almost there and you are gonna meet my brothers, bitch."

I kept walking with my head down and did not react to the comments. I knew better at that point. "The rule is: 'as long as you can see and feel, but can never hear and speak again, it will get better and better.'"

We must have been walking through the corridors for at least five minutes. I was scared to death but kept looking down, pretending not to be able to hear and speak. The inmate kept making similar comments and for some reason the guard never told him to stop. "Are the brothers waiting around the next corner? Will it be quick or will I be picking up soaps in showers for days to entertain the TV audience?"

We finally approached a medium-size room with about ten chairs, two dressing rooms and a window opening where another guard was sitting and looking at us.

"OK, we're here. Get undressed and throw your uniform into that bin over there."

Both the guard and the inmate left the room. I almost panicked, but changed my mind at the last minute. I asked the guard sitting at the window, "What should I wear once I get undressed?"

He looked at me, reached for a plastic bag and said, "Here are your street clothes. Get dressed and sit down over there."

I did just that and the guard said, "That's a smart move. I would advise you to keep quiet once you walk out of here."

I was emotionless, I just sat in the chair for a few minutes and was escorted out of the Cobb County Jail shortly after.

It was late afternoon on January 24th, my mom Alena and her husband Milan were parked several hundred yards from the building. I walked at normal pace, I didn't try to run, so the guards wouldn't get suspicious. As I approached the vehicle, I was hugged by both of them. They were so happy to see me. I did not talk or smile, a complete stage of emotionless overtook my mind and body.

A light blue metallic Dodge Caravan was the vehicle I was expecting, but instead I entered a white Chevy van. "Milan, what's up with the van?" I asked.

"My van broke down a few days ago and this is a loaner from my boss," he said.

I didn't ask any more questions and wanted to go home as fast as possible. The scenery was comforting; the sky was blue, everything was alive, the Sun radiated warmth and positive energy. "What a difference from the grey, dark, and gloomy prison cells. It must be extremely difficult to find your soul and make inner peace with yourself after spending a few years in prison. I hope this was my first and last time behind bars," I thought.

Mom kept trying to persuade me to come to her house to recover and to spend a few days with her. She was persistent, but I didn't change my mind. Romana, Teresa, and Julia were surely waiting for me at home, so I refused. I could not wait to see my family again.

The house was empty and did not feel like home anymore, it felt like an empty prison cell. My wife and daughters were nowhere to be found. Romana, Teresa, and Julia did not kiss or hug me. "What is going on? Where is my family? I am not here to think, I am here to act according to the other people's wishes," I said to myself.

Mom and Milan went to a Chinese restaurant to buy some food and left me alone in the house. Nature was what I craved the most; seeing trees, feeling the Sun and listening to the birds were needed to heal my soul and mind. The jeans I wore were falling from my waist. There were not enough openings left to tighten the belt. My body felt achy and beaten, with several large blue marks on my arms, possibly caused by fighting with the police. I went in the backyard, sat on the grass and tried to relax in the satisfaction of finally being free. It was so peaceful.

It felt so warm and white bright light was all around me.

"Wake up, Joseph, wake up, I brought you some food," Mom said, as she was slightly shaking my body.

I opened my eyes and found myself lying on the grass, on my back, with both arms and feet stretched out as far as possible. I was hurting all over my body. Facial pain was the most annoying; headache, eye pain, and my cheeks felt like they were about to collapse into my face any second. I was unable to open my eyes due to the Sun's brightness. I got up, then went to the nearest restroom, located on the bottom floor, where a large mirror was mounted on the wall above the sink. The restroom was the darkest area of the house. The walls were painted green, with dark hardwood floors and only one florescent lightbulb above the mirror.

"Why are my eyes hurting so much? I need to see myself in front of the mirror." I was not happy with the skinny, wrinkled, and bearded person in the mirror. The appearance of the person was unfamiliar to me, way different from the person I knew from looking into a mirror each morning. The person's vision was blurry and the eyes were dilated to the fullest possible extent. "I hope the Sun did not damage my eyes while I was asleep," I said, then I quickly moved my face closer to the mirror and was able to partially refocus the eyes to their normal state.

The Chinese noodle soup, and fried catfish with vegetables, tasted excellent. I was only able to eat less than half of the portion. A cornbread with milk was the only meal I had eaten since yesterday lunch. I told Mom to go home.

A warm shower and more sleep were exactly what I needed. The bed felt more comfortable and softer than normal. I closed my eyes and after some time noticed that everything around me felt colder. I couldn't feel the bed, my fingers and toes were numb, the heart was not beating at all.

"Joseph, open the door! I brought you a fruit smoothie to go with your dinner!" Mom yelled, as she was standing in front of a glass sliding door leading to the backyard.

I opened my eyes and the area of the bed underneath, around me, the sheets, and my white shirt and underwear were completely wet. I was shivering and felt cold.

"There is no way my body produced this much sweat in such a short amount of time. How long was I out?" I questioned myself and went to the bottom floor to unlock the sliding doors. Mom handed me the smoothie and offered to stay with me for a while.

"Please go home, I want to be by myself and relax," I said to her and she left the house.

I ate some more fish, and noodle soup, and drank the smoothie. "That couch and TV over there looks really good. I'll watch TV, relax and go to sleep, hopefully with no problems," I thought. I sat on the couch, turned on Netflix and, from the many available programs, chose a documentary describing the life in 1980s America. The documentary began to play normally, but there were several abnormalities after about ten minutes into the program. The show criticized the US government in an unusually hard way. The criticism went to such extremes, I no longer believed this had actually happened.

"There is no way something like this would be available on a public or private TV network."

At certain times the program would slow down and speed up. There was the déjà vu; a small segment of the show repeated itself but with different actors. Bright white stars of different sizes were appearing and disappearing near the outer edges of the TV set. I was frightened, turned off the documentary and searched for another program. There was nothing available on Netflix anymore, except the program I just watched. I turned off the TV.

"Nothing is over, the producers are fucking with me. I was made to believe I am in the safety of my house so I can recharge for the next level of the game. This is about to get ugly," were my thoughts.

I turned on the lamp placed on a small table right next to the couch and remembered the unusual sentences said by the police officer during the arrest, just before he touched my shoulder. "So, you met your friends, the aliens from Pleiades, right? This is how it's gonna go from now on. As long as you can hear, see, feel, and touch, you are not saving the world and everything will get worse." I kept thinking.

"I need to figure this out while there is still some time. It's all over if I go to jail again. I have been given clues periodically to figure this out. I am not an idiot, it should be a piece of cake. The aliens from the Pleiades region?" I opened my mouth, was caught in complete surprise, unable to move my head and torso.

"For my fifteenth birthday, on June 30th, 1993, my mother gave me two books about UFOs as presents. One was written about a man (I can't remember the name), a resident of Switzerland who claimed to be the only person in the entire world having in-person contact with extraterrestrial human beings from the Pleiades region of our galaxy, the Milky Way. He was writing about the encounters since the early 1950s. Furthermore, he was writing about the current and future problems our civilization is facing and will face during this difficult time in our history: dangers of overpopulation, religious fundamentalists brainwashing the majority of the world's population to submission, materialism/selfishness and greed, lack of inner spiritual development, false teachings regarding the meaning of life, not taking responsibility for our actions/reactions by shifting problems and solutions to be resolved by imaginary gods, wars for land, water, food, and natural resources, global warming. Several decades later, he was contacted by an extraterrestrial woman named Semjase. The documents regarding his contacts with Semjase amount to over 1,500 pages.

"It has been twenty-four years since I read the book. I need to remember as much as possible. This could be another clue on how to survive this ordeal in one piece," I thought.

At age fifteen, I was not sure if the extraterrestrial contacts were real. However, I knew for a fact the problems facing our civilization that the man described were real. To this day, I never read another book in my life that would describe all the global issues facing humanity in such detail and at same time offer viable/doable solutions to those problems. Even if the man was a phony, I knew he was serious about saving the planet.

The second book listed about forty people claiming to have contact with extraterrestrials from countless regions of the Universe. The book was basically about nothing, describing where and how the contacts happened, how weird the aliens and their ships looked. On many occasions, the aliens performed medical experiments on people who were kidnapped. None of the individuals claiming to have the contacts were described as fakes and phonies, except for one, the Swiss person. The small article described how he faked the pictures of the aliens and ships including physical evidence, such as material composites unknown to Earth's scientists. "Why were books that were contradicting each other to such an extreme given to me at the same time? This could have been another memory implant, so anything is possible. Did this have a purpose? Maybe someone tried to teach me to think logically on my own, to figure things out on my own, to be able to strip away all the endless bullshit filters and to see the world the way it really is, the real world that is facing self-destruction in the near future."

There was one more incident. One evening in spring of 1994, while living at the homeless shelter for single moms, my mother was excited and said, "Joseph, you will not believe what happened. A large flying disk, looking like a UFO, flew above me than quickly disappeared."

"OK, whatever, I'm going out and will be home a little later than usual," I said.

"No, really, believe what I am telling you." She kept trying to convince me.

"OK, Mom, I'll see you later," I said to her, and walked out of the room. I felt sorry for her. "I hope she will come to her senses. She is losing the custody of my sister and it is really hard on her. Hopefully she will stay in reality." I loved my mom and began to worry about her.

There were four possible situational scenarios: the Reality TV show was the most likely, the Heaven vs Hell was the second most likely, then the Matrix, and finally the NSA surveillance, which was the least likely of them all. "There could also be another scenario," I said, and continued to think. "I can only remember flashbacks of the arrest. I can't remember anything on a continuous basis since I smoked the weed. What if the aliens have somehow uploaded data into my brain on how to save the world? There were the blackouts, time perception changed, I spoke faster than normal, heard unrelated words in sentences and my health rapidly deteriorated. Parts of the information on how to save the world were purposely released to the authorities and the NSA was alerted. This would explain the unusual surveillance activity continuing for days prior to the arrest. I was drugged and thrown into jail by the intelligence agency, hoping to break me down, so I perhaps subconsciously released more information. Maybe the information already given to the agencies was so extreme, the government decided to kill me if I provided any additional details, consciously or subconsciously. I was constantly being tricked and monitored to see if I had a mental breakdown, or the agency was simply curious about how much of the 'weirdness' a human being can withstand. My family, friends and the people I knew had no choice but to cooperate. This is government spending at its finest," I thought, and only became more confused due to the complexity of the situation.

None of the scenarios were ruled out, but the Aliens/NSA surveillance hybrid became the most probable. Most importantly, I did not want to give up that easily. The usual symptoms: facial/eye pain, inability to concentrate and different time perception were present. Fighting the symptoms one at a time would be the most logical and practical solution. I drank some coffee to regain the ability to concentrate. With milk and no cream was the way I drank coffee. I was in the tax accounting profession for years and became addicted to coffee at work, especially at Argos; Columbian dark roast tasted delicious and at least eight small cups a day became the standard.

I took my favorite large blue mug with the "Giant Cup of I Don't Give a Shit" statement written in large white letters on both sides. I felt relief as the warm coffee, with a large dose of caffeine, was inside of my stomach. "I have to do something about the time perception. An old-school mechanical watch would work the best. It would be easy to look at and concentrate on the large pointer."

I did not feel like going shopping at all. Walmart, on Terrell Mill Road, seemed like the perfect store to buy a simple watch, to get in and out as fast as possible. The Nissan Leaf was at my sister's house, the Mercedes was the only car available to drive. My wife and the kids were probably at friend's house, unwilling to communicate or help in any way. This was sort of understandable given the circumstances of what happened in the past week.

Music was what I needed to keep my spirit high and to remain focused. I couldn't find my cell phone to listen to Pandora, the car's radio antenna was broken, and so an old iPod from the mid-2000s was the only remaining option. Thousands of songs of different artists were uploaded to the iPod. I turned on The Smashing Pumpkins – *Melancholy and the Infinite Sadness*, Disk 1, the most relaxing album I thought of. My vision increased significantly during the ride to the store. As in prior experiences, everything appeared sharper and brighter than normal.

The Walmart happened to be right across the street from Dobbins Air Force base. Planes were landing one after another, flying low above my head as I exited the car. "Something is definitely going on. I don't remember this place ever being this busy with military activity. I am definitely being followed," I thought, and was not too happy about the situation, but continued with the plan to purchase a watch.

The store was busy with people coming in and out as I headed straight to the area where jewelry and watches were on display. Many types of watches, digital and mechanical, were on sale. I was unable to remember which watch I had already looked at. It was extremely difficult to concentrate again as time was slowing down. The voices of the shoppers around me became blurry and barely audible. I could not understand the conversations at all.

For no reason, someone behind me said, "You are not listening, go home as fast as you can and stay home!" Then the person walked away.

I picked up the first visible mechanical watch and walked to the cash registers with my head down and eyes nearly closed. I did not want to know anything about the surrounding area anymore. I tried not to think about anything else, since I became so lost, like in a twilight zone.

It was around 9.30 p.m. when I returned to the house. All sorts of different thoughts regarding the situation were constantly racing through my head. I sat on a couch, unable to relax. Sharp and dull chest pains accompanied by headaches were appearing unpredictably at different intervals. Both walking and sitting helped to decrease the symptoms. I felt better for a while, but the pains kept coming back.

"I better call my wife." I looked all over the house, including the car, but the cell phone was nowhere to be found. "It has to be at Milli's house or lost somewhere in the area, possibly in the storage area where the weed was hidden."

Social media, especially Facebook, was the only option to communicate with the outside world. "Where is my wife? Why is nobody coming home to see how am I doing? They must know I'm out of jail. Are they afraid of me? I need to ask for help without raising any suspicion and have to pretend I feel good. That is the only way to prevent the agents from storming the house." I didn't want to go to the hospital without Romana. "A person suffering from symptoms similar to mine could easily be declared mentally incapable, drugged, and taken away without consent. If I go to a hospital, I need Romana to protect me from the doctors who like to experiment on patients. I also need protection from the TV producers, from the government, from Heaven or Hell and from the Matrix, if possible." Thoughts were racing in my head as the game headed to the next level. I posted a message on Facebook:

January 24 at 10:19pm
Romana, come home. Can't do it without you because I love you :-)

After twenty minutes, my wife did not reply. I posted another message on Facebook.

January 24 at 10:39pm
We are a beautiful family :-)

I was feeling worse and worse, and began to be impatient. "I need to be more straightforward, so she gets the message," I thought.

January 24 at 10:50pm
Hope I see you before midnight?! Can't promise I still be awake ;-)

"She must be watching TV. I'll try later," I said to myself, and thought about another rule learned earlier today. "You have to keep the good and bad forces of nature in perfect balance. Because of love, the good force will always have a slight advantage over the bad force in the end. Balance, what can a balance mean when I feel this miserable?"

Music, all kinds of music, from classical to heavy metal, helped me to cope with depression in the past. I downloaded the Pandora application to the laptop and created "The Roxette" radio station. Roxette's music was soft, instrumental, and emotional, something I needed to quickly escape the reality.

After a few songs, inner peace, relaxation, and the ability to forget about the situation overtook my mind. The fast and heavy breathing slowed down, the pains decreased and I felt tired. Sleep was what my body craved the most. I went to bed and closed my eyes. The bed felt so good as I was falling asleep. My body was colder, more numbed, breathing took longer, my heart pumped slower and at longer intervals, the deeper I was falling asleep.

"This can't be happening," I said, and opened my eyes. "I still have the same sleeping problem. I need to go to sleep. How will I solve this riddle? Yes, this is it. I need to stay awake until Romana or another person comes to check on me. Balance the forces! I'll drink coffee and listen to heavy metal to stay awake. I'll listen to Roxette or something similar, if I get sick again. I'll repeat the cycle until someone shows up." I comforted myself.

It appeared helicopters and airplanes were constantly flying above or close to the house. I heard the same noises while driving my car on many occasions in the past week. "There is nothing I can do about this. I have to learn how to live with it."

I left the bedroom and went to the office, turned on the laptop, read the news and listened to Metallica radio on the Pandora station. This worked for about a half hour and the symptoms reappeared. Stretching and walking around the house stabilized my body, but I still felt sick. I turned on the coffee maker and went upstairs to the first floor, where the office was. I listened to more Roxette and similar artists until everything felt normal again. I went to bed and closed my eyes. Unfortunately, the same sleeping problems persisted and forced me to leave the bedroom again. This time I was more tired than before, so I took a shower, grabbed the coffee, went to the office, and turned on the computer and listened to more music. The helicopter and airplane sounds were constantly present.

It was late and Romana did not reply. "Let's see if I can get in touch with somebody who would be able to come over, so I can finally get some sleep. The person would be instructed to wake me up if I appear dead; vital signs such as breathing, pulse, and heartbeat would decrease to a barely noticeable level." I hoped to retrain my body to be able to sleep on its own. Sleeping alone in my current mental and physical state was not a good idea, due to high probability of not waking up. "How and why did I lose the ability to control my vital signs while asleep? The producers, the audience, the NSA agents, the aliens, Satan/God and the real Matrix people are a bunch of sick fucking individuals. They all are, regardless who's doing this to me!" I was upset, yet helpless about the situation, and posted another Facebook comment to alert my wife:

January 25 at 1:16am
Romana, please come home now, I don't feel so good, I need a human touch ;-) Now.....
Your love will save me, you can do it....Please...........!?!?
Love you, it is the most powerful thing is the Universe

January 25 at 1:16am
I feel dizzy, please come

I was feeling worse and worse as the body and mind were deteriorating fast. Breathing became harder, the headaches, inner ear vibrations, and the aviation noises increased. To balance the good and bad forces of nature was one of the rules of the game. Zack, representative of the Heaven, and Karolina, representative of the Hell, were chosen as the people I would contact via FB Messenger. Zack was a friend of the family. He and his wife Eva had two daughters; Thalia and Alicia were the same age as Teresa and Julia. The kids frequently played together several times per week as Eva, a stay home mom, watched the kids when Romana and I were at work. All four kids cared for each other like they were sisters. Naturally, Zack, the representative of Heaven, was the most likely person to help once he read the message.

January 25 at 1:20am
Zack, I feel real dissy, please tell Romana to come home now. I need a human touch.
Zack are you home? or online?
zack are you there? Je mi spatne. I am sik.

No answer from Zack was expected this late. Due to the six-hour time difference, Karolina, who lived in the Czech Republic, would be able to communicate with me, at least until I lost consciousness.

The gypsy situation. . .
I met Karolina in the summer of 2016, at a pool in the subdivision where my mom lived. Karolina was of Czech/Romani origin, had a great personality and was a good conversationalist. I invited her to my house several times for drinks. Since 1989, Czechoslovakia kept changing dramatically as each year passed. During the twenty-three years of my life away from the country, I stayed in touch with family and friends, kept reading newspapers and in general stayed interested in the country's affairs. Most Czech people were far better off socially and economically in 2017 than in 1989, most, except single parents, retirees, and the gypsy minority.

For hundreds of years, the Romani people (gypsies in Czech slang) were the community of travelers and entertainers. They were constantly moving through the Czech lands and Europe, from town to town, mostly as successful circus and theatrical performers. They were/still are great dancers and storytellers. The lifestyle is in their blood. In the 1950s, the Communists made the peddler lifestyle illegal and the gypsies were forced to live in apartments against their will, unable to move as they pleased. The people were not used to working for somebody else in ordinary day-to-day jobs. Poverty and feelings of resentment towards the

White majority became the norm. In 2017, most gypsies live on the outskirts of society, unable to break the cycle of poverty, and are being openly discriminated against in education, employment, and everyday life by the majority and the government.

There is a flip side to the story as well; many gypsies became talented criminals and prostitutes, stealing and sleeping their way through life. Many women have a child every four years, therefore never having to work as they are being paid for the rest of their productive life. Regardless of who's at fault now, the Czech government is not doing enough to break the cycle of poverty and to include these people in mainstream society. International organizations have been criticizing the Czech Republic every year for decades regarding the gypsy situation. I always felt bad and ashamed of the Czech government for not doing enough to end the human rights violations. Here is one bad example: to this day the government has failed to build a memorial at the place where the Nazis operated a concentration camp reserved for the gypsies. A pig farm still stands and operates on the premises of the former camp, near the village of Lety.

Karolina openly and honestly spoke about the situation. "You know how it is, some people like us, many people hate us for no reason. It is definitely more difficult for us to find employment than for the majority."

I was curious about the situation and very much enjoyed our discussions.

Back to my situation. . .
For some reason, I thought Karolina would be the perfect representative of Hell. The entire conversation was somehow deleted from Messenger. This remains a mystery, because I don't remember deleting the message. I was only able to remember bits and pieces.

January 25 – about 1:30am
"*Hi, I feel really bad and need immediate help,*" I wrote.
"*Hi what's wrong? I hope you're doing OK,*" she replied.

The pain went to another level. Each inhalation and exhalation was a monumental task, my whole body felt like it was about to collapse into itself, the heart was beating extremely fast. I was barely able to keep my eyes open. It felt like being in a pressure cooker, with the pressure steadily increasing. I tried to concentrate and continued to write.
I need help now, I am dizzy, quick.
I was barely able to lift my fingers off the keyboard to write the sentences and the following thoughts entered my mind. "He will not say

anything to anyone. He will never talk. Only love can provide the ultimate answers to him."

At that point, my whole body started to shake uncontrollably; I was having a seizure. I did not have any strength left in my body to continue to write, my mind was unable to think clearly. I was losing my vision and was a few seconds away from total collapse, resulting in death. I managed to write the following two sentences, lifting one finger at a time, pressing one key at a time, while fighting the extreme gravitational pressure.

Ronnee, Jessica, Christine, Leah I love you
Michael Jackson I love you, save the world

As soon as I finished typing the word "world," the extreme pressure my body was under eased to normal and I was able to move again. My breathing, heartbeat, and vision also quickly returned to normal. I was able to think clearly again and sat there for a while thinking how close I came to knowing the gravedigger in person.

After calming myself down, I began to question the options. "Something is definitely happening and it has to do with love and saving the world. I don't know any more, every scenario is on the table. What if the NSA agents installed a device in the house that is able to wirelessly paralyze or kill a human being? Some sort of electromagnetic waves were shooting at my body. This explains how horrible I felt. The agents probably changed their minds about killing me once they realized I might have more information about saving the world. Anyway, I am not going to screw around with Facebook anymore. I need a friendly person to come by so I can finally get some sleep. Until then, I have to keep the good and bad forces in my body in balance to achieve perfect emotional equilibrium."

Coffee was the number one item that always kept me awake and sharp. I made myself another pot of coffee and went back to the office, and turned on Pandora. The familiar seizure type signs kept reappearing periodically in unpredictable intervals. The sleeping problems also persisted. Listening to all kinds of music kept me in balance, but I had to keep switching the music genres more frequently as the time passed. I was listening to artists like Helloween, Metallica, and Slayer, and at certain points the symptoms of an upcoming seizure started to appear. When listening to artists like Roxette, Bryan Adams, and Mozart, I was falling asleep. "If I listen to heavy metal for a certain amount of time, I'll eventually get a seizure, die, and the Hell will win over my soul. This makes sense since Ozzy Osbourne, the godfather of heavy metal, is 'The Prince of Darkness', anyway. If I listen to classical music or Eighties pop for a certain amount of time, I'll die in my sleep and the Heaven will win over my soul. Well, I don't want my body to boil in water or be crucified on the cross for eternity. I want to stay in the real world, no matter what. I'll keep switching the music genres until Romana enters the house."

After the thorough evaluation, I was plenty happy with the plan but at around 6.30 a.m., it became impractical to switch the music genres any longer. Sickness and sleepiness overtook my body for good. I didn't feel nearly as sick as at 1.30 a.m.; nevertheless, none of the symptoms were going away anymore. I continuously felt sleepy, ready to pass out any minute. The last cup of coffee was long gone, the beans were all ground up and gone as well. Sunlight penetrated the house and birds started to sing around me. The singing was melodic and loud at the same time. It felt like the birds were inside of the house, flying somewhere in the attic.

"I should take a shower, dress, and walk around the house for a while. This will buy me some time," I said. The water, left purposely cold, felt amazing when it touched my body. I dressed in regular jeans and a long-sleeved shirt, since January mornings are usually cold. Breakfast, such as eggs, bagel, and fruit, sounded delicious, but only up to a certain amount; too much food makes a person sleepy. I took my time with the breakfast preparation. The mind needs to be occupied as much as possible to delay bedtime. I also ate slowly to buy some more time. "Romana better be here any minute. I don't know how much longer I can take this," was my thought. After breakfast, I cleaned the dishes and checked Facebook for any incoming messages. Only one message written by Zack was waiting for me.

January 25 at 7:32am
Hey Joseph, not able to help with Ramona, but you sound like you might need to go to the hospital. Is it possible you hit your head when you fell the other day or something else happened?

I couldn't believe what I was reading. This person, living a mile from my house, who I thought was my friend, wrote this and did not bother to drive here, or call my wife, or 911? Nobody from my so-called "online friends" bothered to call 911 that morning. "Don't worry, Joseph. Zack was never your friend. He is just a paid actor, acting according to the instructions," I said to myself. I turned off the computer, lay in the bed and continued to assess the situation until I became too tired and decided to go outside for a morning walk.

The weather was unusually warm; more like late March than late January. The Sun felt warm and comforting, blue sky and birds were everywhere, the air was refreshing as I was able to smell the trees. "What a perfect morning. This couldn't be any better except I am about to pass out and die! Where the hell is everybody?" I was about to start screaming for help, but at the last moment remembered "The Hollywood Rob" rule.

I walked around the house, sat in the backyard and waited for someone to come by. I looked at the clock and it was way past 9 a.m. I hadn't slept almost at all for two days, my body had had enough and was hurting all over. "I've seen too much. Someone has to come to the house. But what if they won't?"

I saw a landscaper working across the street in my neighbor's yard. I remembered the "as long as you can see and feel, but can never again hear and speak" rule. "I can't talk to anyone, not even my family, or I will die. I'll pretend that I can't hear and speak until I get some sleep and figure out the next steps. I had made up my mind.

I opened the garage door and started the lawnmower, like nothing had happened. I'd been cutting grass for a few minutes when members of my family began to arrive at the house, in separate cars, one by one. I looked at the cars and continued to cut the grass. When asked what had happened, a sign language was used to answer that I was unable to hear and speak. My brother-in-law, Jonathan, walked behind me and after a few seconds suddenly screamed into my ear as loud as he could. I didn't even move, my body and spirit were separated and long gone. I was barely able to walk, like a zombie, not displaying any emotions. My body was just there, cutting the grass. My mind was somewhere else, unable to cope with the situation any longer. "Who are these people? Why did nobody come earlier to check on me? At least since 7.32 a.m., they have known I was suffering the entire night! These people are not my family members, they're just actors, paid to drive me insane," were my last thoughts before I completely gave up and surrendered myself to the situation.

I begged Romana to take me to the bedroom, to stay with me so I could finally fall asleep. She refused and wanted to take me to the hospital. I didn't have any strength to argue or come up with another plan adjusted for this situation. I simply went and sat in the car. During the drive to the WellStar Kennestone Hospital, I was looking outside with eyes wide open, just looking and not thinking of anything anymore. I was neither scared nor happy, emotionless is what I had become.

Chapter 5
The Hospital

As the body, the mind and the spirit separate from each other, the human being is not a person anymore. He or she is just an empty shell, materially present but unable to care about the future.

Kennestone Hospital is located in the City of Marietta, about fifteen minutes away from my house. There was a waiting line at the emergency room. Romana helped me to sit down on one of the small sofas placed in the waiting area. She was drinking a venti-size Starbucks coffee purchased in the hospital's cafeteria. I pointed at the cup and slightly moved my right hand towards my face a couple of times for her to hand me the cup. The coffee smelled great, tasted delicious, and warmed my stomach and body to the point I stopped shivering.

"Think, Joseph, you can beat this. It's no big deal. They'll just probably perform a few tests to find out what's wrong and you'll go home," I thought, comforting myself as I was sitting on the couch, looking out a large panoramic window, admiring how beautiful the sky looked.

I grabbed my wife, gently pulled her to sit next to me and kept holding her hand until a nurse told Romana to guide me over to the adjacent room. Jonathan and Milan were told to stay in the waiting room area.

The nurse asked Romana what was wrong with me and was curious regarding the surrounding circumstances. Both the nurse and Romana were visually guiding me through the routine physical checkup examination. The three of us went to a small room, a typical hospital room with one chair and a hard bed covered with transparent white paper. Romana was told to sit and wait with me until the doctor came. I was so tired, half asleep, but somehow managed to stay awake. I became nervous, opened my eyes and kept staring forward at the white wall directly in front of me. When spoken to, I completely ignored everyone; the medical staff and my wife. I did not have to act at all. The fear of losing life makes everyone, including a Joe Blow like me, the Hollywood actor deserving of an Academy Award.

Several doctors performed different medical tests, from making noises behind my head to letting me write on a piece of paper what happened. I didn't know, didn't want to remember anything, didn't want to do anything except to stay in the game and eventually win my life back.

"Everyone is in on this. If I ever figure out who is doing this to me, the son of a bitch is a dead man."

Ideas similar to these helped me to gain additional strength to stay focused. I did not view the medical staff as people trying to help me. "The doctors are excellent entertainers, paid actors, torturers and executioners combined, with total disregard for human life. The doctors only care if the TV network renews their contract for next year. They are not paid by medical insurance, they are paid by the producers, the government and indirectly by the audience." I had to pause my thoughts to prevent myself from completely losing my mind.

After several hours of examinations, combined with seemingly endless waiting periods in between, a doctor walked into the room and said to Romana, "We don't know what has caused this. It appears to be some sort of mental block. We'll try one more test; he'll be taken to the next room and dissected to pieces."

The doctor and my wife were staring into each other's faces during the conversation; she didn't show any emotions, didn't say a word as the doctor finished the sentence. Given the unusual events that had happened in the past several days, I didn't know what was reality and what wasn't anymore. There were an infinite number of possibilities and reasons to justify what and why this was happening to me.

"Many people would have committed suicide before reaching this stage of the game, whatever the game might be," I said to myself. I remained calm, and kept staring at the white wall.

I was taken to a room where an MRI machine stood. "This is it, this is the end," I thought, as I was sliding deeper into the machine, holding Romana's hand. I refused to let go of her hand and the experiment began. A loud and vibrating noise was played at different intervals for at least ten minutes. Every time I heard the noise, my body shook uncontrollably like I was having a seizure.

To my relief, I walked out of the machine in one piece and went straight to the restroom. I washed my face and paused for a few minutes. The thought of going home and falling asleep was priceless. This goal felt realistic and achievable. I left the restroom, went to a nearby waiting area and sat next to my wife.

"Doctors told me that we will go home shortly. Just hold on for little longer," Romana wrote on a piece of paper.

The same doctor who wanted to dissect me to pieces walked in and said to Romana, "We don't know what's wrong with him. He never looked directly into my face. It appears he doesn't view me as the person that is trying to help him, and I don't know what he is thinking of. We have no choice but to observe him for a few days."

Romana, of course, agreed to everything the doctor had just told her. Unfortunately, my wife always blindly believes everything a person of authority tells her. She completely ignored my earlier request; at home, I wanted to fall asleep while holding her hand. I knew she was not going to fight for me to be released. Thoughts of resentment and disbelief boiled within me. "How can a deaf and silent person be held against his or her will? I was not violent at all, just tired beyond imagination. At work, I lost the woman I truly loved, twice in a year. I lost Christine and Jessica as well. I lost two jobs this year, went through a lot of bullshit this week, was in jail, didn't sleep for two days and now this?"

I was placed in a wheelchair and taken to a room. The two-person hospital room looked fairly normal at first. A bathroom with a sink, shower, and a toilet was situated on the right side of the room as I entered. The two beds, separated by a curtain, were also at the right side of the room. A television was strategically placed so both patients were able to watch it simultaneously. I was given the bed closest to a window. The small window, with blinds fully suspended, was located in front of my bed to the right. I was not able to look outside.

Romana held my hand and stayed with me for the remainder of the day.

"I love you. Please stay with me until I am released. I don't want to be alone any longer," I wrote on a piece of paper, as my mind was comforting itself. "Falling asleep without the ability to wake up and being medically experimented on are my deepest fears. The person closest to me, the person I trust; Romana, my wife, would surely wake me up and protect me from any wrongdoings."

To my disappointment, Romana was not allowed to stay with me overnight. A strange idea entered my mind. "I have to fall asleep before my wife can release me to the hospital."

A nurse stopped by to talk with Romana about my medical condition. The nurse kept rubbing her inner ear at an unusually fast pace. I adjusted the bed to a flat position and pretended to be asleep. The nurse deeply exhaled, moved her head down and was apparently relieved by my actions. I questioned the logic but didn't bother anymore to understand the situation. "Was my wife instructed to play the Devil and Angel game? Who knows."

After the nurse left, Romana went to a cafeteria to buy a sandwich and promised to come back shortly to say her final goodbye. On her way back to the room, she was stopped by a nurse in the hallway, just in front of the entrance door. I was not sure what was discussed but she was not coming in. "They won't even let her come in to hug and kiss me, to say the final goodbye?" I thought.

115

Using sign language, I showed the nurse sitting on a leather chair a few feet away from my bed that I needed to use the bathroom. She quickly closed the curtain, handed me a plastic container and blocked me from walking any further. I took the plastic container, urinated, and went back to bed. I knew better, I could not let anyone know I was able to hear and speak. It would have been the end of me, the real me, the person I'd known for thirty-eight years.

When Romana left the hospital, the psychiatrists started to play "The Devil and The Angel" game; a representative of the Hell, the bad doctor, and a representative of Heaven, the good doctor. The good doctor standing in front of me was speaking in a positive way to the bad doctor, who answered in a negative way. Religious themes were often mixed in the conversation. The doctors knew I could not hear and speak, so this behavior was amusing to them. "This is horrible, if these doctors are in charge of a religious patient who is incapable of defending him/herself, it is just a matter of time before the patient is driven to complete insanity. This can't be 'the norm' in all mental institutions," I said to myself. It was obvious the psychiatrists liked to abuse helpless human beings. I heard on numerous occasions that psychiatrists are a little crazy themselves. I had no idea they were this crazy.

At certain times, the staff spoke about all kinds of medical experiments they would perform once the wife was fully persuaded that I was crazy and signed my life away to the mental institution. "The doctors would be able to freely perform medical experiments on my mind and body without any repercussions. It would have been so easy to produce a document listing 'an accident, accidental death,' or the cleanest of them all, 'suicide,' to cover their tracks." I silently analyzed the situation as my body resembled a lifeless statue. All kinds of "toys" were at their disposal to abuse the patients with; helicopter noises, sounds coming from different points of the room, flashes of light hitting your face, a psychiatric person talking complete nonsense, pretending to be your roommate, and an invisible device shooting electric currents to your body. The current was not harmful but was very annoying, especially when directed at your heart and genital area. Many times over, I heard that I would go home in a few minutes. I just kept silent. The worst experience was hearing a screaming woman's voice coming from the adjacent room.

Again, strangely enough, I was awakened by the personnel several times a night. On one occasion, a fake IV was attached to my arm. The next day, the doctors continuously brainwashed Romana to sign the documents. I came up with the plan; to sleep, and to wake up hearing and talking again. I did just that in front of my wife, so there would be a witness. The staff was not too happy about this, making comments such as, "Oh, a miracle has happened, yeah right."

We were told the insurance would not cover the hospital visit if I was released today. The doctors were concerned about my well-being and suggested one more day of observation. Apparently, the doctors had become afraid, they did not know how much I'd really heard. When Romana left, the same game started again, adjusted for hearing, same for the eyes. I was friendly to everybody in order to make them believe I did not hear anything. I tried to convince everyone that I believed it was a normal hospital. I even asked for a razor to shave and complained about damaged photographs given to me by my sister a day earlier. The photographs were damaged on purpose. Blurry faces and barely visible lines printed all over the pictures.

The psychiatrists and my fake "roommate" became friendlier as the evening progressed but they remained puzzled. The staff performed the following test after midnight. I heard my roommate jerking off. The "nurse" sitting in front of my bed pretended to be asleep. The electric currents were going through my body for hours, the person kept jerking off for hours, the nurse was asleep in front of my bed, a helicopter "landed" and kept idling. Another nurse opened the main door, pointed to the exit and stated, "I am trying to make it easy on your department." The doctors hoped I would panic and try to run away. A video showing the attempted escape would be played to my wife, together with a verbal explanation of why I was sedated and "taken away." I, however, got up, calmly went to the bathroom and then back to bed.

I was able to fall asleep around 4 a.m. and was awoken by a doctor right before my nightmares became too real, too scary to be handled by my confused mind. As in prior instances, my whole body was totally wet, the sheets and blanket were fully soaked in sweat. My mood improved dramatically after breakfast. "Just a couple hours and I will be home free. I hope Romana will come earlier than noon to pick me up," I thought.

Everything went well until a nurse offered me a pain pill on numerous occasions. "I better take the pill, or they may think I am crazy." I made the decision and asked for the pill. I pretended to swallow the pill, then went to the bathroom and inconspicuously threw the pill into the toilet.

I wanted to look my best and decided to take a quick shower about fifteen minutes before noon. Nurse was unusually helpful and accommodating; handed me a towel, offered to help with any additional requests I might have. "I have to be in the bed by noon, so Romana can pick me up," I thought, as I was trying to turn on the hot water. The shower tap had a strange design. I couldn't figure it out so I asked the nurse for assistance. Right after she was able to turn on the hot water, I was told to take as much time as I needed. My time perception changed. The nurse placed the towel back on top of the shower and left the room at an extremely fast pace. She moved so fast her body became blurry. I turned off the water and returned back to the room as fast as possible.

I could not believe my eyes when Romana and Julia walked into the room. They were both happy and excited to see me, especially Julia, who ran into my arms with a large smile on her face. She was dressed up and looked like a doll. We kissed, hugged, and played while my wife went somewhere to complete the exit paperwork. About ten minutes passed, a joyful ten minutes, but Romana was nowhere in sight. "I hope she is not being brainwashed again," I thought, and almost panicked, but continued to play with Julia like nothing unusual was going on. Romana finally showed up and the three of us walked out of the room as a happy family. I was walking slowly with no visible emotions, hiding the excitement of beating the system, beating the psychiatrists at their own sick game. "Go home and listen to your wife," said a stranger sitting on a bench. Julia and Romana didn't respond to the comment, neither did I. We just kept walking while my mind was occupied. "I survived but didn't figure out anything. Nothing is over, the game is still on. I better keep quiet and listen to my wife."

As we were approaching the car, a stranger walking behind us said, "We're listening." Again, there was no response from my wife and daughter. Sitting in the car felt like being in a tank, fully surrounded and protected by the metal shell. I didn't want to think or do anything anymore, just wanted to sit there, enjoy the ride and the outside scenery I'd thought my eyes would never see again. As we were driving up from the second level of the parking garage all the way to the roof, the car did not feel like a tank anymore. It felt like an ambulance was taking me to a helicopter parked on the roof. At the top deck the driver, Romana, made a U-turn and slowly drove back down to the bottom level, away from the hospital. The psychiatrists who wanted me back so badly instructed her to perform this theatrical fiasco. Their careers were in jeopardy if I were ever to break the code of silence. My wife, of course, blindly followed the instructions with no questions asked. She didn't even try to give me any indirect warnings. I escaped the gates of Hell, the prison, and the gates of Heaven, the hospital. In the Hell, I would have been killed by prisoners. In the Heaven, I would have been killed by psychiatrists. Which is better? I think there is not much difference at all. Both institutions allow certain people to have almost unlimited power over people who cannot defend themselves. Depending on circumstances, this can bring the worst or the best qualities out of the people in power.

I was relaxed and really hungry when we arrived home. "There's some food in the fridge. I have to go out and buy you the pain medicine," Romana said, and walked out with Julia back to the car, leaving me home alone.

I opened the refrigerator and took out a couple of white Styrofoam boxes. The food looked delicious; fried fish with vegetables. It was exactly the same food my mom bought right after I came home from jail. "What a coincidence," I thought, while eating the food. The situation did not feel normal anymore. "Am I going to be left home alone again, to possibly die? In case I don't wake up, I need to leave a sign for anyone that will come to the house." I placed the remaining half of the fish on a clean plate, left it on the kitchen table and went upstairs to shower and shave. I undressed in front of a mirror. There was a different person standing in the mirror, a totally different person than I remembered. He was skinny, wrinkled, bearded, and bruised, wearing nothing except a paper bracelet. "Any longer at those institutions, this guy would have become a walking skeleton," I said to the person in the mirror.

After the shower, I went downstairs, took a knife and cut the bracelet, then opened the fridge and ate a yoghurt. "I am not touching the fish, no matter what. That'll stay here." I threw the empty yoghurt container into a trashcan and saw the exact same paper bracelet around my left wrist again. "This can't be happening. I removed the bracelet from my wrist a minute ago," I said, and replayed the cutting of the bracelet event in my head multiple times to prove it really happened. I could not comprehend the situation. Hallucinations seemed the only logical explanation at the time. "Another rule; I need to shut up and listen to my wife. The intelligence agency with the psychiatrists are surely monitoring me 24/7. I escaped the gravedigger twice in a few days. This is way too easy. I need to fall asleep right now before I go crazy, or else," I thought, ran upstairs, jumped into the master bed and closed my eyes. My mind was able to completely block all thought process, my eyes only saw darkness while falling asleep.

That afternoon, I was finally able to fall asleep and wake up without help for the first time since the arrest. The "wake up" scenario was anything but usual; I had fuzzy vision, shortness of breath, facial and chest pains. My thought process was supercharged and out of control; generating one positive and associated negative idea about the possible scenarios, one after another, at a faster and faster rate. On the night of the arrest I experienced something similar just before I lost the ability to control the thought process altogether. Ultimately, I was able to refocus my eyes and realized I was in my bedroom, in my bed, in the safety of my house. Sunlight fully shone through the windows and the surrounding area looked crystal white. "No," I said loudly. "No, I don't give a shit anymore about what's going on," then my breathing returned to normal, the chest pains went away, and my eyes were just staring into the room, disconnected from the idling mind. What a relief.

An orange bottle of pain pills was lying right next to me on a night table. I came up with the plan to make everyone believe I trusted Romana. "I'll have to put one pill in my mouth like normal. I will then go to the bathroom, rub my hand against my mouth and throw the pill in the toilet." I did just that and was plenty happy with the acting performance. I had no energy, didn't feel like doing anything except for eating, sleeping, and socializing with my family to a certain degree. I gave up on figuring out what was really going on and decided to play the game day by day, adjusted for each individual situation. The main objective was to stay with my family in the real world, the world I have known my entire life.

Chapter 6
At Home Again

In the following few days after the hospital release, I had no energy and in general didn't feel good. I had difficulty performing and concentrating on everyday tasks, slept most of the time and kept waking up several times a night due to severe nightmares. Fortunately, each time I awoke in my own bed, in the safety of the house, my thought process was at normal speed. The "crazy awakening" experienced earlier appeared to be just a one-time incident. The usual symptoms – inability to concentrate, pain all over my face and the rest of the body – were appearing at unpredictable intervals.

I kept busy by reading the book *Mraky Nad Barrandovem* (*Clouds over Barrandov*) and listening to music. I had planned on reading the book for years but never found the time. The setting takes place before, during, and after the Nazi occupation of Czechoslovakia. The plot is based on a true story; the life struggle of famous Czech actors, performers, and producers of this era. I liked the book but reading every single page was a struggle. The constant back and forth between the pages and chapters was mentally tiring so I napped frequently.

I was not in the best mood either; I was unable to figure out the present situation and the unusual experiences of the past several weeks. I had to keep switching music genres periodically; too much heavy metal caused irritability and chest pains. Too much classical and Eighties/Nineties pop and alternative caused drowsiness associated with facial tingling. To stay in perfect physical and emotional harmony was a challenge.

There was not a cloud in the sky on Sunday morning, the 29th of January. I was feeling much better and wanted to take my family to East Cobb Park for a walk. We drove to the Fuller Park entrance that was closest to our house. East Cobb and Fuller parks are connected by nature trails surrounded by woods on all sides.

"Walk in the woods would definitely help everyone to relax," I said to my wife.

During the walk from Fuller to East Cobb Park, both Julia and Teresa were happy; they continuously smiled and talked with each other and their parents in apparent relief the whole family was together at last.

"Do you remember what you said to Jonathan and Milli just before the arrest?" Romana asked, as we were walking.

"No, I only remember few flashbacks and why talk about it now? Let's just enjoy the day," I said.

"You said something about being followed by aliens. Do you remember that?"

"Aliens?" I replied in disbelief and continued, "You don't believe in fairy tales, do you? That's crazy. To be honest with you, I might have said anything at that point. I've been under a lot of stress lately," I said, and tried to steer the conversation in a different direction.

After a few minutes we reached the first man-made structure; an amphitheater standing before a large open grass area followed by a playground.

Both kids ran inside of the amphitheater and Teresa said, "Look what I found. I have money."

Both Romana and I were a little surprised since she found a twenty-dollar bill.

"You are a very lucky girl. Do you know the president's name on the bill?" I asked and pointed to the picture.

"Jackson," she read loudly and smiled with her eyes wide open.

"Good, you are smart girl. That's a lot of money, save it and buy something useful," I said.

We continued to walk to the playground where we played. A kids' birthday party was in full progress just in front of the playground, near the cooking grills; the food smelled good, everyone was happy, and kids were running around. The kids and adults played all sorts of games: sand bag toss, circle toss to reach a specific target, and flying air rockets.

"This is fun. Let's go there," Teresa said.

Romana didn't want to meet the people since it was a private birthday party.

"Come on, let's go, it doesn't matter. I am sure the parents will let our kids play the games with their kids." I tried to persuade her, but she refused to go with us.

The three of us had a great time since the birthday family welcomed us with open arms. All of us played the games and ran around the field. Within twenty minutes, other families unrelated to the birthday party joined and played with everyone. I had a nice conversation with the granddad of the ten-year-old birthday girl. We talked for at least thirty minutes about ourselves and our families. He answered every single question with a smile and without hesitation, no matter how private the question was.

"What a nice guy and friendly family. I wish everyone would be like them," I thought, after saying goodbye to him and his family. It was about lunchtime so we walked back to the car and drove home.

After lunch, I became exhausted and irritated. "I need to save myself. I should stay out of everyone's way until I feel better."

I remembered the rule and went to the bedroom. I slept, read the book and listened to music until dinner time. I didn't want to think about the possible scenarios and solutions, or why this happened or what might happen next. I was happy to be alive and grateful for the precious time spent with the family earlier in the day.

After dinner, the kids wanted to watch a movie. It had been a while since the four of us watched a movie together.

"Romana, come on over to watch a movie with us. I'll find something appropriate for all of us," I said.

Netflix is one of the best entertainment deals out there. For less than ten bucks a month, you can watch unlimited amounts of movies, shows, and fairy tales, commercial free. I was searching through movies similar to *Pirates of the Caribbean*, the movies anyone from three to a hundred years old would enjoy watching, and came across *E.T. The Extra-Terrestrial*.

"That's a great movie. I must have been about seven, right at Teresa's age, when I saw it the first time," I said.

Everyone, including my wife, became excited and wanted to see *E.T.* As expected, both kids enjoyed the show and were asking the right questions up until the end. I loved the movie as well, it reminded me of my childhood. One sentence in particular stood out. As E.T. was saying goodbye to the little boy, he made the following comment: "I'll be right here," and pointed his finger to his head.

The next morning, January 30th, started like any other morning after the hospital release. I felt fine at first but quickly became tired, especially after eating breakfast. The facial pains appeared again and my time perception changed. At certain times, everyone and everything was moving just a little slower than normal; however, voices and sounds remained at the same speed.

"To feel better, I need to start functioning again. Where is my phone? I can't remember seeing it any time after the arrest. It still must be somewhere at Milli's house. I'll get it today, as soon as we're finished at marriage therapy."

Romana decided that seeing a marriage therapist would be a good idea. I also felt the marriage was not where it should have been. About a year ago, she grew more distant and wanted to hang around with her friend Eva as much as possible.

We arrived at the therapist's office, located on Roswell Road near Buckhead, a few minutes before the scheduled appointment time of 11 a.m. and sat in the waiting area. The place was small but cozy; there were two chairs, a water pitcher, magazines, and peppermint candy. An older, white-bearded heavier gentleman walked out of the office with a younger man dressed in a suit.

He turned to us and said, "Good morning, I am Mr. Milton. How are you?"

After the introduction we went to his office, which appeared more like a large closet, with a two-person couch and chair separated by no more than five feet and a small night stand. There wasn't room for anything else. I thought the setting was very unusual, especially after I found out he used to work for KPMG performing full background checks of potential candidates.

"My wife chose this guy," I thought. "His prior client, the younger guy, looked like a typical agent. The office setting in general is strange. Yes, he is the post-hospital NSA government caretaker of mine."

I was tired and decided not to talk unless I had to. I blocked the agent idea out of my mind and viewed Mr. Milton as the person who was saving the marriage. He was relaxed, friendly, and fair to both parties, and the meeting went well. Individual stress therapy with someone else was recommended for the both of us.

In the afternoon, Romana had plans with the kids and refused to give me a ride to pick up my car and the cell phone. I used her phone to call Milan, who had no problem driving me to Milli's house. I called my sister to let her know Milan and I were about to come to the house. We were going to see each other for the first time since the arrest and I didn't want to scare her by staying in her house alone. I dressed for the occasion: black Levi's jeans, black Kenneth Cole long-sleeve shirt, black Kenneth Cole Reaction winter coat, "Iron Man" sunglasses and black Nike sneakers.

"Whatever the scenario might be, I'm sure looking good for it. The NSA can follow me as long as they want and I'll just give them a hard time from now on," I thought, and admired myself in front of the mirror.

The coat was my favorite; comfortable fabric, nice collar and just the right length, ending slightly above my knees. I took it to every single European trip except in summer. This was the coat Leah liked as well. I have one memory that stood out among the others. . . At the end of 2016, Leah and her tax group were sitting and waiting for an airplane at Flint, Michigan airport. She noticed me, started to smile and looked directly into my eyes for at least ten seconds as I was approaching her. I was looking and smiling at her as well.

Milli and her family live in Canton, about a twenty-minute drive from my place, on almost an acre of land in a ranch-style house built in the Sixties. Most houses in those days were built ranch style, surrounded by trees to save electricity. The world population in the mid-Sixties was 3.3 billion, less than half of the 7.5 billion in 2017, therefore, a house near a city on an acre of land was easily affordable for a blue-collar family.

Milli and Asa welcomed us as soon as we arrived. Jonathan was also in the house, unable to go to work due to short-term disability. About a week ago, he had an accident while skiing in Snowshoe, WV. While skiing on the Western Territory side of the mountain, a gust of wind blew him to the ground so hard he cracked his wrist, scapula, shoulder and fractured a collarbone. The pain must have been excruciating since he was still unable to sit in a chair and drive a car. I felt sorry for him, especially when all the circumstances were factored in; it happened on the second day of their vacation, on a flat surface while he was almost at a standstill. The wind gust must have been at least 60mph.

The four of us sat down in relief that we were finally able to get together. We talked about everyday items, Jonathan's accident, the arrest, and the next steps in my life.

"Jonathan, I need to ask you few questions. Can we go outside for a minute?" I said.

"Sure, no problem," he replied, and we walked to the backyard.

"Please tell me everything you can remember about the arrest. I can only remember a few flashbacks; I smoked some weed, broke the aquarium, went outside of the house, was in an ambulance, two cops standing in front of me, waking up in a police car, arriving at prison and that's it. This scares me, I want to find the cause of this," I calmly said to him.

"I don't know why this happened. I never seen you acting like that, it wasn't you. You might have smoked some, but you were drug tested in jail and everything came back negative," he sincerely answered.

"Really, the tests came back negative? That's strange, weed usually stays in your system for weeks," I replied, and clearly remembered several deep inhalations of the weed, knowing for sure I smoked some.

Jonathan continued to speak. "It's possible you have a quick metabolism, I just don't know. Anyway, you went outside of the house, was really noisy and the neighbor called a cop. I called the ambulance, but you refused the medical help. Then you fought with the police; Black guy and White woman. You kicked the woman officer and were thrown hard in the cop car by both of them. The Black cop mentioned, 'Is this necessary? Do we really have to do this?' I talked them out of pressing charges and said the truth. You lost a job and were under a lot of stress. This was not the person we knew. This wasn't you. We never seen you act like this," he said.

I was able to see genuine concern on his face.

"Thank you for sticking with me and for downplaying the situation with the cops. I don't know why this happened to me. Let's move past this. I'll get a job asap and Romana will be happy. Sorry for all the trouble I caused you and I feel really bad Asa was present. I hope he wasn't scared of me," I said in relief, happy to communicate with Jonathan in a normal way without the crazy "side effects" experienced in the past several weeks.

It appeared nobody in my family knew what was really going on in my mind.

"Don't worry about it, Joseph. Milli and Asa ran out of the house as soon as you acted weird. He didn't see anything," he said, trying to comfort me.

"Good. Were you able to save the fish?" I asked.

"No, but we told him the fish got sick in the aquarium and had to be released to a river."

I was plenty satisfied with the answer and we went inside of the house to play with Asa.

Asa and I always liked to play with kid guns, to shoot foam bullets at each other. We did just that every time our families were together. Everyone, including Julia and Teresa, enjoyed shooting from the pistols. It's a shame Romana never saw us having this much fun together. She didn't seem to enjoy outdoor activities, such as primitive camping, either. She was more of an indoor person who loved to spend vacations in full-inclusive resorts, killing time by eating, drinking, and endlessly lying by a pool. Asa and I took the guns and started to play by shooting all over from one end of the house to the other.

"This is great, when a bullet is shot, I can track it from a barrel to a target. I'll try to catch one," I thought, and asked Asa to shoot directly at me.

I almost caught the bullet and asked him to shoot again from a greater distance. He was, however, shooting from the same distance. I didn't want anyone to suspect my time perception changed so I stopped playing and pretended to feel tired.

"Has anyone seen my phone?" I asked.

"Yes," Milli answered. "It's in the drawer, inside of your car."

"It was great seeing everyone again, sorry for all the trouble I caused."

I said goodbye and walked to my car, where the phone was exactly as Milli had said, in the drawer. While driving home, I did not feel good; I had chest pains, facial muscle soreness and my eyes were hurting. I had to stop at my mom's and talk with her about a letter she received from the mortgage company. She had low income, unable to qualify for a mortgage on her own. The mortgage on the house she owned had been under my name since 2005, the last time we refinanced.

Shortly after my arrival I quickly became irritated, snappy, and could not listen to her advice regarding everything from nutrition to my marriage.

"Stop right now, don't say another word!" I abruptly said to her.

"But Joseph, avocado is healthy—" she said.

"Shut up, I had enough of you! All my life you caused me nothing but problems," I snapped back at her, then threw the letter on the cul-de-sac, jumped into my car and drove away as fast as I could. "That woman, if she wasn't my mother I would never want to see her again. I had enough of her already."

I was angry, needed to relax somewhere as fast as possible, and wanted to walk the trail from Fuller to East Cobb Park. The chest and facial pains were intensifying, the closer I was approaching the park. I parked and exited the car as fast as possible, feeling like my heart was about to explode. A black vehicle parked next to my car; a man looking like an agent exited, turned his head towards me and kept staring for a few seconds.

"Yeah right," I thought. "The agents must have bugged my car with some sort of device generating a strong electromagnetic field."

I justified the situation and slowly walked into the woods, but the pain didn't stop. "It has to be in the Leaf's wireless key since the phone is in the car."

I buried the key next to an easily recognizable tree and resumed the walk, then tried to run, but felt worse after a few steps.

"Nobody is around to help me in case of a collapse. I better pick up the key and drive home as fast as possible," I said to myself, as the pain intensified.

And there he was; the agent I feared approached me and smiled like he knew what was going on in my body from both a physical and emotional perspective. I gathered the last remaining strength left in my body and ran as fast as possible to the car. I drove home, obeying all traffic laws so as not to raise any suspicions.

"Romana will surely take me to the hospital or, in a worst-case situation, I'll die home in my bed," I thought numerous times.

Unfortunately, Romana was not home. The pains slightly decreased, I lay in my bed and tried to relax. Airplanes and helicopters constantly flew nearby. At one point, it seemed if a helicopter was idling above the house.

"I'll probably die or will be kidnaped for interrogation."

I was helpless and didn't know what to do anymore. To close the eyes and wait for help was the best and only available option. The helicopter must have been idling for at least five minutes and for no apparent reason slowly flew away. The chest pains decreased in similar speed as the helicopter engine sound decreased. My symptoms went away and there was total silence.

"Am I in a grave?" I asked. "It sure feels quiet and peaceful."

It was so easy to close my eyes and fall asleep.

The first thing I wanted to do on Tuesday, January 31st was to read news on my cell phone. Reading news right after waking up is sort of my habit anyway, especially on off days. Local news is great for local events. I mostly access foreign sources on the internet for national and world news because most news generated by the US media companies caters to special interest groups. The news is limited, biased, and doesn't provide the whole picture. On TV, most of the airtime devoted to news is wasted in pointless debates to influence the public to have certain opinions. It makes sense because of limited ownership; in 1983, fifty companies controlled 90% of the media market in the USA. Today, only five companies control the same 90% of the market.

After waking up, I felt close to normal and happy to be in the bed. I reached for the phone to surf the internet and experienced the same problems when looking at the screen. Flashes of light were shooting into my face at unpredictable intervals, the colors were sharper than normal and touch-screen functionality of the device was off the charts. A simple one-time finger touch mostly did not work and a page moved slowly up and down or to the sides. The zoom was either too much or too little, nothing in between. I tried as hard as I could to at least read something. This seemingly miniscule task became impossible since the symptoms returned; the dizziness, facial pains and inability to focus were increasing the longer I looked at the phone. I had to stop.

"Is someone doing this on purpose?"

As soon as the thought ended, I heard the engines and tire noises of several cars that drove by. This was strange since noises from passing cars were always barely audible while being in the master bedroom. It sounded as if Old Canton Road was right next to the house instead of at the normal distance of about 200 feet.

I stayed in the bed and tried to fall asleep, but could not, as thoughts were racing in my mind. "Are the aviation and street noises somehow related to each other?" And again, after I finished my thought the loud street noises were audible again. "Yes, I am in trouble! The psychiatrists and agents conspired against me by installing speakers in the house to drive me crazy when nobody is around. At least I'm still alive and on TV! :-) It's OK, I need to learn to live in my new dimension."

I brushed my teeth, washed my face, styled my hair and dressed in the usual jeans and T-shirt outfit. It was time for breakfast. I went downstairs to the kitchen to make myself a small dish consisting of one slice of toast and one of papaya. All the noises were gone but my physical symptoms were present. I sat down and removed the cell phone from my pocket and placed it on the dining table in front of me. The symptoms slightly decreased. I walked away from the table and the symptoms disappeared altogether.

"It's in the cell phone. The producers bugged my phone with a device that shoots strong electromagnetic radiation to my body. I'll do a little experiment."

I approached the table and inserted the phone into my pocket and the symptoms – dizziness, chest and facial pains – appeared again. I quickly reached for the phone, placed it on the table and walked away and again the symptoms were gone.

"I need to get rid of the phone as fast as possible. But how, how am I gonna do this without raising suspicion? I am under constant surveillance and can't just take a rock and smash the fucker. The phone has to stay away from my body until I figure something out," I thought, and placed the phone in the kitchen cabinet above the refrigerator.

Watching the news on TV was the next logical step. Picture quality of the TV was way above average; bright sharp colors, the characters in focus were positioned more in front of the TV, very similar to 3D-picture quality, and again there were the ever-present vibrating flashes of light. I gave up on LCD screens altogether, turned off the TV and went upstairs to lie in a bed. I continued to read *Clouds over Barrandov* and was finally able to relax. The book looked and felt like a normal book; the pages were not vibrating, and letters were not coming out of the paper, what a relief.

I either slept or read the book until lunchtime. The weather was warm, the sky was cloudless. After lunch, I went outside, took my shirt off, lay on a blanket and continued to read the book. At 2.30 p.m., Teresa arrived from school. Both kids changed to swimsuits, took their books and lay next to me. We read and played all sorts of games; holding and flying the "kid airplane" above my head, hide and seek.

"Why don't we take the blanket and go to the Sope Creek park?" I suggested. "We can lay on the grass next to the pond, play and read our books over there."

The pond is in the middle of woods and is full of life most of the year. There are plenty of fish, frogs, turtles, and birds. The kids always loved to go there.

"What do you think?" I asked the kids.

The girls smiled, jumped up and down and eagerly agreed.

I came up with a plan in my head: "Perfect, I'll drop the phone in the pond and make it look like an accident."

The children took their books and ran to the garage to sit in the Leaf. I picked up the blanket, went to the kitchen and grabbed the phone.

The symptoms appeared again, and I walked to the garage like nothing was going on. My symptoms decreased, but didn't disappear completely, as soon as I threw the phone on the floor right next to me.

"This sucks! My car must be bugged with a similar device," I thought, and turned around to make sure the car was not affecting the kids.

What a relief, the girls were smiling and talking with each other. The parking lot at the park was unusually busy for Tuesday afternoon but we were able to find a spot to park. I picked up the blanket, phone, and a water bottle. The symptoms immediately worsened; my chest was under such pressure, I was barely able to breathe. I tricked the kids into walking next to me as fast as possible by playing a game; whoever reaches the pond first is the winner.

"Strange, if I hold the phone right next to their little bodies the pressure eases. I guess the producers want to kill me and not the kids."

We reached a wooden dock located at the edge of the pond, near the main trail. Julia and Teresa walked to the other edge of the dock from where I was standing; the chest, facial pains, and pressure increased to an almost unbearable point. It felt like I was about to collapse.

"I need to do it now or never."

I threw the blanket with the water bottle on the ground and calmly typed the pin. My back was facing the pond. I took a step back and kept moving the phone in front on my face like I was searching for the appropriate amount of sunlight to improve the screen's visibility, then lifted my right foot and gently touched the outer rim closest to the water with the heel. I applied additional pressure to my left foot and jumped into the water backwards. Hundreds of needles suddenly penetrated my body.

Swimming in an open body of water in January surely felt cold, even in Georgia. I quickly dropped the phone and exited the pond as fast as possible. Both Julia and Teresa couldn't comprehend what just happened; they stood still with their mouths fully opened, asking questions about why and how this happened. I quickly took off my shirt and wrapped the blanket around my body.

"Come on, girls, we have to go. I'm freezing," I said.

"But Daddy," Teresa said, paused and continued, "why did you fall into the water? Will you go back to get your phone?"

"No, Teresa, the water is too cold and the phone is already damaged. Let's go home," I replied to her.

After several minutes, I was finally able to convince both girls to walk back to the car.

At the parking lot, a man on a bicycle approached us and said, "Hi."

I was caught in complete shock but said, "Hi," as well.

130

It was Zack, the person who wrote the sarcastic message on Facebook and didn't bother to call 911.

"Hey Joseph, what's up with the blanket? Did you go for a swim?" Zack asked, in clear amusement.

"Man, you won't believe what happened. I tripped, fell in the pond and lost my phone," I answered, in the friendliest way possible.

"Is your phone still in the water?" he continued.

"Unfortunately, but what can you do," I said, and buckled the kids into their car seats. We said bye to each other. He continued bicycling towards the pond; the kids and I drove home. Zack was a business consultant and normally traveled Monday through Thursday almost every week. This was unusual, and I began to get worried.

"Why was he so concerned about my phone? I hope he will not try to find it. The NSA definitely sent him over here to check on me."

When we arrived home I acted brilliantly in front of my wife, who believed every single word that came out of my mouth.

"Joseph, what's wrong with you and your phones lately?" she asked in disbelief.

"I had an accident, ask the kids, they were there. Fortunately, the phone cost only $170, not $700. I'll get something cheap again," I answered.

"You are cheap, it only took you ten years to buy a new couch and you had to make a scene at the store."

Romana clearly wanted to pick a fight and argue. I knew exactly where the conversation to argue was heading; my employment situation and flirting with women.

The hopes of flying to the Czech Republic were high. A haircut was desired. I called my hairstylist, Khuan, located in the nearby city of Smyrna, and made an appointment for 7.30 p.m. that night. I drove my wife's car, a Toyota Highlander, and not the Leaf due to persisting facial, chest pains and fatigue. Strangely, the symptoms were present in much lesser strength or not present at all when driving a gasoline car. I was nervous, alone in the darkness of the night. This was the farthest distance away from the house I'd been since the arrest.

"Are there any surprises waiting for me? What is the next stage of the game and will I complete the journey in one piece?" I questioned the situation.

Khuan is an immigrant from Vietnam, has a people's personality and is an excellent hairstylist. We share life stories every time he cuts my hair. He has been cutting my hair since 2000, for seventeen years already. This occasion was no different than any other visit except I was tired and didn't feel like discussing anything.

After my hair was trimmed, I said goodbye, walked outside and saw a person sitting in a dark blue Dodge Ram pickup truck eating a sandwich. Three words crossed my mind as I entered the car: "agent" and "being followed." The engine started; shortly after, my chest and facial pains resumed and increased to such an extent that breathing normally was a monumental task.

"Not only had they bugged the Leaf, the keyless entry and the phone, but now the Highlander is also bugged with the device to make me sick, to crash the car. I need to get home, to a witness, any friendly witness right now, before I collapse again," I thought, and tuned in a fast Metallica song to keep my mind occupied, away from the fatigue and pains.

The car left Khuan's parking lot, all four wheels touched Spring Road and I placed the pedal to the metal to get away from the Dodge as fast as possible, then maintained speed right at 55mph. The pains increased to unbearable levels; my eyes were barely able to see the road ahead, slow and long deep breaths were the only way to force some air into the lungs, my chest was about to explode. I turned the volume of the song to the maximum to stabilize my body and mind. Just before the Atlanta/Spring Road intersection, a few seconds in front of me, a black Mustang was slowing down to almost a complete standstill.

"You will not force me to stop and give up, not now, or never as long as I am alive, fuck you!" I said loudly, and at the last second, just before rear-ending the Mustang, I steered the car to the left lane and floored it again.

The light at the intersection was flashing green, the speed of my car was climbing to 65, 75, 80 and I saw another car at a standstill in front of the Mustang, while both vehicles were quickly disappearing in my rearview mirror.

"I better slow down before I crash or kill someone. There is a Nam Dae Mun farmers market less than a minute away. I have to exit the car right now, before I pass out," I thought.

I parked at the right side of the store, next to empty shopping carts, exited the vehicle and within a few seconds all symptoms, except eye pain, had disappeared. I shopped at this store on a regular basis until spring of 2015 when we moved from Smyrna to East Cobb. The store offers a large selection of basic to exotic good-quality fruits and vegetables for reasonable prices, way below what the typical grocery store charges. I needed to calm down and assess the situation. Buying fresh produce seemed like the next logical step. I took my time; went to the bathroom, shopped around and paid the cashier, like every other person at the store.

A young man, an ordinary-looking man in his mid-thirties, dressed in blue jeans and a light-grey jacket, passed by me and looked directly into my eyes while a cashier was placing the purchased items into plastic bags. He unsuccessfully tried to hide his emotions, but his face was silently giving him away by showing, "What are you doing? You can run but you can't hide."

Leaving the store, entering the Highlander and driving home was the only option besides throwing the groceries in a dumpster and walking home.

"If I walk home and tell the story to my wife, I am a dead man. She will call the psychiatrists who will advise her to bring me back to the hospital."

My hands were shaking as I turned the key and started the car. The engine was smoothly idling, my face was staring into the darkness of the night, my body was waiting for the symptoms to appear again. I was nervous, but otherwise felt fine. I slowly drove off and religiously obeyed traffic laws. The shortest route home was to drive around the new Braves stadium, currently under construction. The car crossed Cobb Parkway and ascended to the top of a small hill where everything was beautifully lit up: new hotel, new office building, new residential development and the stadium itself. I slowed down to 25mph, opened the window, looked outside and admired how fast the construction had progressed. I was being followed by a black SUV but didn't care anymore.

My body was flooded with the feeling of victory, "I won, at least tonight, and was given a break to enjoy the scenery, to recharge for the next level of the game," I said and drove home without experiencing any unusual incidents.

At home, I was unloading the groceries. Romana approached me, slightly bumped into me and continued to walk to the kitchen in silence without saying "Hi" or anything else. She poured herself a glass of wine and walked upstairs to the master bedroom. My worst fears were confirmed. The NSA agents had forced her to cooperate. She feared for her and our children's safety but couldn't tell me anything since the whole house was bugged. At least she was smart enough to give me a signal by bumping into me. It appeared the agents were amused by the situation. I almost died and crashed the car, went to the store, was given a break and left alone thereafter.

"This is my house, my family, and nobody has the right to drag my wife and kids into this. I will give them a clear message to stay away."

I was upset, turned on the TV and watched the movie, *Braveheart* (1995). Less than an hour into the movie, Mel Gibson screamed as he rallied his soldiers, "They can take our lives, but they will never take our freedom!" Shortly after, the Scottish soldiers raised their kilts and waved their naked butts at the English. I said to myself, "Perfect, I am sure the agents will get the message," then turned off the TV and went to bed.

On Wednesday February 1st, I woke up in a good mood. The phone that made me so sick was lost forever in the waters of the Sope Creek pond. The manual stated the phone would be irreversibly damaged if submerged under water for more than 30 minutes. Shopping for another phone became today's priority. I wanted something cheap and possibly used. After the T-Mobile authorized dealer sold me the death-ray-emitting cell phone, I didn't trust or want to go anywhere near the store.

"How about the independent cell phone/repair store owned by Middle Easterners on Windy Hill Road? They surely would sell an unlocked, possibly fully cracked cell phone," I thought, and left my house within a few minutes.

Unfortunately, the store was no longer in business. I remembered the young server from Ru San's Sushi Bar who mentioned there was a small independent cell phone store right next to the retailer. I found the restaurant on Google Maps but not the cell phone store. It did not exist. I had little more than an hour of free time before my scheduled doctor's appointment, a hospital follow-up with primary physician, Dr. Reddi. I made up my mind to find the retailer, no matter what.

On my way to Kennesaw, there was more than the usual amount of traffic on I-75 in the opposite direction. I began to worry I would not make it to the doctor on time. "Dr. Smart Phones" was the name of the small retail store. I picked up a used Samsung Galaxy, the only phone I liked from the variety of only four phones available for sale, and asked the cashier if the phone was unlocked. The answer was "Yes" and I was also given friendly advice to use CM Security, the free antivirus program. I paid cash and negotiated a small discount of 5%. Due to system error, the cashier was unable to print a receipt.

"Don't worry about it. I have to run to a doctor. I am sure you will remember me in case I have a problem with the phone." We said bye to each other and I left the store.

I arrived at the WellStar Medical Center on Roswell Road just on time and was welcomed by Dr. Reddi's assistant, a young Indian girl in her early twenties. She was friendly and kept smiling during conversations. I described my symptoms and circumstances surrounding the hospitalization.

"I see a note here from October stating a low pulse of 46. Did you ever follow up with a cardiologist?" she asked.

"No, I totally forgot and still have chest pains from time to time," I answered.

Dr. Reddi decided to perform another EKG test and told me to take my shirt off and lie on the medical bed.

The doctor left and the pretty young assistant entered the room, smiled at me and said, "Well, I am going to have to shave your chest before the sensors can be attached."

I remembered a situation that happened in October 2016; two young and pretty assistants also had to shave my chest before an EKG examination. It was sort of fun but, most importantly, I had a story to share with the girls at lunch.

A couple short memories. . .

The next day, in October, I went to the cafeteria at my usual time right around 12.10 p.m. Christine and Ronnee were sitting at a table opposite each other. Jessica was sitting alone, at the table right next to them, and smiled at me as I walked in.

"Great, today I will entertain Jessica. It's her turn," I thought, as I was heating up lunch in a microwave, standing a few feet from the girls.

I sat down opposite Jessica and said, "Hi guys, you won't believe what happened yesterday."

"Hi Joseph, so what happened?" Jessica asked, and I began telling the story.

"I went to a doctor for a yearly physical exam. It was discovered I had a very low pulse of 46 and an EKG test was ordered. The doctor's assistant stated she will have to partially shave my chest for the sensors to stick. She left the room and I heard her laughing with another assistant saying, 'We will have to shave his chest, ha, ha, ha.'"

Jessica jumped into the conversation. "That's mean, I can't believe they were laughing at you."

I then continued to talk. "Well, both assistants were girls in their early twenties, who then entered the room with razors in their hands and said the following sentence while smiling: 'We are going to shave your chest and won't even charge you for it,' and I replied, 'That's great, next time I need a wax I know where to go.'"

The four of us had a good laugh. The lunch was great, we also talked about a movie called *Borat*. I mentioned that, during one particular sporting competition the official Kazakhstan national anthem was accidently exchanged for the Kazakhstan national anthem played in the *Borat* movie. The wrong anthem was played to the Kazakhstan athletes during a medal ceremony.

Mark came to the lunch and pulled Ronnee into the hallway to discuss a business matter. Christine was on her phone, sitting on a couch at the other end of the cafeteria. It was just me and Jessica sitting alone at a table. I seized the moment.

"You have the exact same hairstyle like the other day," I said.

"I don't remember," Jessica said.

"But I remember, the other day you had the hair pulled back, just like today, and wore the black costume. You look great."

At that moment, we were both happy and smiled at each other. I didn't have a chance to say anything else as Ronnee had come back and joined us. This was the perfect lunch. Jessica was sitting at a table alone and waiting for me. She knew I would come to the lunch that day. It was Tuesday, I always went to the cafeteria on Tuesdays. I had a chance to flirt with her and show my appreciation right there at the lunch. I didn't, however, have a chance to show her my affection. A gentle touch on her hand would have been the perfect ending to the perfect lunch.

After the lunch ended, I was in a great mood for the rest of the day. In the afternoon, Sue and I talked about work-related and personal matters and I shared the story with her.

"One time, I waxed my legs and it wasn't the most pleasant thing," she replied.

"Have you ever waxed down there?" I asked.

She raised her head, smiled a little in clear amusement I had the courage to ask her this question.

"Yes, and it hurt like hell," she answered

"This is great, I can't believe I am having this type of conversation with my boss," I thought, smiling and looking directly at Sue.

She was still my boss and I didn't want to push my luck by asking her any more inappropriate questions. I thought about the conversation later in the afternoon.

"What if Christine, Jessica, and Ronnee told me they waxed their legs. Would I also have asked them about waxing down there? I most certainly would have and who knows where the conversation would go in the future. :-)"

Back at the doctor's office

And again, a young nurse was shaving parts of my chest for free as I was replaying the two memories in my mind. The EKG results were within normal limits, but I had more important symptoms to worry about.

"Why am I having all these facial and chest pains? What's wrong with my right arm? A touch of anything feels different with my right hand than with my left hand. The arm tingles and I have a 'freeze' feeling on the dorsal side of my hand."

I was puzzled by these symptoms and suspected possible nerve damage. The doctor ordered blood work and an X-ray of my right hand. I never had pains when having blood drawn except for today, when the procedure was very uncomfortable. Nerve damage seemed the most probable cause of the additional sensitivity. I went downstairs to the ground level of the building, where the imaging center was located. A young female assistant introduced herself and stated she would be the person in charge of the X-ray procedure. How lucky I was, all these pretty young nurses were catering to my needs. We walked through a long hallway, to the X-ray room. I was told to sit in front of the X-ray machine, to place my hand on a square plate and hold still.

The nurse went to the operator area but quickly returned and stated, "Please bear with me for a minute, I need to make a few adjustments."

"No problem," I said.

She walked away, back to the operator area.

"I'm not going to sit right in front of the machine while she's performing her so-called 'adjustments'. I know exactly what's going on. On NSA's direct order, I'll receive a lethal dose of radiation. They will kill me in a similar way to how Putin poisoned Alexander Litvinenko," I thought, and got up from the chair, walked across the room, sat on a chair right next to the operator area and continued to think. "I am away from the X-ray machine as much as possible and really close to the nurse. She can take as much time as she wants 'adjusting' the machine."

In few minutes the nurse came back and said, "OK, everything is ready. Let's take the picture."

I went back to my original seat. She placed a heavy rubber cover over my lap.

I looked into her face, smiled, pointed my left hand toward the cover and said, "Good thinking, this is the most important item I need to save."

She smiled back and said, "It will definitely protect you."

The nurse took the X-ray fairly quickly and walked me back to the waiting area. I was happy to be out of the room and remembered "The Hollywood Rob" rule, to stay calm no matter what. I became thirsty and slowly walked to a water fountain, then used the restroom. Body language was the key. I acted as if nothing unusual happened until I paused, closed my eyes for a minute and relaxed in the safety of my car.

I couldn't relax for too long as I had another appointment scheduled in the afternoon. It was with behavioral therapist, Patricia Keller. Coincidently, her office was located in an office park right next to the WellStar clinic. Patricia was an older lady in her fifties, not too attractive per my taste, but she had class. It didn't matter to me if she was attractive or not.

As the marriage therapist said, "Joseph, the behavioral therapist shouldn't be someone you want to have lunch with."

I took his advice and was happy that at least she is a woman. I love to socialize with all kinds of women; young, old, attractive or unattractive, I don't care. The women, however, have to have class and intelligent conversation is a must. If I can't have intelligent conversation with you, I'll never talk with you again, no matter how beautiful you are.

The therapy session lasted less than an hour. It was more about introduction and the surrounding circumstances that led me to her office. After leaving the office, I was hungry, tired and went straight home to take a nap. I woke up in less than half an hour but didn't feel right. I had difficulty concentrating and remembering events that had happened recently. Performing seemingly miniscule tasks more than one at a time was a struggle. I had to keep reminding myself of what I was doing all the time. For example; when making breakfast, I placed a glass inside of the refrigerator's opening to pump filtered water, then turned around and applied cream cheese and marmalade on a piece of toast.

"Is this enough cream cheese? Should I put more or less of it? What about some fruit with my meal? What should I get? I am being watched by the producers or the NSA all the time? What about Heaven vs Hell and Matrix? How are Christine, Jessica, and Ronnee doing, are they OK? I wish I could at least talk to them, I miss them so much. Hollywood Rob is the golden rule. Am I doing everything in the correct order? Maybe I should go to the bathroom first to wash and brush my teeth, then make breakfast."

I walked to the bathroom and continued to think. "Should I first wash my face or brush my teeth? What is the correct order? I don't want to raise any suspicions. How did I do it before I got sick? I look horrible, I need to shave and brush my hair first. Oh shit, the water is running!"

I ran back to the kitchen and the water was flowing from the fridge to the glass and to the floor. I realized, this was more or less a problem all the time since I left the hospital. My thoughts were constantly racing between the ordinary stable world I knew before December 15 2016 and the world after December 15 2016, the new world, the new space-time, the new extreme dimension where anything was possible. The uncertainty of the new world, the constant thinking about what may happen next, to figure things out as fast as possible, to save my life as fast as possible, made everything so difficult. It became impossible to concentrate and stay focused. To fall asleep was the only thing that cured the problem, but only short-term until I woke up. To go outside, listen to the birds, look at the trees and sky, to lie down on a blanket, to close the eyes, relax and finally be able to block the thought process was another short-term solution frequently used.

"What about the long-term solution? Does it even exist? What if it doesn't? Is this going to get worse and worse until I die?" I often thought.

I couldn't even imagine being alone all the time. At least my family was around and forced me to stay in the old world most of the time.

Thursday, February 2nd was another busy day. My wife and I had an 11.45 a.m. appointment with our marriage therapist. I wasn't particularly happy at the prospect of seeing this government-appointed guardian of mine but had no choice.

"It will be OK as long as I act normal, no matter what. This strategy worked fine so far."

I reminded myself to act natural then asked Romana about Europe. Since leaving the hospital, I questioned her on numerous occasions to let me travel to see my family, especially grandmother, who's almost eighty. She gave me an evasive answer every time I asked her, so this was the last try for a while. I didn't want to give her any reasons to throw me out of the house. After coming home from the hospital, she became cold, distant, and unsupportive of my problems. In her mind I was fired, and went to the jail and the hospital on purpose. As soon as I returned home, she had many questions about my life insurance and wanted me to sign a document giving her full authorization to disconnect me from life support. I had a difficult time comprehending why she acted the way she did.

"Only a paid actress or wife extorted by the intelligence agencies would act this way," was the only explanation I was able to come up with.

Nobody likes to get fired, or goes to jail and hospital on purpose.

The therapy session went fine except for my symptoms; my eyes were slightly dilated, I had facial pains and my right arm was hurting. There was one instance which made me a little nervous.

"Joseph, tell me a few examples of what you like about your wife," the therapist asked.

"Well, she is a strong woman who doesn't fall under pressure—"

He interrupted me and said, "Yes, she doesn't fall under pressure. That is an important quality don't you think?"

During the sentence he slightly jumped, turned his body toward me and his wide-open eyes were looking directly into my eyes.

"I agree, this is an important quality. That's what I love about her," I calmly answered in a steady voice and didn't move my body at all. I thought, "The agent is trying to trick me into talking."

I was alternating my sight between the floor, walls, and the therapist for the duration of the session.

At the end, the therapist asked us, "Would you like to schedule the next session a week from today?"

I raised my head up and answered, "I was hoping to go to Europe for a few days before I start looking for a job."

He looked at my wife and said, "It is not up to me. Would you let him go?"

Romana answered without hesitation, "Yes."

Chapter 7
Vive la Europe

The first thing Romana said when we walked out of the office and entered the car: "I booked you a 6 p.m. flight to Munich."

"Thanks for letting me go. It's already 1 p.m. and we're in Buckhead, let's hurry up. I need to get home asap. Can you please give me a ride to the airport?" I asked.

"No, get your own ride. I have to take care of the kids," she answered, irritated.

I wanted to leave the house at 3 p.m. at the latest to avoid the afternoon rush hour, so I kept pushing my luck.

"Why don't we pick up Teresa from school a little earlier and all of us can go to the airport?"

Again, the answer was, "No."

I was able to reach Milan who, as on a prior occasion, had no problem driving me to the airport. I was excited about the upcoming trip and was determined to make the flight, no matter what.

During the drive to the airport, I encouraged Milan to drive as fast as possible and noticed a camera mounted on the windshield in front of me.

"He must have been involved in video recording for some time and just now makes it obvious," I thought, but did not ask him any direct questions.

In my mind everyone, including Milan, was in on this. I was leaning towards both the Reality TV show and the NSA scenarios, but had no idea which one became my new dimension.

The flight to Munich departed from the newest section of the Atlanta Airport, Concourse F at the International Terminal. We safely made it to the airport and there was plenty of time to look around, admire the architecture, sit down and relax for a few minutes. Since leaving the hospital, I quickly became tired after performing any everyday task and had to nap two to four times per day. Today was no exception, but I was so excited to get away from everything, from this madness.

"Maybe I will be left alone, to recharge my batteries for the next level of the game."

Romana was a flight attendant for one of the major airlines and my departure was not guaranteed, since I flew standby. The line at security checkpoints appeared to be less than thirty minutes long.

I called my car mechanic, John, regarding Milan's van, which was falling apart. I had to make the call since Milan doesn't speak much English. I had known John for more than ten years. It is difficult to find someone who is honest, doesn't perform unnecessary repairs, or overcharge. John is one of those people who is always friendly and positive. Every time I went to his shop, JW Auto in Austell, he offered me a beer and we talked for a while about anything that was happening in our lives. I consider him more of a friend than just a car mechanic. Milan's blue 1999 Dodge Caravan had severe engine and transmission problems, something the average person would not consider worth repairing, but not him. He was always emotionally attached to his vehicles and drove them until all four wheels fell off and it became impractical to repair the vehicles any longer. It would have been considered more of a restoration project than a simple repair.

Why all this emotional attachment? Milan grew up under communism where everything was scarce. For example, in the late Eighties, the average lifespan of the cheapest Eastern-made car available on the market was twenty-eight years. The Trabant automobile was made out of laminate and had a simple two-stroke engine, which the average person was able to rebuild on the side of a road within a couple hours in case of unexpected malfunction. There wasn't even a fuel pump since the gas tank was placed above the engine. The car was literally made to last a lifetime, since people in East Germany had to wait between eleven and fifteen years to buy one. There was a downside to this "simplicity" as well. Trabant produced thirty times more emissions than the Mercedes S500 of that era. Anyway, Milan's thinking regarding automobiles was similar to a person living on the island ninety miles south of Key West. In 2017 Cuba, it is not uncommon to see 1950s American automobiles that have been on the streets for sixty-plus years, maintained literally from nothing. As expected, John quoted close to three thousand dollars for the repair.

I had to place my shoes, belt, watch, and everything that was in my pockets on a plastic tray just before entering a full body scanner. My jeans almost fell to the floor as soon as I took off the belt.

"Did I really lose all this weight during such a short period of time?" I questioned myself when entering the scanner.

"Spread your legs more and keep your arms risen! Didn't you hear me?" said a female TSA officer in an impatient tone of voice.

Her wide-open eyes met my eyes for a few seconds.

"I better do what she says or I'll go back to jail in no time. Again, I am being tricked to act out of the ordinary. She thinks I am just a junkie wearing loose jeans," I said to myself, and was relieved after the security checkpoints were passed, but facial pains, especially eye pain accompanied with light sensitivity, had resumed.

My worst suspicions had become reality; the eyes were fully dilated when I looked into a mirror mounted in a men's restroom. "No wonder the TSA agent thought I am high as a kite when she saw my eyes. I am lucky she didn't give me anymore problems."

At a duty-free store, I bought a couple bottles of Belvedere vodka for my dad, then went to the gate. Belvedere is smooth and tasty Polish vodka, but Dad had never heard of it. Stolichnaya, Grey Goose, and Belvedere are my favorite vodkas, especially when mixed with cranberry juice to make a Cape Cod.

The facial pains had become too severe for me to keep my eyes open. I pretended to be asleep and just listened for my name to be called, hopefully to receive a confirmed business-class seat.

"This is definitely a setup; to make me panic in a public place was the ultimate goal of the producers or the agents. That's why I was somehow drugged to make my eyes dilate. Maybe the marriage therapist or Romana placed something in my drink today." I came up with this explanation and hoped to get a seat, any seat in coach or business, I didn't care anymore. I thought of my friend Brant, who I knew from Houston's restaurant. We always tried to stay positive and laughed, even during the most difficult times.

One particular memory crossed my mind; I used to fly to Europe quite often in the early 2000s and shared my stories with Brant.

"Most of the time I got lucky and sat in business class when flying overseas, and usually talked to the person sitting next to me. You wouldn't believe how many interesting people I met on those flights, like directors and CEOs of large companies. The conversations were quite interesting," I said to him.

"That's great, Joseph, so what do you tell them, what do you have to offer when asked what kind of work you do?" Brant asked.

"Well, this is what I tell them," I answered with a serious face. I paused for a few seconds then continued to speak. "I am a student at Kennesaw State University pursuing a degree in accounting. I qualified for Pell Grant and HOPE scholarships. My construction company went out of business last year, right after Lehman Brothers. I just filed for Chapter 7 personal bankruptcy and my daughter, Teresa, was born in September. I work part time as a debt collector for a small collection agency."

Brant opened his mouth, laughed as hard as he could and said, "That's great, Joseph, you are one of a kind; the person who always finds a way around the system. Do you also tell them you drive a Mercedes to school?"

I then answered, "That's why I would like to get into taxation, to look for loopholes. Shit, the Mercedes, you have a great point! I didn't think of this. In order to get a parking pass, a car has to be registered with the school. What if the parking pass data is somehow available to the government office that awards Pell Grant? Only the poorest students are eligible for the scholarship. The Mercedes is almost fifteen years old but still, I don't want to raise any red flags. If someone starts digging into this, it's not rocket science to figure out I cheated on my tax returns."

I was genuinely worried, but Brant comforted me. "Don't worry, they're not that sophisticated. To be safe don't buy any late-model cars."

"Joseph T., please come to the counter," a female gate agent stated over the loudspeaker.

I walked to the counter, presented my passport and was given a boarding pass with seat C9 specified.

"Great, a business class seat, this can't get any better," I thought, and walked onto the airplane.

The departure was delayed by an hour due to stormy weather. Using my cell phone, I purchased a connecting flight from Munich to Prague, leaving the next morning. I had to purchase a regularly priced ticket since Romana was on short-term disability, so unable to purchase deeply discounted tickets (90% off) on partner airlines. My eyes were still hurting so I placed a fully open newspaper in front of my face to cover the dilation. I was lucky to have a standalone window seat. And then, for no reason, an older female flight attendant asked me if I would like anything to drink. Her eyes met mine at full stare for a few seconds, her facial expression changed to "puzzled." I thought for sure I am the reason for the delay. It was still being decided if I should be allowed to fly overseas.

I stayed calm and looked around the cabin. All female flight attendants were ladies approaching retirement age. The airline industry is based on seniority and many of the so-called "senior mammas" cherry-pick the best flights and work a couple times a month. The younger flight attendants, like my wife, always complain about them.

"Why would any flight attendant want to retire early while in their forties or fifties? They have employer-sponsored health insurance, can work a few days a month and fly around the world for free. Who is going to provide affordable health insurance in case of early retirement? Not the government, that's for sure. Many older employees have been with the company thirty or forty years, did their time and deserve to work a few days a week and 'cherry-pick' trips. Delta is full of older female and obviously gay male flight attendants and truly is the employer for all people, regardless of race, gender, age, and sexual orientation. I think it's great. This proves the US antidiscrimination laws work much better than, for example, in the EU or South Korea, where the flight attendants are forced to retire at a certain age. There is only one negative comment about the airline I can think of; per several pilots, Delta was deliberately driven to bankruptcy to reorganize, to be allowed to dump pilot pension plans. Is this just a rumor? Who knows, right?"

As I was finishing my philosophical thinking, the plane finally took off. I just sat there in disbelief, glued to the seat, surprised we were leaving the country. Fatigue overcame me. I put down the newspapers, closed my eyes and tried to get some sleep. I woke up just before the five-course dinner; a glass of chardonnay, shrimp appetizer, creamy vegetable soup, garden salad with vinaigrette dressing, another glass of the gourmet chardonnay, steak with vegetables, fully loaded ice-cream sundae, grapes, strawberries and two glasses of dessert wine. This was exactly the type of food my body craved at that time. The meal itself was worth every penny I paid for the ticket. There was a line of people in front of the restroom. I stood next to the exit doors and looked around. Unexpectedly, in almost perfect synchronized order, three men that surrounded my seat got up and stood behind me in the line. The men, well-built, masculine, and tall, looked like agents.

"I am being followed and there is nothing I can do about it. Crossing borders doesn't mean anything anymore. The intelligence agencies have presence everywhere, in any city or village in the world where their service is required. The local governments don't even know it or are powerless to stop them."

I assessed the situation and continued to stay in line, yawning, and pretended to be extremely tired. The agents didn't bother me at all, they just stood there in complete silence. The silence, the uncertainty, the not knowing what might happen next, made my heart race. This was nothing new since I had been in similar situations before. At least I knew how to act. After I brushed my teeth and used the restroom, I went to my seat without looking around. I didn't want to see or experience anything else, I just wanted to quickly fall asleep and arrive at the destination as soon as possible.

In Munich, I missed the connecting flight by twenty minutes. Purchasing a last-minute flight ticket would have cost at least $500. I looked around for alternative transportation and ended up purchasing a ticket for a bus leaving that afternoon, with estimated arrival in Prague five hours after departure.

The bus stopped at Prague's main train station, from where I took a train to Tišice village, located about fifteen miles outside of Prague. I arrived at the house shortly after 9 p.m., exhausted and hungry, but happy to see my grandma, aunt, and the three cousins: Matyáš, Ondra, and Štěpán. Grandma's meal was excellent. Smoked beef with red and white cabbage and potato dumplings is one of my favorite dishes. I had two portions. Everyone was astonished at how skinny my body looked. I told them the story, minus the inner thoughts. Due to light sensitivity, I had to keep covering the eyes with my hand and finally asked for the light, suspended above me, to be turned off.

On Saturday, Cousin Ondra and I went out to the city with Marcel Peter, a childhood friend of mine. Marcel is an interesting individual and we have lots in common. He grew up without a dad and was able to brainwash his mom into letting him do pretty much whatever he wanted from an early age, just like me. He is more like family since his uncle, the crazy boyfriend Káža Peter, was shortly married to my mom. They were married in 1994, at the courthouse in Marietta, Georgia, and divorced around 1996. In the good old days, we frequently hung out at the Stardust Casino and did all the fun stuff the City of Prague had to offer. He was always one step ahead of me, always pushing things one step further than everybody else. I was fourteen and Marcel was twelve years old at the time, but looked like he was at least sixteen. Here are a few examples:

Marcel was never afraid of anything and knew what he wanted from life. At age ten, he was brave enough to have sex with a girl for the first time. At age twelve, he had multiple girlfriends, ranging from thirteen to twenty years old. On one occasion, he stole $100 from Uncle Káža's jacket while he used a restroom when visiting the family. Káža complained to everybody about Marcel on multiple occasions: "I went to use the toilet and he stole $100 from my pocket. That was the most expensive piece of shit that ever came out of my body."

On a few occasions, money strangely disappeared from his mom's closet (most people were paid in cash in those days). The mom hired a technician to install a panzer plated entrance door with three independent locks; however, somehow the robber was always able to break into the apartment without damaging the locks or the door.

Mom gave Marcel money to buy new shoes, but he bought a glass of whisky and we played pool at a nearby bar located at Prosek, about ten-minutes' walk from where he lived. He told his mom the money was lost and kept walking in his old shoes, the only pair he had: sneakers with the sole halfway detached. Prosek is a newer part of the town built in the 1970s and it is known as the classic Communist apartment development complex; all the grey rectangular buildings looked exactly the same, boring and ugly. The apartments themselves looked the same, with the same interior decorations and fixtures. The only difference was the amount of rooms each unit had. The Communists built the apartments for survival, not necessarily for enjoyment. We were kids and didn't care about where we lived. To stay outside, have fun and wander around the city was everything we ever wanted to do at that time.

On one occasion at my middle school, the whole class, with the teacher right next to me, walked out of the main building to the cafeteria to have lunch. As we were walking outside, passing through the main entrance door, there was Marcel leaning his body against a taxicab and smoking a cigarette.

He waved his hand and yelled at me, "Hey Joseph, how do you like my unannounced visit? Come on, let's go! We'll take a cab to the casino and have lunch at the McDonald's above."

I separated from the class without saying a word, walked to and entered the cab as fast as possible, and said, "Dude, are you crazy, smoking right in front of my teacher? You'll eventually get me into trouble."

Marcel then answered with a calm tone of voice, "Don't worry about it. There is nothing she can do."

He was right, nothing ever happened as the teacher didn't even bother to bring it up.

At the age of sixteen, Marcel's luck ran out. He was arrested for breaking into cars and stealing the radios. He was released from jail after six months and completely turned his life around. In 1998, at age seventeen, he met his future wife, Ivana, and started a business selling cell phones. Marcel eventually became a real estate agent and a well-respected attorney in and around the city of Neratovice, where he resides. Marcel remained a down-to-earth person, regardless of income, and lives below his means in a two-bedroom apartment of a similar style to the home where he lived as a child. Money is your best servant, but your worst master. The world would be a much better place if more people were aware of this rule.

"Who would have the balls to sue a law school over admission discrepancies? The building is full of lawyers," I asked myself on numerous occasions.

Marcel not only sued the West-Czech University in Pilsen, but he won, and the school had to admit him. Based on countless political and nonpolitical discussions we had over the years, Marcel had reached a certain point in his life and wanted to make a difference by bringing back to political and public life the ethics the country was known for in the 1920s and 1930s. He has high political ambitions and once said, "I am third Christian, third Jew and third Arab; the perfect person to negotiate peace in the Middle East. Who would want to throw me away from the negotiation table?"

Marcel has a gift; with stone-cold face and smooth tone of voice, he can convince most people of anything, regardless of subject. He will maintain his standpoint no matter what and until a person is fully convinced. I became confused on many occasions. The CIA and NSA would love this guy, he is the human lie detector, someone who can analyze and read people very well. He even uses zodiac signs to assess personality types of potential business partners and competition. Marcel is the perfect politician. In 2009, a newly formed political party called TOP 09 welcomed him with open arms. He moved up fairly quickly and eventually developed a friendly relationship with Miroslav Kalousek, the Czech Republic's Minister of Finance from 2007–2009 and again in 2010–2013.

Conveniently, Neratovice is only ten minutes away from Tišice and when I am in town, he always picks me up when we go out. Marcel drove his car, a 2011 Škoda Octavia, to my grandma's house where Ondra and I entered the vehicle. After he and Ondra were introduced to each other, we talked about our families and how things are in general. It's been a while since we saw each other and we had a lot to talk about. The discussion steered to two subjects: politics and Europe's refugee crisis.

"How are the politics treating you?" I asked Marcel, then continued, "I read that Kalousek and Babiš (current Minister of Finance) are not the best of friends. They publicly keep accusing each other of who stole more money, and when."

Marcel loves talking politics and gave me a quick answer. "For Babiš, it's more about power. In my opinion, he would like to establish a dictatorship similar to Putin's Russia, where he would be the king. Also, Babiš has plenty of money already; couple years ago, he and his party voted to extend the biofuels subsidy, in fact giving his company, Agrofert, five billion crowns."

"What about Kalousek? He's no angel either, right?" I asked him, with a smirk on my face.

Marcel looked away and didn't give me any answer. I could tell he didn't feel comfortable discussing the subject any longer, but I was persistent.

"Come on, Marcel, it's no secret that Kalousek stole billions while he was in charge of the Pandur purchase and other defense contracts in the Nineties. For some reason, he is a huge advocate of church restitutions and a supporter of the gambling industry. Tell me, your secret will stay with me."

He looked back at me and said, "The party (Kalousek's TOP 09) insiders conservatively estimate he 'cleaned' and hid about seven billion crowns ($350 million) in such a way that nobody will ever find it."

I was in total shock and said, "I thought it was two billion at most, seven is a little too much. He is smart, like Klaus (Minister of Finance and later President). I am sure Klaus 'cleaned' some money as well."

Marcel answered, "That's right, he also 'cleaned' billions of crowns. Did you know that Kellner is Klaus' 'white horse'?"

The conversation was interrupted since we had to decide where to go. A hookah bar close to Náměstí Míru (Peace Square) in Prague 2 was chosen as the place to start the evening. U Bassama Shisha Lounge is cozy, a small place with five tables and a couple of couches, situated in the basement of a historical apartment building built in the 1910s. The owner is a pleasant Middle Eastern man in his late forties who immigrated to the country more than twenty years ago. At the bar, the refugee crisis seemed like the perfect subject to discuss.

"What do you guys think about the refugees? In my opinion, the situation will worsen in the future because of bad politics. I am sure most of the refugees are nice people, but when it comes to social views on life, they have the mentality of 15th-century people. Think about it. These people lived in oppression and terror most of their lives. They are used to women being enslaved or stoned to death because of adultery, and things like public executions and mutilations. The people have no idea what freedom is. That is why they should not be allowed to enter a host country without some sort of training on democracy," I said, and knew this wasn't going to be the easiest discussion because I was sitting with two sun-men (*Sluníčkář* in Czech) who welcomed the refugees with open arms, without thinking about the repercussions that might happen twenty or thirty years down the road.

They both maintained their standpoint and Ondra answered, "I know there may be a few terrorists mixed in, but 90% of the refugees really need help. They will eventually assimilate."

Marcel entered the conversation. "I am not too happy that millions of people are crossing Europe's borders. There is nothing we can do but to help them. You know who caused the crisis, right? It's the Americans. Saddam controlled the region with an iron fist. This wasn't the best thing for the people, but it worked to a certain degree. The region was at least sort of stable. The U.S. Army brought down Saddam and left Iraq defenseless and unsecured. This created a void, a no-man's land in the region. ISIS is not about religion, it's about money. The same people and their friends that were in power under Saddam created ISIS."

I then said, "That's an interesting point. As always, it is all about money and defense contracts. That is the reason why the USA doesn't want to quickly defeat ISIS. We could defeat ISIS in a matter of weeks if we wanted to, since the U.S. Army is the most powerful force on the planet. The government is using the war against ISIS as an excuse to increase defense spending, to appease the armament industry and, of course, to make more money for the industry and the politicians themselves."

We each had a fruit drink consisting of cranberry juice with club soda, but Marcel was the only one who smoked apple-flavored hookah. I like the apple flavor, but didn't smoke anything that evening.

"The only way to help the refugees is to set up an enclosed perimeter of, let's say, fifty square miles somewhere in Spain, and build apartments, schools, and hospitals. The refugees would return home after the war is over," I said.

"Politically, this could never work," Marcel quickly answered.

I looked directly into his eyes and answered with a strong tone of voice, "If Grandma Merkel is going to invite the whole Middle East to Europe there will be total chaos. You will see a terrorist attack on a weekly basis. I understand that 90% of the refugees are decent people, but what about the other 10%? For example, if I give you ten pieces of candy and tell you one piece has been poisoned, would you still taste at least one?"

Both Marcel and Ondra were listening and not saying anything. I therefore continued to speak. "You wouldn't take any, would you? So why accept the refugees without proper screening and a completed pre-assimilation process? In the long run, Merkel will do more damage than Hitler. This is why we need more people like Donald Trump in the government. He is the best thing that happened to the US in a long time. You know a lot of pissed people voted for him. We, the common people, are sick and tired of corporations that continue to outsource more and more jobs overseas each year, until one day, the hamburger flippers and financial speculators will be the only people able to find jobs. Do you guys know the real cause of most wars and misery around the world?"

Both Ondra and Marcel looked at me and answered "No" almost simultaneously, and I said, "It is religion. Organized religion is the source of most human misery and suffering. People are brainwashed to hate each other because of different religious beliefs. It is a pyramid scheme that keeps the people on the top in power and most of the population under control. Look at the history; most deaths from unnatural causes are attributed to religion. Long story short, the world will never be free unless it gets rid of organized religion."

Marcel diplomatically stated that we should not continue to have this discussion any longer. I looked around and the bar was empty, except for a few older Middle Eastern men, including the owner, who were sitting a few feet away from us playing chess and quietly listening to our conversation. I got the message and we continued to talk about everyday subjects. Before we left the bar, I walked into a narrow corridor where the restroom was located. The owner was walking towards me, holding a case full of beer. I said "Hi" and he said "Hi" as well, while fully avoiding any sort of eye contact. I had a nice and long conversation with him about a year ago, so he had to remember me. It was sort of understandable he didn't want to talk to me today, since I presented myself as Trump's advocate, defending his immigration policies.

The next stop of the evening was a dance club, U Zlatého Stromu, located less than 200 feet from the Charles Bridge. The club is a multilevel place with several different bars, dance floors, and many different compartments where people can sit, talk, and drink. Three young, beautiful, and topless girls were dancing all night on top of a bar table in one of the rooms. A lesbian show was on the program that evening as well. The three of us had a few drinks, danced with girls and fully enjoyed ourselves. The politician, Marcel, is a well-networked individual. He contacted a girl who was willing to have some fun with the three of us. After all that had happened in the past couple of months, that was exactly what I needed. For all I knew at that moment, it might have been the last fuck of my life. We left the club right after the lesbian show ended and drove the car away from the city center to pick up the girl. We didn't have to pay for a hotel room since Marcel, the real estate agent, had a key to an empty but fully furnished apartment that was on sale. Ondra changed his mind and didn't want to participate in the activities any longer. This was understandable. He was in his early twenties and had just moved to an apartment together with his girlfriend and baby, who was born a few months ago. At least he touched the girl's naked butt before exiting the master bedroom.

It was close to 5 a.m. and everyone except me was tired. My biological clock was still ticking in the US Eastern time zone, 11 p.m. was the real time my body was experiencing. Marcel and I traditionally end a night by eating a kebab purchased from a small vendor located in the downtown area, right across from Máj department store. My preference would have been a Waffle House, if I were able to find one. We skipped the closing ceremony and drove home.

Overall, the trip was going very well. I did not experience any of my usual medical symptoms, except for eye pain and sensitivity to light. Even those symptoms went away after about week. I felt very close to normal and was able to forget about the possible scenarios: Reality TV game, the Paranoid NSA, the Matrix and Heaven vs Hell.

"Did I really experience all those events? I feel as normal as ever. Maybe everything was just a bad dream. Is this going to resume once I return to the USA?" I thought, and immediately went over the physical evidence: the Facebook posts and the fact I didn't have a job confirmed the incidents happened for real. The idea of writing some sort of a book first entered my mind a few days into the trip. I spent each morning with my grandmother discussing the family history and suspected that many of the events that happened to my family over the past one hundred-plus years are somehow connected to the recent unusual experiences. I hung around the house a lot and spent as much time as possible with my other two cousins, Štěpán and Matyáš.

Štěpán is the classic middle-school kid who spends most of his free time on social media sites or playing video games. He rarely goes outside to play with his friends. Times have really changed since I was a kid. To stay home was the worst punishment imaginable. But, overall, he is a great kid who helps his single mom with many household items, including eating half of everything that is in the refrigerator in the middle of a night.

Matyáš is almost thirty years old and still lives with his mom. Why move out if you have a free place to stay and hot homemade meals cooked from scratch on a daily basis, by his mom Simona or his grandmother? He lives the classic bohemian lifestyle; is around one or more free-loving girlfriends, enjoys life to the fullest each day by camping, exploring caves and historical sites, partying and not caring what may happen tomorrow from social and financial perspectives. At least he has been able to hold a steady job since 2012.

From 2010 to 2012, Matyáš lived at my mom's house in Marietta, Georgia, and picked up some useful work ethics such as to get up from the bed and make it to work on time. He was not afraid of anything, including driving my mom's 1992 Toyota Corolla with broken AC to the Great Lakes and back. He and his friend, also a young man from Czech, slept in the car most of the time. In the middle of the night, in downtown Chicago, they picked up a hitchhiker and were robbed at gunpoint. The money was lost, but their lives were spared. Matyáš and his friend had picked up many hitchhikers in the Czech Republic before and didn't think this might happen to them. Matyáš' stay in the USA was cut short when he was arrested by Gwinnet County police on I-85 after a minor car accident. Unfortunately, an immigration officer at the Gwinnet County jail checked his background and scheduled him for deportation.

My mom bailed him out of the ICE immigration prison by placing her house as collateral. He legally left the country six months later. I was sad but happy at the same time, when he said the final goodbye and left for the airport. I knew we would never be able to hang out together like that ever again. I was happy to see him go because there was no future for him in the USA. Unless a bride was found, Matyáš would always be illegally working rough jobs, like cleaning grocery stores at night. The stripping chemicals used to scrub the floors caused him to cough blood on numerous occasions. Mostly the Polish Mafia conveniently employed and underpaid illegal workers from Eastern Europe to clean Walmarts, Krogers, Publixes, Big Lots, and many other stores. The workers, of course, were not provided with any safety equipment to mitigate the risk of poisoning caused by the chemicals.

I visited my stepdad, Milan, and his wife, Ivana. They have been together since the mid-Eighties, hiding the relationship in the early days from their spouses. This visit was unlike any other experienced before; Grandma, Aunt Simona and Štěpán accompanied me on the visit. For some reason, Milan lives about twenty miles from Tišice, but the two families are not in regular contact. It has been at least a couple years since the last time Milan saw my grandmother. I had a chance to thank him for wiring me nineteen thousand dollars two weeks prior to the arrest.

In the middle of 2016, Milan and Ivana sold their business and retired. One of the main reasons the businesses were sold was due to a recently passed law (EET) that targets mainly small business owners. The new requirement is to electronically connect to the central tax department and live report every single item sold.

"Many small restaurants and pubs are barely staying afloat. Is it fair they have to immediately report every single bubble gum or beer sold, while in the meantime, high-ranking government officials are passing favorable laws to help them, in fact, steal billions of crowns from taxpayers? I don't know the answer to that question but the Minister of Finance, Mr. Babiš, surely does," I thought, while relaxing on a comfortable couch at Milan's house.

I had visited Europe many times since moving to the USA in 1994, but had never hung out with my stepbrother, Patrik. This time was different. Patrik, his wife, and I went out and had dinner in a nearby pizza place. A few days later, we had lunch and went out to the Model Train Museum. We were able to catch up on our lives and relax in general. His business, a small commercial laundry, was also not doing too good, far from the golden Nineties, when everything and anything you put your mind and money into worked and was profitable. The profits eroded over the years, due to economies of scale and increased competition.

And, lastly, I visited my biological dad, Josef, and his wife, Kamila, numerous times. The visits were great and probably the best to date. Kamila normally doesn't talk much but this time she was able to keep up with Dad, who always talks way more than anybody else. The three of us were finally able to communicate on the same page; we discussed and made fun of the crooked politicians. We also spoke about our lives, everyday problems and pleasures, and thoroughly discussed the family history from his side. My dad always picked on his dad because of political views. My granddad grew up in the 1940s, and in the late 1950s became a Communist supporter. To this day, he didn't return his red book and remained loyal to the party. Dad was the exact opposite; he disliked and to a certain extent fought against the Communists his whole life. This created a huge friction/wound between Granddad and Dad which to this day has never healed. We discussed the circumstances of my job loss, arrest, hospitalization, and the memory loss (less the inner thoughts) while a show about alien abductions played on TV.

"Sounds like you were abducted by aliens," my dad said, as a joke.

My face froze as I looked directly into his eyes and thought, "This better not be another possible scenario. I need to get those books as soon as I get back. Mom surely still has them in her house."

I remembered the mysterious Swiss man, his alien contacts, then replied to my dad, "Yeah, right, you could not come up with a crazier explanation than this. All these people claiming to have contact with or be abducted by aliens are actors. I know the people because I live in the USA. This is Hollywood! All they want is money and fame. It's such bullshit."

"It doesn't seem like bullshit to me," he said.

I quickly changed the subject of the discussion to something else. Dad, for some reason, was a big believer in that aliens do exist and we'd had similar conversations before. In the back of my mind, I also believed life exists somewhere else besides the Earth, but to this point always had other things to worry about. Other things, like going to work, providing for and spending time with my family. My dad, on the other hand, had all the time in the world to think about aliens since he was already retired.

Sometime in the middle of the trip, I bought two tickets to see a *Macbeth* opera in the old National Theater, standing on the bank of the Vltava River, overlooking the Prague castle. My preference would have been *Don Giovanni*; unfortunately, the opera was scheduled to play next month at a different theater. My grandma was almost eighty. I had a feeling this could be the last time the two of us had an opportunity to see an opera together, especially at the National Theatre. This wasn't the only cultural event I experienced during my trip. The whole family went to see a musical performance played by The Charles University orchestra, where Cousin Ondra was singing. We had third-row seats and the performance was amazing. I had a chance to admire all the beautiful college girls who were performing or walking around the Municipal House concert hall, dressed at their best.

A few days before my departure, I went to a late lunch with my childhood friend, Honza Dosedla. I've known him since elementary school and we always hung out every time I was in town. He suggested we go to the U Fleků pub. This was strange, since for the past ten years we always met at a different pub, called U Houtků, in Žižkov; an older area of town located away from the tourist-filled city center. About fifteen years ago we went to the U Fleků pub all the time but haven't been there since. According to written documents, the pub has been continuously brewing its own beer, dark 13-degree lager, since 1499. According to legend, the place has been brewing beer since the mid-1300s. This is kind of cool since the original owners possibly died of the Black Plague that ravaged Europe during that time. Anyway, I arrived about an hour ahead of schedule, sat down at a window table closest to the exit door, had a few beers and talked with a couple of middle-aged ladies sitting right next to me. An older gentleman played harmonica, so I gave him 200 crowns to play some of my favorite folk songs, such as "Škoda Lásky" and "Co Jste Hasiči." Once Honza arrived, I ordered my favorite dish: half an oven-roasted duck with bacon, potato, and bread roll dumplings, accompanied by cooked red and white cabbage and, of course, another pint of the black beer. He ordered a goulash with bread roll dumplings. We spoke about the events that had happened to me over the past couple of months (again, less the inner thoughts). He listened continuously for about two hours and then said, "You're not gonna believe what happened to me. I was hospitalized with a nervous breakdown in the middle of December, an ambulance was called to my work. The diagnosis was stress-related breakdown and I have been taking it really easy since then. A doctor prescribed me some psycho pills, but I refused to take them."

I was in total shock but remained calm. "I hope you feel better. How are your wife and kids?" I said to him, and thoughts were racing through my mind at the same time: "Who is this person? Is he an actor or the friend I've known for over thirty years? Are the producers fucking with my mind again? All this is too coincidental."

I started to talk about the music from our childhood. "One concert I regret not attending was the legendary one, the one that happened in 1991 at Bzenec, where all the great bands like Tři Sestry, Orlík and Braník performed together."

"Something like that is never going to happen again," Honza answered.

Here is some background information explaining why an event like that is extremely rare. For a few years after the 1989 Velvet Revolution, the whole country was in total happiness and euphoria, including the shaved skinheads and the long-haired anarchists. To my knowledge, this was the only time in the history of the planet the two groups that traditionally hated each other came together and did a joint concert. The main sponsor of the festival was the well-known cultural and political weekly magazine, *Reflex*. The band Braník was/is and will be the only openly racist band that has a logo and the name of its sponsor, also named Braník – the fifth-largest brewery in the country – printed on the back cover of the album, *Power*. It is the only album the band ever recorded. The band's slogan, *Braník pije* (drink) *Braník*, is printed right below the logo.

Another popular skinhead band of the time was Orlík. The band's debut album, *Oi*, was one of the best-selling 1990 albums in Czechoslovakia. Even someone like Lou Fanánek Hagen, the front man of Tři Sestry punk rock band, who is normally reserved, got carried away by the unique atmosphere of the event. In a TV interview given during the concert, he made a few unpleasant comments about the gypsy minority. No one – the event organizers, the sponsors, the bands themselves or anybody else – was ever sued for racial discrimination or for supporting human rights violations against certain groups of people. The early Nineties was unlike any other period in the modern history of Czechoslovakia. It was a no-man's land, a paradox, some sort of twilight zone where everything and anything was possible. It was a period of lawlessness where, to a certain extent, you could say and do whatever you desired without any repercussions. Even if the political system were to change in the future, this type of lawlessness will never happen again.

"How did we first find out about the Braník band?" I asked Honza.

"You don't remember?" he answered, and continued, "I came across the album by accident when my mom and I went Christmas shopping. I said to my mom, 'Look, Mom, these songs like "White Europe" are great. Please buy me the record.' She looked at the album and beside 'White Europe' saw the 'Fuckable' song, then answered, 'No, Honza, this album is inappropriate for you!' and bought me the *Vysací Zámek* album instead."

I then remembered the surrounding circumstances and said, "That's right, she refused to buy you the cassette, so I immediately ran to my mom, who gave me the money with no questions asked. I bought the album and we listened to it the next day after school." (In March 2017, I unsuccessfully searched for the original cassette. It's a shame. It would have been a collectible, since only twenty thousand records were released.)

I remembered about our other favorite records of that era: *Rebelie Punk 'N' Oi* (1990) and *Ultrametal* (1990). These two albums feature a nice collection of bands that were forbidden to legally exist until late 1989. This is real music, way different from the mainstream commercial garbage that's coming off assembly lines these days. "Well, because we are all over fifteen, there is not five of us and shaking our asses on TV and singing other people's songs. . ." Dave Mustaine of Megadeth once said, when asked, "What was it about the music business or music itself that made you say, OK I've had enough?"

156

The year 1990 was incredible for Czechoslovak music. Many artists that were unable to perform released their first official albums. Tři Sestry – *Na Kovárně to je nářez* and Orlík – *Oi* fully capture the unique spirit of the era and are my two favorite albums from that time. The two bands heavily advertised their first albums on TV since there were hardly any domestic and foreign corporations willing to pay ridiculous amounts of money for a few-second time slots. The commercials were memorable. Tři Sestry video clip: a man with guitar enters the Na Kovárně pub and within a few seconds, the bartender kicks him out and breaks his guitar over an asphalt sidewalk. In the Orlík commercial, the group members ride a wooden cart going downhill, while laughing. Other bands like Tublatanka – *Žeravé Znamenie Osudu* and Arakain – *Thrash the Thrash* became the symbols of the Velvet Revolution for younger people.

By 6 p.m. I had about eight pints of beer in me but, oddly enough, I wasn't drunk or had any kind of buzz at all. The *Macbeth* opera was scheduled to start at 7.30 p.m., so we left the pub and walked to the Main Train Station, positioned just above Wenceslas Square, to meet Grandmother. Honza knew my grandma very well since she had been his third-grade elementary school teacher. We both attended the same class until seventh grade, when I was kicked out of the language school for receiving one D grade. I attended normal middle school until we moved to the USA.

It felt special, sort of magical, sitting in the National Theatre for the first time in at least a quarter of a century. The opera exceeded my and my grandmother's expectations. Most importantly, I was grateful for having the opportunity to experience such a special event with my grandma. What a perfect ending to the perfect trip.

I didn't want to take a bus from Prague to Munich again. I purchased a flight ticket to Frankfurt, from where I flew standby to Atlanta.

"Lucky me, another free business-class seat!" I thought, as I entered the US-bound airplane in Frankfurt.

I had plenty of time to recap the two-week trip. It was a great trip, since I was able to do everything and see everyone according to plan. Most importantly, except for Honza's coincidental hospitalization, I was left alone by the producers, intelligence agencies and everybody else, as a matter of fact. During the second week of the trip, I felt normal and did not have unusual inner thoughts and did not experience any weird events. I was almost sure my life would get back to normal upon my return; to start a business or find a job, go to court, to see the marriage therapist, would be the only few things required to resume living the life I had known until December 2016.

"How are the girls doing? I miss them, and the lunches, they were so much fun. I hope nothing bad happened to Ronnee."

As I thought about the three women from Argos, I became sad and hopeless. I was in love with Ronnee and didn't have a clue what to do about it.

Chapter 8
The Legal System

On Friday, February 17th, I arrived in Atlanta after ten long hours. As a child, I could never have imagined myself someday living in this city. The city's existence first became known to me from watching the movie *Cyborg* (1989). The Hartsfield–Jackson International is unlike any other airport in the world. It's the busiest in the world, with over 100 million people flying in and out each year. The logistics is the best feature of the airport. Terminals are connected by a local subway system; each terminal equals one subway station. It's impossible to get lost.

This is in sharp contrast to the Charles de Gaulle Airport in Paris, where a network of illogical bus lines must be used to travel among different terminals. Over the years, I almost missed many flights leaving Paris. It appears the Charles de Gaulle Airport was built to be inefficient on purpose; to create unnecessary government jobs instead of convenience for the passengers. The French are the work inefficiency experts; going on strike because of a threat that the thirty-eight-hour work week would increase to a forty-hour work week. At least they are known to be great lovers. I guess all this extra time away from work is needed to learn and practice this type of social skill.

I turned on my cell phone while the plane was taxiing to a gate and received an urgent text message from František (Frank) Přibyl's daughter, Karolina, stating Frank was in trouble and she needed my help. The message was vague and didn't give me any additional details. I had known Frank since 1998 when he began to fix my car. We didn't start to talk or hang out until I met my wife, in 2005. Romana also knew Frank; he was fixing her old car on a bi-monthly basis and helped her purchase another vehicle once her old "lemon" totally fell apart. She had so many breakdown stories and remembered very well the thousands of dollars wasted on the old Nissan. In 2004, Frank helped her to buy a 1999 Ford Taurus 3.0, Flex Fuel. This car was such a great and low-maintenance vehicle that my mom still drives it to this day. As of 2017, the Ford has accumulated almost 300 thousand miles on the original engine. I responded to the message, but Karolina refused to give me any specific details over the phone. We agreed to meet the next day at the Starbucks located in Tucker, about halfway between Marietta and Snellville, where she lived.

I had no luggage except for one carry-on bag and going through the immigration/customs was a breeze. An alarm went off at the last security checkpoint. The TSA officer opened the luggage and looked into a plastic bag full of Czech candy. He laughed, then closed the bag. The candy bag hid countless sweets, like Tatranky, Miňonky, Milena chocolate, Studentská Pečet, Lázeňské oplatky, Kinder eggs. It was taking about half the space in the carry-on bag. To my relief, the officer didn't discover the illegal Kinder eggs I forgot to declare at customs. Some insurance wizard, together with government bureaucrats, determined the small toy parts inside the eggs pose a choking hazard. What happened to parental responsibility? When I was a child, Kinder eggs were one of the most popular candy/toys on the market. I've never heard of or seen kids dying from consuming or playing with the products. The small mechanical toys had to be assembled. This actually helped children to develop patience and fine motor skills, not to mention the endless fun when playing, collecting and exchanging the toys with other kids.

Romana, with the kids and Eva, Zack and their daughters, left on the day I returned, to go skiing at Snowshoe, WV, for a week. It was difficult to understand why my wife didn't wait for me to come back. She knew I wanted to go with them well in advance. Luckily, I called Milan, who again agreed to pick me up at the airport. He picked me up more than two hours after the agreed time. I was tired, irritated, and barely able to control my emotions while talking with Milan during the drive home.

"What are you doing? Why are you not going faster than 55mph?" I almost yelled.

"I am saving gas. You drive yourself home next time," he answered, and tried to appease me by going faster.

"What are you doing? You're following way too closely. Do you want to get us killed?" I said.

We were going back and forth like this until we drove off the Delk Road exit on I-75. This was the strangest ride from the airport to date. My thought process was way faster than normal; I said something to Milan and before he had a chance to react, I asked him something else. Finding the UFO books was the mission of the evening, so we first drove to my mom's house. To look and don't ask was the best strategy to find the books, since the NSA might have bugged Mom's house as well. I tried not to think about being in the Reality TV game show since the producers and the audience would have known all my thoughts and actions live, as they were happening, and any kind of disguise or sneakiness would have been pointless.

"Here it is, one of the books found!" I said in excitement. I continued to search for the second book in a small bookshelf standing next to the main entrance door but, unfortunately, the second book was nowhere to be found. Then I saw seven original *Rychlé Šípy* scout magazines, printed in 1969, 1970, and 1971. The magazines reached cult status because they were banned by the Communists within a few years after the 1968 Soviet invasion of Czechoslovakia. The paper prints were discolored yellow, with some of the cover pages detached, and looked way different than they had around thirty years ago, the last time my eyes saw them. I placed the magazines on top of the UFO book, had dinner consisting of a healthy home-cooked meal full of vegetables, and asked Milan to give me a ride home.

Upon entering the house, I sat at the kitchen table and opened the UFO book. Sadly, this was the incorrect book; it was the one with all the empty stories, but the small article regarding the Swiss man was there in the middle of the book, at the same place according to my memories. Eduard Albert "Billy" Meier is the person's name. We live in a digital age and this was the only information required to perform further research using a cell phone. To return the book back to Mom, to cover up the tracks that I was on to something, seemed the next logical step. I was exhausted and didn't have any energy left to Google Bill. Loneliness and sadness overtook my emotional state of mind, the place felt so dark and empty. It was difficult to comprehend why my wife wouldn't wait for us to go skiing together. The answer was received in the form of a letter placed on my nightstand. The letter basically stated: the kids love you, but I have no feelings for you any longer and want a divorce. I was blamed for being fired, arrested, and hospitalized. To take a shower, lie in bed, and fall asleep as quickly as possible was the only thing I was able to figure out at that moment to keep myself from dropping tears.

"They will be gone for the whole week and maybe everything will change once we see each other again," I reassured myself, while falling asleep.

The Sun was shining into my face when I woke up the next day, at almost at 10 a.m. Jet lag is no fun. To watch TV, sleep, eat, and read books is all you want to do for a few days after an overseas trip. I read over the letter several times and couldn't understand the reasons behind her decision. Emotionally, she was cooler than normal last year, but I didn't see this coming at all. A loving and supportive wife should understand when her husband gets fired, arrested, and hospitalized, especially since this appeared to be a total body shutdown. The marriage therapist was pretty sure a total body shutdown had happened because of excessive stress and informed Romana of his opinion. What was the problem? Why wasn't she supportive and understanding, especially after I assured her we'll get through this? She became a different person once I returned home from the hospital.

I left the house at 2.15 p.m. to meet Karolina at Starbucks. Unlike the Nissan Leaf, which was bugged, the Mercedes didn't cause chest and facial pains or any other discomforts. Using GPS didn't seem necessary, since Starbucks coffee shops are clearly visible from the road.

Depending on the Global Positioning System too often takes away the small adrenaline rush generated by the body when a person is lost. I took the Lavista Road exit, turned right, continued to drive for a few miles and turned around when the four-lane became a two-lane road surrounded by private residences. It turned out the coffee shop was hidden in a small shopping center, away from the main road. My wife and I normally split a venti-size coffee with cream, no sugar. We have done it for years, since I like paying $3.00 instead of $5.00 for the same item separated into two cups. During my early years in the USA, my sister, mom, and I frequently shared one drink while eating at fast-food restaurants. Why not, if you have unlimited refills on non-alcoholic beverages everywhere you go? Unlimited free refills were unheard of in Europe at the time. I purchased a tall coffee with cream, sat outside and closed my eyes.

Karolina and Frank's roommate, Roman, showed up within a few minutes. I had known Roman for years but didn't expect him to accompany Karolina to the meeting. Roman is a fun guy to hang around with, especially on ski lifts, because he always has a flask of hard liquor hidden in the interior of his jacket, close to the heart.

"Hi, Joseph, thank you so much for coming. It's good seeing you again," Karolina said.

I couldn't wait for her to tell me the story.

"Hi, it's great seeing you as well. It must have been at least ten years ago, the last time I saw you. You were a kid back then, no more than fourteen years old," I said, while secretly admiring her beauty, especially her eyes and hair.

Her mom was Russian and she had a distinct European look, the kind of look I was used to when living in the Czech Republic.

"She has the exact same eyes with the same genuinely sincere look, the exact same color and type of hair pulled back in a bun, just like you, Ronnee. She reminds me of you so much and I wish it was you sitting here with me, drinking a cup of coffee," I thought. I looked elsewhere to hide my emotions and continued to talk.

"Tell me, what happened to your dad?"

It appeared Karolina didn't know where to begin or how to explain it. She looked downward, back into my face and started to talk.

"Well, Dad's wife and the baby flew to Czech Republic for a few months to see the family. Dad went on Craigslist, met a girl and drove to Tallahassee, where he was arrested, because the girl in the ad was fourteen. It's all over the news," she said, and almost began to cry.

I kept staring into her face in disbelief, with my eyes and mouth fully opened. It took a few seconds to realize what was happening. . .

"This is another piece of the puzzle the producers prepared to make the

162

game more interesting. Everyone around me is getting sick or arrested. On second thought, the NSA might have framed Frank in order to scare me, to drive me crazy. Maybe Frank wasn't really arrested, because he's an actor, like everyone else."

There were too many ifs or maybes, therefore, I had no choice but to play the game according to expectations.

"I knew your dad for almost twenty years and would never think he may do something like this. Did he know she was fourteen?" I asked.

"I spoke with him a few times since the arrest. Dad was giving me indirect answers since the phone calls were recorded. This is what I understood; he was persuaded for two days by both 'mom and daughter' undercover agents to drive to Florida, the email communication was hacked and slightly adjusted by the FBI agents. It seems weird and I have to research it more closely. Dad has a court date on Tuesday. Can you please go down there with me to be a character witness and drive his car back to Atlanta? There is a chance he may be placed on house arrest until the trial," explained Karolina.

I didn't know a great detail about Frank and we were not that close friends, we hung out two to three times per year at the most, but I felt sorry for the girl. She seemed so innocent, beautiful, sad, and helpless at the same time. It was impossible not to help her. The family was out of town and it's not like I had at be at work on Tuesday anyway. Before I said "yes" there were a few unanswered questions.

"How did Frank treat you when you were a child? He wasn't beating you up or anything like that, was he?"

She quickly said he had not. I wasn't so sure since she kept looking down, away from my face, while stating her answer. Here is the reason why this question was asked; on one occasion, Frank said he slapped his then three-year-old stepson several times so hard his butt was red. He did it because the little boy kept pooping himself and, on that occasion, spread the poop all over the TV. Supposedly, from that point on, he never pooped his pants again. He presented the story as a good method of raising a child. I felt awful when hearing the story, especially since he laughed about it. If Frank was cruel to children, he deserved to be in jail for some time, even if innocent of his current charge. I felt this might have been karma for his past wrongdoings. I am a strong believer in that each person is responsible for his/her actions and associated reactions; consequently, problems caused by humanity will never be solved by imaginary gods.

The hearing was scheduled for Tuesday at 10.30 a.m. and we agreed to meet at 4 a.m. in front of Frank's house.

During the drive home, I kept thinking about how odd the situation was. Karolina's face appeared in front of my eyes, then changed to a facial image of Ronnee, the image I remembered from the day our eyes met at full stare in the cafeteria. Ronnee had perfect facial proportions and her wide-open eyes were looking deep into my eyes, trying to extract enormous amounts of information out of my soul within a matter of seconds. As a result, feelings and sensations which she was no longer able to control overwhelmed her mind and body. Ronnee no longer cared about the surroundings of her physical body since her mind inadvertently entered a different dimension; the dimension where everything and anything was possible, where the whole world belonged to her. Tears came out of my eyes as Ronnee's face kept appearing in my mind. "Am I ever going to see and talk to her again? She knows that I am forbidden to contact anyone at Argos. She probably can't contact me because her life, like my life, is in danger. I hope she isn't dead yet. The uncertainty regarding life and death pertaining to the person you deeply love is one of the worst feelings a human being can experience. I don't wish this on my worst enemy." My mind was being occupied with these and similar thoughts until I came up with the solution; to write her a letter.

A garage clicker is the most convenient and handy invention you can find around a house. I was irritated on numerous occasions when the remote was displaced or didn't work. How inconvenient it had become, something as simple as entering and turning a key inside a lock. On this occasion, the remote worked. I parked the car and entered the house, where my thoughts resumed on the Ronnee situation: "A letter, what kind of letter, a love letter, perhaps? No, because she will think I lost my mind. She has three terrific kids and has been in what appears to be a great marriage for twenty-plus years."

I kept going back and forth on the scope of the letter and after a few hours made up my mind, "She means a lot to me and I need to somehow warn her of the potential danger. I'll truthfully write her about my whole life and indirectly include some of the weird events that happened in the past couple months. I'll just write whatever enters my mind and, maybe, I'll figure out why those recent events happened. Even if I never see and talk to her again, at least she will fully get to know the real me without any bullshit filters or images, the real Joseph, who was her past lunch companion."

That evening, on February 18 2017, I wrote the first lines of my letter to Ronnee.

For the next two days, I wrote almost continuously, except for a few breaks such as to eat and nap. The inspiration was received by listening to music and walking the wooded trails of Sope Creek Park. During one of those walks I called my grandmother in Florida, who said she had been injured in a fall and didn't feel good at all. I felt bad for her, but at this point was not surprised. I was getting used to the accidents, nervous breakdowns, and arrests that were happening to friends and relatives. It was more of a routine, like catching a cold or flu. It was a shame, because I planned to visit my grandma and two aunts in a few days. Deerfield Beach would surely provide additional inspiration. Listening to hard rock/heavy metal when writing about the fun stuff from my childhood provided the needed inspiration. Listening to love songs and Eighties pop helped me to remember many events about the four women. Many times, pure silence was the most helpful occurrence for my writings.

On Tuesday, February 21st, I woke up at 3 a.m. and drove to meet Karolina, according to the plan. We picked up another character witness, a guy named Renda, who was Frank's friend. All his other friends refused to help him in this critical time of his life, when he needed the help most. We were the only two people willing to testify at the federal courthouse in Tallahassee, Florida.

During the five-hour drive from Atlanta to Tallahassee, the three of us had some interesting conversations. I found out a few details about my new friends. Karolina was living alone, with no boyfriend or roommate, paying rent of $1,200 per month. She recently bought a brand-new Nissan Altima and was able to negotiate a really good deal; $600 per month for five years. :-(Both Renda and I told her to return the car and move out of the apartment to her dad's paid-off house as soon as possible. It was clear to the two of us that Frank would not be leaving prison anytime soon. Renda went through a rough divorce; his then-wife stole many valuable items from their home and on many occasions threatened to call the cops, stating she felt terrified by him. I shared stories of losing my job, the arrest/hospitalization and the situation with Romana. Both of them basically told me to file for a divorce and find somebody else. Karolina kept persuading us Frank was framed by the FBI. She was able to pull the email communication, including supporting background codes.

"You see, the times of these messages don't match. There's proof the communication has been modified," she said to me and Renda.

"Look, Karolina, I am not an IT expert. I am going there to testify as a character witness and not to argue about falsified FBI evidence. Give this information to a lawyer. Frank needs a good lawyer anyway and as soon as possible. If what you're saying is true and we start to ramble about it in the courthouse, we could end up dead. The FBI, together with friendly local law enforcement, could easily plant drugs or weapons into my car and house. I would be arrested and 'accidentally' killed in prison. Many agents do think they're above the law, above the common people, and they act accordingly. If this is your plan, please let me out of the car right now. I don't want my two daughters to grow up without their dad," I said, and maintained my position from that point on.

"No, no, I don't want to put us in any danger. We'll stick to the original plan. I agree, the FBI will do whatever is necessary to keep this hidden, especially after the case received so much media attention," Karolina reassured me.

Renda fully supported my point of view. I had good feelings Karolina would stay calm and keep her mouth shut about the emails.

About an hour away from Tallahassee, we stopped at McDonald's to change clothes and have some breakfast. I ordered an egg white McMuffin sandwich, which appeared to be the healthiest breakfast item on the menu. In my early twenties, I experienced rapid weight gain accompanied by low energy levels due to frequently eating in fast food restaurants. In my opinion, McDonald's is the worst offender, since they heavily advertise to children; building their future customer baseline in total disregard for people's health and well-being. After breakfast, I changed into a black suit. For a one-day trip, Renda had brought a full-size suitcase packed with clothes. It took him about twenty minutes to change, which was a little odd.

We didn't make any more stops until we arrived at the courthouse.

After passing through the same full body scanner used at airports, I thought to myself, "The federal government must have done something wrong to take extreme measures like this to shield itself from its citizens."

"Everything out of your pockets and take off that watch!" an older security guard dressed in a business suit said, in an unfriendly tone of voice. Before I had a chance to react, he said, "Didn't you hear me?"

I looked directly into his eyes and replied in a snappy but firm tone of voice, "Yes, I heard you!"

The watch caused an alert, requiring a manual scan. Shortly after, I experienced the usual facial pain symptoms and sensitivity to light in both eyes. I went to a restroom, looked in a mirror and was horrified to see the eyes fully dilated. Focusing my eyes on the middle finger placed in front of my nose only slightly helped to decrease the dilation. "Having this condition in a federal courthouse surrounded by police, detectives, and agents is a big problem. Anyone who sees my face will think I am on drugs. If Karolina starts to ramble on about the tampered FBI evidence, I'll be picking up soaps in prison showers in no time. The hearing is about to start; what am I going to do?" I thought. I exited the restroom and kept walking with my eyes looking down towards the marble floor.

I sat next to Karolina and tried to avoid any eye contact with her, Renda, and especially the agents sitting around the courtroom. Within five minutes, two detectives called Renda and me to follow them outside of the courtroom, to the hallway. We were asked to give our names, for the record. I had no choice but to cooperate, but both first and last name were misspelled when written down on a piece of paper. I told the detective to correct my last name, but left the first name misspelled on purpose. "To buy myself some time before the detectives figure out the mistake and to postpone a full background check," were ideas that entered my mind. Fortunately, nobody said anything about the dilated eyes.

"To provide emotional support to Karolina is the main purpose of your trip," one detective said.

"The judge will not ask you any questions anyway," the second detective said.

A public defender with Karolina entered the hallway and, together with the two detectives, disappeared into an adjacent room, leaving us outside. Renda and I were strictly forbidden to join the group for the upcoming discussion.

"I told you," I said to Renda, "if you come here without a lawyer, you are going to be treated like low-life. All these people you see around here live on a different planet with their own sets of rules."

He agreed and we both returned to the courtroom. Within ten minutes, Karolina joined us, and the session began. Frank didn't look good at all. He had aged by at least ten years and, due to lack of clean contact lenses, both his eyes were infected. He turned around, smiled at Karolina, and an agent immediately blocked Frank's view, using his body. He was no longer able to communicate with us. As expected, Karolina was very emotional throughout the hearing and comforting her didn't help much. At least she kept the concerns about tampered FBI evidence to herself. Posting bail or imposing house arrest were denied, as the judge sent Frank back to prison.

The public defender offered information on what to do next and invited us to his office after lunch. Lunch sounded great and nearby Backwoods Bistro was chosen as the place to eat. Renda wanted to change into gym clothes as soon as possible and took his suitcase to the restaurant. Again, it took him twenty minutes to change clothes. In the meantime, Karolina and I had much-needed alcoholic drinks. The lunch was cancelled as time became a precious commodity.

We left the restaurant and walked to the federal building, where the public defender's office was located. A security guard asked us for our IDs and told us to write our names in the visitors' book. Renda had left his ID in the car and I conveniently stated the same reason, fully aware my ID was in my pocket.

"There is no way I'll give anyone my real name, not at this point," I thought.

Luck was on my side that day; the public defender stated we were "OK" and didn't have to present our IDs. I signed my name as illegibly as possible and we took an elevator to the office upstairs. The public defender was friendly and gave us some much-needed information on what might happen next.

We left the building and drove to the nearby prison, where Frank was incarcerated. Karolina was unable to see her dad due to missing documents. She had mailed the paperwork via registered mail to the prison's office almost two weeks ago, but for some reason the prison did not receive the package.

It was late in the afternoon and anything to eat sounded great. We stopped at the nearest sports bar and had unhealthy but delicious fast food, consisting of burgers, fries, and wings, topped off with some light beer. To pick up Frank's car, a 1997 black Mercedes C280, was the last stop before our drive home that evening.

At home, I couldn't help but think about Frank and his arrest. "Everyone who is at least half intelligent knows not to respond to a Craigslist advertisement where a mom, together with her fourteen-year-old daughter, are looking to have some fun with complete strangers. It's obviously a set up! Didn't Frank watch the famous NBC show, *To Catch a Predator*? Apparently not. It appears the FBI is targeting for arrest the less intelligent people. Less intelligent people have less money than smart people. They are much easier to convict than smart wealthy people who can afford armies of good lawyers. On many occasions, the smart and powerful ones prey on children at churches, sometimes with help from the victims' family members who, at that point, are brainwashed beyond the point of no return. Warren Jeffs is the perfect example but, unfortunately, he is just the tip of the iceberg. Most of these abusers will never get caught, since even the most respected church leaders are more than willing to cover their tracks. (On May 13 2017, Pope Francis announced that the Vatican has a 2,000-case backlog in processing clerical sex abuse cases.) Marie Collins once said, "The Church . . . wouldn't have covered up for them if they were stealing parish funds. They covered up for them if they were raping young children. How could men in leadership have done that?"

Why hasn't the FBI conducted any undercover operations to go after the pedophile clergy? Is it because the clergy in this country is above the law, above the government?

While in bed, I thought of one instance involving Frank and Ronnee. On December 21 2016, during the last lunch with Ronnee, we discussed maintenance on our old cars and how expensive everything is if you go to the wrong person. Many car mechanics automatically think your pockets are bottomless and full of cash if you drive a BMW or

Mercedes, regardless of the car's age. Coincidently, Ronnee's husband also owned an older Mercedes. I suggested Frank as the person to go to. He truly is the Mercedes expert who can figure out and fix anything, including electrical issues, for very reasonable prices. I've found only one other person this honest. His name is John.

"Joseph, I would like to have his phone number," Ronnee said. Our eyes met and she looked at me in a certain way.

Her face was giving out a silent secret that could only be decoded by a person with similar feelings. A simple, genuine, loving kiss was what Ronnee craved at the moment. I felt the same and wanted to kiss her, but being in the cafeteria at work surrounded by co-workers had ruined the moment.

"Does she also want *my* phone number?" I thought.

To this day, I haven't had a chance to give her my number.

I was able to give Frank's phone number to Leah. In 2015, her daughter Maggie's Mercedes broke down; the battery was dying. At the last minute, Leah drove the car to a shop where she didn't know anybody and was charged almost 200 dollars to replace the battery.

"You got ripped off. I would have gladly changed the battery for you free of charge. Why didn't you ask your husband?" I said, while writing Frank's phone number on a sticky note.

"Even if I bought the battery, Tom would never change it. It would be sitting in the garage for weeks," she said, in a non-caring but disappointed tone of voice.

"Leah, you really do everything around the house." I smiled a little and continued to speak. "Call this guy if you have any kind of problems with the car." I gave her Frank's number.

Leah never contacted Frank, at least not to my knowledge. Maybe it's for the best Leah and Ronnee never hooked up with Frank, as they both have teenage daughters.

There was one more story I remembered about Frank that night. About five years ago, I walked into his old mechanic's shop located in Lawrenceville. There was a rectangular, average-size calendar hanging above his desk with an imprinted picture of a fully dressed young woman. Even though the girl was dressed, she was absolutely gorgeous: perfect hips, upper body and facial proportions, with brunette hair pulled into a bun, my favorite women's hairstyle.

"Who is this hot girl?" I asked, while staring at the calendar with my mouth partially opened.

I closed my mouth, then continued to talk. "I really would like to have my way with her."

Frank was sitting in his chair, he leaned back and laughed as hard as he could, then said, "That's my daughter."

"Really? I didn't know that," I said. "She is beautiful. I don't mean any disrespect. Last time I saw her she was a kid, about fourteen years old."

"That's OK, man," Frank replied.

We started to talk and I found out Karolina used to be a model. No matter which modeling agency in Atlanta hired her, it was always the same story; the owners wouldn't give her any decent work until she had sex with them. Karolina never slept with any of the owners and eventually left the industry, disgusted and disappointed.

The next day I woke up with one purpose only, to continue to write the letter to Ronnee. Deadline for completion: only five more days remained before my wife and kids return from vacation. To my surprise, to write was not as hard as I initially thought it would be. Keeping my emotions under control was the greatest obstacle to finishing the letter. The moments experienced right after I was fired from PulteGroup kept entering and blending in my mind, together with all the beautiful memories of Ronnee. This created an emotional tornado.

"Tears are falling out of my eyes and I would do anything for a kiss," I thought.

Mixed feelings of sadness, joy, and happiness were present when a photograph of Ronnee was projected in front of my face. I had to stop writing once I realized I would probably never speak with or see Ronnee again in my life, just like it happened with Leah. To fall asleep was the only short-term medicine that worked.

I woke up and figured out one important piece of the puzzle: "In order to write from your heart, you have to be in a different state of mind. A person has to find the key and open the door of another dimension, where everything and anything is possible, where the reality as we know it no longer exists, where time doesn't matter and where different sets of values exist, totally different sets of values to those we're used to in our material world."

Since about December 2014, I had been in love with Leah, heartbroken when she left Immucor, reassured of my love for Leah once hired at PulteGroup, really heartbroken when fired from Pulte, in love with Ronnee like with no one else in my life and extremely heartbroken once fired from Argos. I was continuously in a different state of mind for over two years. The exorbitant amounts of additional chemicals and hormones my body produced for such a long time allowed me to find the key and open the door to this new dimension. There were some unexpected pleasant side effects as well, like losing over thirty pounds in eighteen months. To this day, I don't crave sweets or junk food at all. I drink water, coffee, and eat small portions of mostly healthy foods, when hungry. Time was becoming scarce, so Mom brought me some delicious healthy home-cooked meals on multiple occasions.

There were periods I was able to stop writing, turn off the computer and not think about anything. This made me happy because I wasn't really able to do this in the past couple of months. Up until the overseas trip, thoughts of the different scenarios or trying to figure things out continuously entered my mind.

My first tennis match of the 2017 spring season was scheduled for the evening of February 23rd, at the Highland Pointe subdivision, about a twenty-minute-drive from home. My favorite black Nike sneakers were made out of cloth, the worst possible material for tennis shoes. I had no choice but to wear my other shoes, also Nike sneakers. I had not worn that pair since late 2015, as the right shoe had a defect; a line of connecting material that was hurting my foot, right above the toes. Interestingly, for the first time ever, the shoe felt perfectly fine. This was my first time playing tennis at the Highland Pointe subdivision. The development was the classic "Brady Bunch" houses built in the 1970s, with plenty of front and backyards. The houses were gently placed in the forest with the least amount of damage possible to the surrounding trees. There was a large pond next to the tennis courts. The scenery of the pond, hills, trees, and houses was beautiful.

"I wish new constructions were built this way instead of cutting down every single tree and placing the houses right next to each other. Privacy is nonexistent in those communities," went through my mind.

A frozen, dull, and tingling feeling bothered my whole right arm for some time. With certain movements, my right wrist was hurting as well. To talk with another human being and to clear my head was the purpose of this match. I didn't want to cancel the match until the pain was unbearable. My opponent was a well-built, mostly baldheaded man in his late forties, with a small but fresh scar on his forehead. I was able to warm up my arm and resume the game. Matt seemed normal at first, but became very irritated every time he lost a ball. At certain times he said, "Fuck this and fuck that," and threw his racquet away. He played way above the beginner's level of this game; to win and not have fun was his mission. He registered at this level on purpose.

"Who cares if you or I win, this is not Wimbledon's final. It's all about the fun," I said, to calm him down.

He would have been a much better player if he had stopped caring about winning the game. A bad mood is the result of many mistakes.

"What if he has a gun in his car? Will he shoot me in case of a loss?" I thought.

To let him win was the medicine he needed to calm down and I gave him just that. Towards the end, Matt became a really friendly and outgoing person, the discussion was great.

It was dark during the drive back home; my eyes were hurting and the colors of neon lights and street traffic signs were brighter and sharper than normal. Seeing way better than normal was beautiful, but scary at the same time.

"Why is this happening again? Matt really was the weirdest opponent I had met to this day. Hopefully, he wasn't an agent trying to provoke me, to get me arrested again. Romana paid for vision insurance, I better make an appointment as soon as possible."

Again, uncertainty about what was really happening entered my mind. Everything about the possible scenarios was just speculation. It was difficult to switch my thoughts to a different subject, since I had to drive the car, to look at the road in front of me, to see all the gorgeous colors. At home, the computer became my savior as I was able to shift my thought process on writing the letter.

I had a court date scheduled for the next day and began to organize my thoughts on how to defend myself. I didn't hire an attorney. I wasn't too worried. My only experience with the judicial system, besides traffic, was in 2004 when I had to pay a fine for selling artwork on the street. "No big deal, it is only a misdemeanor charge. What's the worst-case scenario anyway?" Surprisingly, I was facing a $1,000 fine and a year of incarceration, should the worst-case scenario materialize. "An attorney surely would be nice, but who cares. It doesn't matter, because the producers or the agents are running the show anyway."

My mind was occupied, and the phone rang; it was Renda. I told him my concerns surrounding tomorrow's court date.

"You can't go to any court without an attorney, don't you know that?" Renda said. "Let me tell you a story. About ten years ago, I went to court without an attorney to settle a case related to a suspended driver's license. All my friends told me I will pay no more than a $500 fine. I basically went there for a $700 refund since the bail was $1,200. I didn't speak much English at the time and had a difficult time understanding the judge. 'So, you are with Russian Mafia, right?' the judge asked. 'Me? No, I am Czech,' I said. He said something that appeared to be the amount of the fine and I started to walk towards the door to exit the courtroom. A cop blocked me and stated, 'Where are you going?' 'To cashier, for money,' I said. He put handcuffs on me and said, 'You were sentenced to eleven days in jail. So, you are a Russian Mafia, ha, ha, ha.' This is how they wiped their asses with me."

I listened to the whole story without saying a word.

After digesting the conversation, I said, "They gave you the maximum sentence. Tomorrow, I'll tell the judge to postpone the case until I get a lawyer."

Renda answered, "Yes, this is how it works here. The whole system; the judges, prosecutors, and lawyers, are hand in hand. They'll be happy you have spent money and the judge will give you a break. This is not the end of the story. I was forbidden to wear any gold during my parole period."

I was getting more confused. Not to wear any gold jewelry, what was wrong with that picture?

"They can't tell you not to wear gold, don't bullshit me," I said, so he would tell me the truth.

"Yes, they can. I came to the courtroom wearing my gold chains and earrings. I found out later the judge placed a ban on me wearing any gold jewelry."

We also talked about Karolina and the whole situation regarding Frank, who was facing ten years to life in prison. This harsh sentence sounded absurd to us since there was no harm done to anyone and, at age forty-eight, Frank had no prior criminal sex offender record. After the conversation ended, I couldn't help but laugh at Renda's arrest. It was funny until I realized the judge had no real evidence except him wearing a lot of gold jewelry, no basis to accuse Renda of being connected to the Russian Mafia. The judge obviously didn't like his appearance, therefore gave him the maximum sentence and made up the silly gold jewelry ban to teach him a lesson. The judge knowingly violated Renda's constitutional rights.

The sunny, cloudless morning elevated my spirit as I entered the State Court of Cobb County. For some reason, the citation stated 8 a.m. as the start time of the court session, but the door of Courtroom 1A didn't open until 9 a.m. Playing with a cell phone, sitting around or admiring the courthouse's architecture, were the most common activities people choose to do to kill the extra hour. The usual facial and eye pains reappeared, preventing me from reading news on my cell phone. I suspected my eyes were dilated as well. I went to a nearby restroom where my worst fears were confirmed. To return to the courtroom, to look down, to not act suspiciously and to listen to every word coming from the court officials was the perfect plan to hide the symptoms.

As a result of different time perception and elevated hearing ability suddenly experienced while sitting in the courtroom, my brain was able to simultaneously process multiple conversations coming from several different directions. From the vision perspective, everything around me became sharper and brighter, individual skin pores of people sitting next to me became clearly visible. I was scared to death; I looked towards the floor and closed my eyes.

"Nothing is over, I am probably going back to jail. The symptoms appear every time I go through a body scanner or metal detector. Have I somehow become super sensitive to electromagnetic radiation?" I thought, and tried to relax for my interview with the prosecutor.

The county had recently established a new program for first-time family violence misdemeanor offenders; a case by case evaluation and associated therapy was the requirement to have the case automatically dismissed. I was more than happy when this offer was presented to me. Of course, I accepted, received detailed instructions listing the next steps, left the building and drove home as fast as possible. The instruction package listed general conditions in lieu of prosecution:

1. Do not violate any laws of any governmental unit.
2. Do not drink alcohol.
3. Do not take drugs unless lawfully prescribed to you.
4. Avoid persons or places of disreputable or harmful character.
5. Support legal dependents.

I unknowingly clarified item #1 with the prosecutor before accepting the offer.

"Let's say I accidently run a stop sign. Will you kick me out of the program?" I asked.

"No, only if you get arrested," the prosecutor answered.

This made me happy since I religiously ignored stop signs placed at intersections such as malls, where you can clearly see the oncoming traffic from every direction well in advance. Item #2 made sense. Item #3 also made perfect sense; in fact, legalizing medical marijuana. Item #4: avoid persons or places of disreputable or harmful character.

"Hmm. . . what does that mean?" I thought. "Only in America could somebody write something this vague and ridiculous to intimidate people. Should I avoid swingers' clubs or churches? I better avoid the churches because they are full of pedophile clergy these days. The priests and pastors would try to corrupt my good morals, that's for sure."

I finished the analysis and closed my eyes for a few minutes, hoping the symptoms would disappear. I woke up and the symptoms were gone. The letter – the memory, the portal to my past life, the only available means of communication left with my beloved women – had to be finished, no matter what. Every time the computer started, I inadvertently found myself in a different world.

My writings were nearing the end, love was missing in the letter. Love is the most powerful force in the Universe. Love was the reason why I wrote the letter in the first place. I had to write about my feelings for Ronnee.

"How should I write about it?" I thought.

Anything, it didn't matter what, as long as my heart was the source, the generator of those feelings that would be transposed onto a piece of paper. I wrote without thinking, everything that entered my mind at the moment. To write about the genuine love was so easy. I really didn't have to do anything except to feel the presence of my loved one.

Chapter 9
Going Back to Normal?

On Sunday the 26th of February, shortly after lunch, I wrote the last word of the letter. This wasn't just any ordinary letter. The letter was twenty pages long, an 18,000-word large document summarizing my life, my opinion on today's world, my beliefs and feelings.

"Perfect timing," I thought. "My wife and kids will be here this evening. Tomorrow is another day and my brain is fried, I'll do the final review tomorrow."

I was excited about the accomplishment and prepared for the second tennis match of the season, scheduled in the evening at Loch Highland subdivision, not too far from my house. The right hand was still bothering me but I was able to warm up the wrist to play the whole game. It was a good game overall. My opponent, Paul, was friendly, positive, and didn't care if he won or lost. What a difference compared to Matt. We talked about our jobs. Paul was an IT expert, and I told him a few stories about indirect tax. I couldn't help but share my grievances regarding the big four accounting firms.

"I heard conversation about tax. Hi, I am Matt. I used to work for PWC, corporate tax," said a young-looking man playing tennis on the adjacent court.

Matt was about my age, resembling Mark Zuckerberg to a certain extent.

"You used to? I guess the so-called work/life balance failed to materialize," I answered, and we both laughed.

"I left the CPA firm to work for the industry and what a difference. I am much happier when it comes to work/life balance," he said.

We talked some more between sets and I asked, "Do you know Corey Self? He is one of the founders of City of Brookhaven. He used to work for PWC tax in the early 2000s. I used to work with him at PulteGroup. What a great guy with an impressive personality."

"I never met Corey in person, but heard about him. I started after he left," Matt said, and continued to play.

I couldn't help but think about Leah, how much I missed her from time to time. I hoped Corey was taking good care of her. He did an amazing job flirting with her, something I wasn't able to do at that time.

What an incredible feeling when I arrived home, opened the door leading to the living room and both daughters jumped into my arms. It had been three weeks since I kissed and hugged my beloved children. That was a long time, especially at this early age of three and seven, they changed so much and appeared sort of taller than in my memory.

Romana said "Hi" and told me to move to a different bedroom and abruptly ended the discussion.

The next day, on Monday morning, I had an early breakfast with the family before Teresa had to catch a school bus. Romana gave me a list of projects to be completed that week: file 2016 income taxes, find a job, patch drywall in the kitchen and Teresa's bedroom, which became my bedroom as of yesterday. To get her off my back, I agreed to everything she said and added another project myself: to seal leaking holding tank of the backyard water fountain. My priorities were somewhere else – to finalize and send the letter to Ronnee. I wasn't sure how to send the letter. It could have been easily intercepted if sent via email or directly to her at work.

"For all I know the NSA, together with Argos, are monitoring Ronnee twenty-four hours a day, seven days a week, waiting for me to make a move. Even if she isn't monitored this closely, her boss, Mark, may open the letter. Jessica is the perfect person to receive the letter. She is Ronnee's friend and doesn't have a boss that is constantly breathing over her shoulders."

I made up my mind and decided to mail the letter to Jessica. The return address presented a small challenge. I didn't want the letter to fall into the wrong hands, in case it wasn't delivered. Quality Care for Children was the perfect return address, since Jessica was on the Board of Trustees and would eventually receive the letter, in case it was returned. The projects and finishing the letter were postponed, spending time with the kids became the priority for the rest of the day.

In the afternoon, we went to East Cobb Park where there is always so much to do, like playing at the playground or walking the trails. Upon our return, we had more fun together until Romana called us to eat dinner. The kids have all kinds of toys: endless amounts of dolls, dishes, puppets, cars, airplanes, Lego, you name it. Playing soccer inside was also a lot of fun, since there is plenty of room to build a "soccer field"; the second living room with adjacent formal dining room was converted into one large play area shortly after we moved to the house.

"Formal dining room, you never use it unless there are guests. It's a waste of space, so let's convert it to something we can use every day," Romana said back in 2015.

I couldn't agree more and replied, "Teresa and Julia would sure appreciate a large playground. They can't run around the town the way we used to when we were little."

After dinner, I drove to the nearby Walmart to buy large envelopes, return address stickers, blank printer paper and a stapler. It became impossible to concentrate and efficiently select the products, a chilly reminder of when I purchased the watch. I stopped comparing the products, quickly grabbed one of everything and walked to the cashier. Aviation noises, the same noises I heard so often before I went to jail and hospital, were audible during my drive home. I didn't know, I didn't want to know what was going on anymore. I went to speak with my children as soon as I entered the house and ignored the noises until they had finally subsided.

It appeared this was going to be a long evening before my mind and body would be able to fall asleep regardless of thoughts, exhausted to just the right level.

"Why not watch some old movies? Something that always made me relaxed and feel good, something I haven't seen in a while," I thought. I went to the laundry and found an original bundle collection of Schwarzenegger DVD movies: *Commando*, *Predator*, *The Running Man*, and *Total Recall*, purchased in 1998.

I lay in my bed, turned on the computer and inserted the DVD of *The Running Man* (1987) movie. A strange desire to be totally disconnected from the outside world entered my mind. Oddly enough, I thought this was necessary to fully enjoy the movie, filmed exactly thirty years ago.

"I am most definitely being monitored at this moment," was my reasoning.

I disconnected the computer from the internet.

The more I watched the movie, the more different it was when compared to the last time I saw it, back in 1998. There were many instances combined with inner thoughts; somehow the movie fitted perfectly into the puzzle of my whole life, the recent experiences, my knowledge and beliefs of the current world and my love for the four women.

"Is this why I watched the movie endlessly, once a day for several weeks, when living behind the Iron Curtain? Was the mind of the ten-year-old boy trying to decode hidden messages, the messages which only now I am able to see?"

I didn't know what to think or what to do at that point, more information was needed to confirm my suspicions. I was, however, able to fall asleep peacefully that night.

The next morning, I reviewed the letter for the last time and attached a handwritten note for Jessica, asking her to give the letter to Ronnee and meet me for a cup of coffee. I chose the UPS store on Delk Road over a US post office because both the mail to and return addressees were going to be printed on the envelope by the UPS store, thus avoiding any handwriting whatsoever which could be recognized by Argos employees, especially by mailroom person Steve, who knew my distinct/ugly handwriting very well. I entered the UPS store and there was no one there except for a man; an employee standing behind the counter. I was given an envelope to place the letter in. The background music changed to classical as I was walking back toward the counter to mail the letter "certified." The payment was processed and the receipt with the tracking number given to me for my records. I turned around and there was a line of at least ten people who were smiling directly to my face, standing in total silence. It felt awkward.

"Who are all these people that appeared in the store like ghosts? I hope this is not some sort of warning sign given to me by the intelligence agency."

Emotionless a person has to be to play this game right. I looked down, walked out of the store and drove to the LA Fitness gym on Roswell Road.

Memories of the gym and restaurant
At the gym, lack of energy, combined with facial pains, arm pains and the wrong state of mind, prevented me from having a decent workout. I lifted some light weights but mostly daydreamed. The normal workout routine consisted of three, two-hour sessions per week; thirty minutes cardio on each day, chest/biceps/triceps on Wednesday night, back/shoulders on Saturday morning and legs on Sunday morning. This was a far cry from the late 1990s/early 2000s when I worked out five to six times per week and concentrated on smaller muscle groups. Being single and the atmosphere of the old gym, Main Event Fitness, made the rigorous workout routine possible.

Back in those days, thanks to my favorite "healthy sounding" energy drink, Thermo Hydroxadrine, a person could have a great workout even when dead tired. On many occasions I walked into the gym tired, barely able to walk after working a double shift at Houston's restaurant the day before, bought the drink and sat on a couch for twenty minutes. What an out of this world feeling when the ephedrine alkaloids expanded the sockets in my lungs and supercharged the lungs to allow much higher air intake per breath. I was able to lift the whole gym at that point.

"Drugs, don't drink this!" George Hyder, who was the head of Steel Ballet fitness program, warned me on multiple occasions while I was consuming the energy drink.

"OK, George, I won't next time," I answered, to get him off my back while entirely dismissing his advice in my mind. "Look who's talking, an ex-steroid user."

Many times, George said how much he regrets taking steroids in his early twenties. "Joseph, even if you do a couple of cycles it will stay with you for the rest of your life. Your body will rot from inside out."

George passed away in January 2001, at age thirty-seven, due to multiple organ failure. My worst nightmare became reality; a seemingly healthy, well-built individual I talked with almost daily, with no warnings, forever disappeared from everyone's life. My last memory of George was him training a person, standing and facing a pulldown machine. He was gone the next day. George, his achievements, and later his spirit, became an inseparable part of MEF. People missed and talked about him for years, until the gym closed. There were other interesting people attending the club:

1. A person wearing a mask and plastic clothes, throwing away the gear after each workout.
2. Toothpick Rambo; a gentleman in mid-thirties wearing a camouflage bandana, white tank top and really tight shorts. He looked into a mirror after each set while performing one of the following: flexed his biceps or moved pecs up and down – one at a time or moved his butt cheeks up and down – one at a time. He frequently ran on the sidewalks of Powers Ferry Road, wearing his uniform and boxing like Rocky.
3. The Heavy Guys; a couple of well-built males lifting only very heavy weights; moving the free weights two to four inches per repetition, thinking it is the perfect workout.

To drop the weight to the floor and scream as loud as possible after each set was the zenith of a workout for many bodybuilders and wrestlers. Many times, the whole upper floor of the gym shook when dumbbells weighting 200 pounds or more were dropped to the floor. MEF was the only gym in Atlanta and probably the whole US where this behavior wasn't against the rules. I asked at other gyms about the rule and always received the same answer; the average people and especially women feel intimidated by the noises. I've never seen any women that were intimidated. On the other hand, MEF was no average gym, that was for sure. To see Lex Luger warm up; bench press 315 pounds, 18 times, on his first set was intimidating enough for me to stay in reality and warm up with my usual 135 pounds. Who wouldn't know the owner, Lex? He talked to everybody at the gym regardless of background. On one occasion I waited on him at Houston's restaurant, located right across the street from the gym. Lex and his girlfriend, Ms. Elizabeth, were sitting at a four-top table, at the far corner of the restaurant.

We were talking about the usual everyday events but I couldn't help myself, I had to tell him, "The other day I measured the diameter of my arm, it's seventeen inches!" I was excited and proud of the achievement.

"That's great, Joseph, most people don't come even close," he said, as they both smiled directly into my eyes.

This comment made me feel really good because it came from the person who knew very well how much effort is needed to achieve something like that.

"And I did it without steroids," I replied.

While going through the light workout routine at LA Fitness, my thoughts then shifted to memories of Houston's restaurant. In 1998, I walked into the restaurant in the middle of a lunch rush hour and asked for a manager. I introduced myself, said a couple sentences about my restaurant experience and asked about open wait-staff positions.

"I am really busy as you can see. You are hired, come back tomorrow to speak with the assistant GM. His name is Joe," said a gorgeous, classy young woman named Summer, and that was the end of the interview.

Summer was a great manager, fair to everyone but tough if you didn't do your job 100%. On one occasion, I forgot to "manicure" a table – to take an empty sugar package from a guest's table – and she immediately took me to the "Hobart" (back of the restaurant) area and tore me apart.

After her motivational speech she said, "Joseph, you have a heart."

I had no idea why she made the statement and have been puzzled by it ever since. I am able to picture the moment and see Summer in front of my eyes making that statement like it happened yesterday. The place refused to carry any of the mainstream beers, such as Budweiser or Miller Light. The owner, George Biel, wanted to offer his customers a different experience when it came to beer. This was great and as a result the restaurant offered my favorite beer, Pilsner Urquell. Lex was a regular customer and made several requests for the restaurant to carry his favorite beer, Coors Light. One day, after many countless and unsuccessful Coors Light requests, he lost it. Lex got up from the table and walked towards the open grill/kitchen area and screamed at the manager in such a way the whole restaurant heard him: "I don't care the owner doesn't like Coors Light. I am the customer and not him! Next time I come back, you better have Coors Light!!!"

I've never seen anybody that pissed off over a beer. Maybe he had a bad day or forgot to take his dose of pain pills and roids, or was just upset when he realized that a "wall" not a person was listening to him every time he made the request. Anyway, the point was made and going forward, the managers always had a case of Coors Light hidden in a walk-in cooler in case of the arrival of this "special guest."

For a waiter like myself, the restaurant business was a hit or miss lottery of guests from different backgrounds. The salary was $2.30 per

181

hour, just enough to pay the taxes. Our livelihood depended on a mixture of guests of four different tipping categories:

1. Above average; 20% +
2. Average; 14% to 19%
3. Below average; 6% to 13%
4. Way below average; 0% to 5%

Given great consistent food and service, experienced waiters knew how to accurately categorize their guests upon arrival to the restaurant. All sorts of direct and indirect signs were used to read customers' minds; wardrobe/appearance, age, sex, race, educational level, nationality, and accent. Most people tipped average. Many business people and regulars tipped above average. Most rednecks, foreigners, and uneducated people tipped below average.

There was one category of guests that all servers, regardless of race and background, feared like the Devil of the crucifix. They required the most maintenance and almost always tipped way below average. These guests usually arrived late at night, shortly before closing time. They wore lots of gold jewelry, sunglasses, baggy pants, and a FUBU jersey. We called them the "Fucked Up Black Underachievers." It appeared many of them thought they were entitled to a free meal with service. On many occasions, they drank Hennessy cognac, Heineken using a straw and unusually sweet alcoholic beverages.

"I have to go back and cut down a fruit tree to make this Pina Mulata and Frozen Strawberry Blackuiri," I joked with my buddy Brant, who was also my workout partner, and other servers on many occasions.

The food ordered by this group consisted mostly of well-done or fried extra-crispy protein, with extra sauces and extra-crispy fries with extra ketchup. Even the water had to have a straw, extra lemon or extra maraschino cherries with extra grenadine.

"It always takes so long to correctly enter these orders," I complained to Brant while he was standing next to me, entering his order into the system.

"No kidding, there should be one key, the special guest key, making everything extra-crispy and adding extra sauces," he said, and we both laughed.

On one night, my friend, a server named Gary, had his section full of the late-night arrivals.

"You have the real winners tonight," I said to Gary, and laughed at his face while rolling silverware.

"Joseph, don't even go there. I am so ashamed of my people," he answered, while making his drinks, then walked away in a not so good mood. This was a strange comment.

"Are they not tipping on purpose, or due to lack of education? Maybe they're thinking this behavior could somehow make up for all the injustices that happened to their people during the past 400 years." I tried to figure out the right reason.

I was almost fired for reading guests more than I should. A server named Rizwan complained to manager Margie that I refused to serve his six guests sitting next to my seven guests because of racial reasons. Due to lack of extra-large tables, the party of thirteen had to split between two different tables. This was during a short period of time when the restaurant didn't allow servers to enter an automatic 18% gratuity to parties of five or more guests. Since servers had to pay 2% of gross sales (tip-share) back to the house, I didn't want to work for free and refused to swap tables.

"Riz, you take care of your part of the group and enjoy it," I said.

Margie called me to the office shortly after. "We are a place of business and serve all guests. With these skills you should be working for the Third Reich and not here. I am not firing you, but don't let this happen again!" she said.

"It's a party of thirteen and I can't give them good service. I have two other tables as well. Riz tried to give me the table because he didn't want to take care of them," was my justification of the situation.

I was lucky, Margie was a woman who took it easy on me and gave me a break. The wait staff made fun of me for months due to the fact Margie recommended the Third Reich as my next place of employment. I never figured out why Riz complained, especially since we were laughing at each other's tables on almost a daily basis. In a few days, we became friends again and continued to laugh at each other's guests until I left the restaurant in 2004.

As mentioned earlier, the servers were from different backgrounds, including LGBT. I had made fun of gay guys since about the age of seven, but never made fun of lesbians because I viewed the idea as sort of hot. The pleasant thought of two or more women playing with each other always made me kind of excited. The longer I worked at the restaurant, the more I became accustomed to the idea that gay guys are normal, no different than the rest of us human beings. They looked the same, talked the same (except for one girlish guy), had the same feelings and behaved the same way as me. To certain extent, I even flirted with a couple gay guys at work; to keep them in suspense – them not knowing if I was straight, bisexual or just curious was the excitement this game provided for me.

"Come on, guys, give me a break, I would never do anything like that. I am straight as can be," I said, to cool them off when the game became too hot for my standards.

"Straight as can be? Yeah right. Straight to bed, that's what you are," a person named Erik answered.

There were two people, Juan and Charles, who stood apart from the usual crowd. The couple adopted a baby boy via private adoption. For years, Juan told me how difficult a time the State of Georgia gave them because of the adoption.

"I don't know what to do anymore, the government here is making our lives miserable because we're gay and adopted a child. We wasted tens of thousands of dollars on legal fees and there's no end in sight. We'll have to move away, probably to Florida, to live a normal life."

Many times, Juan, Charles, and their son came to the restaurant to eat. The smiling and talkative little boy was always hugged and kissed by the loving parents. It appeared he was loved beyond imagination. At that moment, I realized it doesn't matter if a child grows up with mom/dad, or mom/mom, or dad/dad, as long as the child is loved and has a happy childhood. The little boy was surely better off growing up with Juan and Charles instead of in some government institution.

There was one more story that came to my mind before the workout was finished. After about a year, I moved up in seniority and didn't have to work lunch shifts any longer. The lunch shifts were always hit or miss; a server made anywhere between $25 to $90 working on weekdays between 10.30 a.m. and 2.30 p.m. It all depended on how fast the tables turned. An unlucky server had the table section full of female secretaries who were drinking chamomile hot teas, eating grilled chicken salads dry, with dressing on the side, and were yapping about bullshit for hours at a time. No wonder I didn't want to work anymore lunch shifts unless absolutely necessary. Oddly, I kept being asked to work the lunch shifts by the same group of people, usually girls, over and over again.

My answer was always the same, "No, I can't work the lunch shift."

A pretty, young, and persistent girl then asked again, "Come on Joseph, work for me. You have nothing to do anyway."

"I am busy, I can't do it," I answered.

"What are you going to do that's so important that you can't work for me?" she asked, clearly to irritate me.

"Gym, bike, pool," I snapped back at her.

"What do you mean by gym, bike, pool? Come on, work for me," she asked again.

At that point I gave up and told her everything. "Let me explain something to you. I get up at 9 a.m. and go to the gym. I eat lunch around 12.30 p.m. After lunch, I ride my bicycle at Chattahoochee River. At 3 p.m., I go to the pool to work on my tan and at 4.20 p.m., I have to be at work. So, you see? I can't work for you because it would mess up my workout routine."

"You are such an asshole, screw you!" was the typical answer received after the thorough explanation.

"Well, if you really mean what you just said, you don't have to tell me twice," I said, and smiled into her face.

At that point the girl clearly received the message and walked away without saying another word.

About two weeks later, she asked the same question again.

"Sorry, can't do it, gym, bike, pool!" I quickly answered, without pausing my walk, without looking into her face, just laughed loudly as I was walking away leaving her standing in front of the salad area in total shock, with her mouth partially open. I learned to appreciate this type of work/life balance while working at KPMG.

Daydreaming was over
After almost two hours, I left the LA Fitness club, not remembering most of the repetitions performed. The stories of my past life combined with music played on Pandora kept my mind occupied and away from the gym. At home, there was a flyer attached to a white magnetic board nailed to a wall close to the kitchen table. The yellow flyer displayed a fundraising event organized by the Chick-fil-A restaurant for Taylor, a little girl who suffered brain injury due to a car accident. My daughter Teresa was the same age as Taylor and attended the same school, East Valley Elementary. The fundraiser was going to be good lesson for my daughters, especially for Teresa.

"Girls, let's go to Chick-fil-A and make a donation for this girl who is really sick. Anybody's life can change in a few seconds. You should enjoy every day as much as you can," I said, and they were both looking at me, requiring additional information so their small brains could process the meaning of what was said.

"Is she going to be healthy, why is she sick?" Teresa asked.

I explained the situation in more detail and we drove to the Chick-fil-A store located on Roswell Road, about two miles from the house.

"Here is $20, put it in the collection box," I said to Teresa as we were entering the store.

The place was really busy, tables were full and about eight people were waiting on the right side of the cash registers for the food to be ready. The famous Chick-fil-A cow mascot was playing with the countless small children running around the store.

"Where can we place the donation for the Taylor Grace Fundraiser?" I asked the cashier when our time had come to place the order.

"We don't accept cash donations, you have to buy the food in order to contribute," the cashier answered.

I was stunned by the answer and asked, "What percentage of sales is going towards the cause?"

I don't know," she replied.

"You don't know? Can you please find out for me?"

She went and talked to some person who appeared to be her boss and came right back. "We will give away 10% to the cause," she said.

"That's it, you will only give out 10% of the sales?" I asked and placed an order worth almost $13. "Out of the $20 dollars I originally wanted to give to the cause, the little girl will only receive $1.30. This can't be right. This corporation always presents itself as the pillar of the community. It has to be a mistake. They can't be this greedy."

While we waited for the food, I reasoned why the percentage was this ridiculously low, then walked back toward the cash registers and asked a person who appeared to be the manager.

"I heard you are only going to give out 10% of gross sales to tonight's fundraiser," I said, looked into her face and maintained a certain facial expression that demanded the truthful answer.

The young blonde lady who happened to be the marketing director stopped smiling and gave me the "What the fuck?" look, and answered, "It's 14%, but if you spend more than $15 per order, we will give out 20%."

"Really? Can I verify this on your website?" I asked, refusing to move an inch.

"It's not on our website," she said.

I persisted and asked another question. "Are you going to post the percentage of sales and the donated amount on your website?"

"We don't post the percentage of sales anywhere, but I will post the donated amount within a couple days," she said.

The kids and I sat at the only open table to eat our dinner, consisting of two chicken sandwiches, fries, fruit cup and a drink. I went on the store website to see where the dollar amounts from the past fundraisers were posted. I didn't find the information or anything about past fundraising events. The current February 28th fundraiser was not even posted on the calendar where other events were listed. Something about this whole situation didn't seem right.

"Why do you need a marketing person at a fundraising event? Why don't you have the event listed on your calendar? As an organizer of this charitable event, don't you want to raise as much money as possible to help this little girl, who is almost brain dead?"

I became sick to my stomach, unable to eat any more food. Evidently, the store didn't give a shit about the little girl's health, she was just being used as another marketing tool to generate sales. That's why there was a marketing person present at the so-called fundraiser and the store employees gave me conflicting information. Flyers of the child's photograph were distributed outside, away from the store, but there was nothing inside the store to remind people there was a fundraiser going on. I left the place disgusted, without saying a word to my little girls.

The next day, Romana and I drove to Buckhead to see our marriage therapist, Mr. Milton S. Gay. She quickly looked into my face with a slight smirk, started to talk, and kept talking most of the session, blaming everything on me and unwilling to give me another chance to save our marriage.

"If you can't move beyond the past events and are unable to give him another chance, there is no point in me continuing to be your therapist. Is that what you want?" he asked.

Romana, without any hesitation, said, "Yes, the marriage is over. I don't want to give him any more chances. He deserted us by travelling to Europe and broke his promise by extending the stay another week."

Mr. Milton and I looked at each other and then both looked at Romana. I couldn't believe she wouldn't give me another chance.

"It appears the intelligence agency forced her to do this, to divorce me, to kick me out of the house. Once I live alone, I could easily be kidnapped." I figured out the answer but remained calm, as usual, and didn't ask any unnecessary questions.

Later in the afternoon my health symptoms started to worsen. Facial and chest pains made completing any of the projects impossible. I had to lie down several times per day and take naps for the symptoms to decrease. (This continued sporadically until around the middle of April.) Driving the Nissan Leaf made me feel even worse, so I drove the Highlander as much as possible. In the mornings, my problems resumed again. I had a very difficult time making any kind of decision, including the most miniscule ones: "Should I make toast or eat the bread plain? Should I put cream cheese on the bread? If yes, how much? Oh, I forgot to make a coffee. How strong and how much should I make?"

It took way longer than usual to finally calm down and eat a meal in peace. My eyes were hurting and dilating sporadically. Throughout the day, I kept moving around and worked on the different projects, but was unable to finish any of them. On many occasions, I couldn't remember what I did a couple hours ago.

I also played with my children quite a lot. Our favorite activity was playing soccer with a large inflatable plastic ball. At certain times, it appeared the ball was moving slower than normal, changing directions in a way considered impossible. It literally felt like being in a video game, some sort of twilight zone. My abilities to kick and throw the ball with both feet and hands improved dramatically.

"I had no idea I was ever this good. What happened to me in the jail? Did my brain somehow get rewired to have this ability?" I thought.

I was even able to play with and juggle two balls simultaneously. I became anxious and didn't say anything to my wife and kids. The kids had a great time and laughed when the tricks were performed. I, however, never performed this in front of Romana, thinking she would give me up in case of ever being placed under a lie detector.

On most evenings, Teresa and Julia both wanted me to read them books, different books to be read at the same time. Having two heads to accommodate the request would have been nice but that never happened. After a ten-minute explanation and back and forth arguing, the girls realized they would have to compromise. They were taught from early childhood to share, respect, and love each other. One day their parents will rest in peace, gone forever except in their memories. They will only have each other to depend on and ask for help.

After Julia and Teresa fell asleep, I departed to my new, much smaller, but cozy bedroom. I had all the time in the world to see some of the DVDs my dad gave me. To watch the endless struggle of Václav Havel was the topic of several different recordings. Throughout his life, he always stood apart from the crowd, tried to solve all the problems the society was facing with love and respect for other people, including the Communist oppressors. In one instance, he helped the secret police agents that followed him twenty-four hours a day to dig out their vehicle that was stuck in a ditch, buried in snow.

Havel explained the situation: "People in the mountains always have to help each other, no matter what. I left the cottage, walked to the car and offered assistance to get them out of the ditch. The three of us were eventually able to get the car back on the road."

I remembered seeing a political campaign billboard with a large heart printed under Havel's initials. During his life, he was ridiculed by many people in Czechoslovakia for using too much love to solve problems. Somehow, he figured out this was the only way to heal the world, to solve all the problems the country and humanity was facing.

"How is this possible? Maybe, early in his life, someone taught him to think logically on his own, to figure things out on his own, to be able to strip away all the endless bullshit filters and to see the world the way it really is, the real world facing self-destruction in the near future." I thought of this as the only logical explanation for his actions.

When watching the documentaries became too much for my brain to handle, I switched to the Schwarzenegger action bundle set and watched *Total Recall* (1990). This movie also perfectly fitted into my current life. Someone was able to erase Doug's (Schwarzenegger) memories and implant a whole new identity into his mind. This fitted the "Reality TV game show" scenario perfectly.

"Is this another clue given to me by the producers, to tell me that I am being correct regarding the game show scenario?"

My mind became confused, tired, and unable to figure anything out. Not to think, to forget and fall asleep was the solution to escape the reality.

On the evening of March 2nd, I finally had a chance to sit down and find out more about Eduard Albert (Billy) Meier, the Swiss man I read about more than twenty years ago. Times have really changed for the better. There was so much information available on the internet, way more information than any single book could handle. Bill is an interesting individual; he lived in many different countries, worked hundreds of different jobs and all his life remained dedicated to his cause, to warn humanity about upcoming dangers. As a young man he accidently lost his left arm, but remained positive and able to overcome life's difficulties.

The next morning, on Friday, March 3rd, I had a meeting scheduled with a person named Fareed to remodel apartments in College Park. I had a suspicion the money would not be great, but drove there anyway since I was just starting the business and needed the work. Also, Fareed was the only person that paid me back in 2007, when most builders stopped paying their sub-contractors. He actually called out of the blue, after we had not spoken for ten years, and informed me about the upcoming project. Fareed reminded me of the last project I did for him; installing trim in a Muslim mosque located on Hank Aaron Drive in downtown Atlanta.

I drove the Mercedes to the meeting and was stopped by a police officer at the gates of the run-down apartment complex on Washington Road.

"What's up with all this security? It looks like I'm entering a military compound," I said to the officer, who smiled and replied, "The complex is partially empty and has to be protected."

Fareed looked different, sort of older than the last time I saw him. He and his friend showed me the building I might potentially renovate. I drove home shortly after.

Coincidently, this was also the day of the long-awaited Snapchat IPO, offered at $17.00 per share. Unfortunately, I couldn't place a "to buy" order the day before since the stock was not yet available to the public. Shortly before 9.30 a.m., I messaged Marcel Peter and asked him about the stock.

The reply was soon received, "I wouldn't touch it unless it was less than $15.00 per share."

I disregarded his opinion and wanted to purchase ten thousand dollars' worth of the stock at $17.50 per share, but was unable to do so even when the market opened. The same reason appeared on my phone screen; the stock is not yet available for trade at secondary markets. I was upset. "What secondary market, this is AMEX, right? Oh, you mean the market for the average people, the small investors."

The stock remained unavailable to ordinary AMEX investors for about two hours and finally went on sale for $22.30 – screw this price. I refused to buy a single share. "What a scam the IPOs are; for the first two hours the stock wasn't available to the general public but only to a selected few entities predetermined to make a killing that day. This is what I call pure capitalism; the rules of the game are made by the rich for the rich to get richer, while the others are forced to sit, wait, and smile while this bullshit is going on right in front of their faces."

I was driving home, analyzed the situation and became tired and irritated the more I thought about it. Lunch tasted great, to fall asleep with a full stomach felt even better.

I woke up and drove to Cumberland Mall, located not too far from the house, to make my appointment with an eye doctor at Visionworks and to pick up a gold bracelet my grandmother gave me in 1998, when I first visited the Czech Republic. I almost lost the bracelet in the early 2000s when it opened and fell from my arm. It has been in a drawer ever since, forgotten, collecting dust. About a week ago, after shopping around for the best price and the type of repair, I dropped off the bracelet at Helzberg Diamonds. At Visionworks, a young, pretty girl in mid-twenties, wearing glasses, took my personal information so the eye exam could begin. The doctor tested both eyes by placing different types of lenses in front of each eye and asking me how I could see. I remembered the enhanced vision experienced multiple times in the past month and became afraid, not knowing how to react.

"Should I really tell her truthfully how I see? If the tests reveal the enhanced vision ability, the NSA will definitely perform medical experiments on my eyes. The Bush administration already sold the idea to the public; it's OK to torture other human beings in the name of national security," I thought, and decided to give the examiner conflicting information.

I was not the best actor and became hesitant at certain times, not knowing what to tell her.

"Don't try to figure this out, just tell me what you see," she said.

I wasn't experiencing any unusual effects at that moment. I changed my mind and reported everything truthfully.

The doctor was happy with the information given and said, "This is how you see normally without glasses when I take all lenses away."

Everything become blurry and I wasn't able to see anything except for flashes of colors and light that made no sense. I kept quiet and continued to play whatever the game might be.

"OK, we are done. Go up to the front and pick your frames and lenses."

"I really need glasses?" I asked, in a sad tone of voice. "Yes, you do," she said.

I felt this was karma; at elementary school, I laughed directly into other children's faces for wearing glasses.

"Jessica, nothing personal, but I probably would have laughed at you as well since at that time I wouldn't have known what else to do with you," I thought, and walked up to the front of the store to pick glasses.

I had a difficult time concentrating and kept going from one type of glasses to the next, not remembering what I had seen and tried. I gave up and asked the same young lady, who was more than happy to help me select the right lenses and frames. The sad faces of many of the children I laughed at kept appearing in front of my eyes. Consequently, the look of the glasses was the most important factor. "How do I look? Do I still look good?" I kept asking the girl these and similar questions over and over after placing a new pair of glasses on my face. After numerous tries, I picked a pair of small, thin blue frames I liked the most.

"You really look good in these," she said.

"You think so?" I said.

"Yes," she said, and smiled, while looking directly into my eyes.

Judging by her facial expression, it appeared she really meant what she had just said and wasn't bullshitting me to make a sale. She recommended non-glassy, polarized HD lenses and I agreed. For the first time in my life, I was covered under vision insurance and only paid $220.96. Without the insurance, the bill would have been $734.00; $614.00 for the glasses and $120.00 for the examination. The original intention was to buy colored contact lenses to cover up dilated eyes.

"At dance clubs, people on drugs would be ecstatic to see one person with two eyes of different color. I would definitely look awesome walking around town wearing colored lenses, like Marilyn Manson."

In my mind I couldn't help but combine his and my appearance. The young lady advised not to buy the colored lenses or any contact lenses for that matter because of eye irritation.

I walked out of the store plenty satisfied and had a couple of missed calls from unfamiliar numbers. I called the first number and Debbie, the Argos HR Manager, said "Hello."

"Hi Debbie, I had a missed call from you," I said.

Debbie immediately spoke in an upset tone of voice. "Joseph, what do you think you're doing!! You're supposed to have no contact with anyone at Argos. It is disturbing!"

My body instantly felt chest and facial pains accompanied by breathing difficulty, knowing very well she'd read the letter intended for Ronnee.

"I am sorry, Debbie," I said, and hung up the phone, unable to continue the conversation.

I quickly walked to Helzberg Diamonds to pick up the bracelet.

"Would you like some water?" asked a smiling young man standing behind the counter, who held a small bottle of water.

It looked like the person was reading my mind, knowing exactly what happened just a few seconds ago. I gratefully accepted the water, calmed down and relaxed within a few minutes. The bracelet was fixed according to my expectations. I left the store and walked to the parking lot.

"Did Jessica at least allow Ronnee to read the letter before running to Debbie?" was my biggest worry. "The package was mailed on Tuesday and most likely arrived today, around 10 a.m. The phone call wasn't received until this afternoon, because both girls read the letter at lunch before contacting Debbie. At least the girls are doing good and nothing bad had happened to Ronnee, unless the intelligence services or the TV directors forced Debbie to lie. I hoped this was not the case, it was impossible for me to find out."

This answer was satisfactory enough and, while sitting in my car, I called the second number.

"Hello, this is Debbie," answered the person at the other end of the line.

"Debbie, I am so sorry, I had another missed call and didn't know this was your number," I said politely.

"Joseph, what is going on?" she asked, in an almost caring tone of voice.

I quickly answered, "Nothing."

"You are not welcome at Argos anymore. If you contact anyone again, I will call the police," she said, but this time sounded calm and reasonable.

"I promise, I will not contact anyone, and thank you for the warning," I said to her in a calm tone of voice.

We said "Bye" and ended the conversation. Luck was on my side that day, Debbie didn't call the cops without speaking with me first. She was a woman who gave me a break that day. I had talked with her on several occasions at Argos. She always smiled and was a good conversationalist.

"This English chick, although a little older, is probably a lot of fun to hang out with," I said to myself, and drove home.

In the evening, I took the family to dine at a nearby restaurant called Sage Social Kitchen and Bar. Upon entering the restaurant, there were beautiful chandeliers hanging from the ceiling, everything was decorated in stylish dark wood and the servers wore black uniforms. The place looked exactly like the Houston's restaurant on Powers Ferry Road. Laughing people at the bar and live music made everything sort of cozy. There was hardly anyone sitting at the tables, we had the restaurant to ourselves. Chicken tenders with tomato/garlic pasta were ordered for the kids, braised lamb for me and a steak for Romana. We had multiple servers taking care of us and everything was excellent. Teresa gave $5 to the guitarist to play and sing Nirvana or a Pearl Jam song. Everyone was happy, especially the kids, who both behaved at their best. Teresa drew a picture of the whole family with several small hearts around it.

"See, Romana, we all love each other. Everything will be fine, just give me some more time, I promise," I said, while pointing at the picture, then called the waiter and ordered a piece of chocolate cake with one scoop of vanilla ice cream.

As we were leaving the restaurant, satisfied, both greeters, two beautiful girls in their early twenties, smiled and said goodbye. Two servers opened the double entrance doors, also smiled and said goodbye. It was almost dark but the street lights and the moon provided enough light. There was an Eighties Cadillac Coupe Deville in showroom condition parked in front of the restaurant.

"Everyone, look, this was my first car Granddad and Mom bought, twenty years ago. I haven't seen this car in a long time and never in such perfect condition," I said.

That evening, I thought more about our dining experience and it wasn't right; everything was too perfect, including Romana, who was happy like nothing ever happened.

On the next day, Saturday, March 4th, Romana was not in a great mood at all.

We had a small argument about the whole situation that had happened in the past three months and she said, "Jonathan told me you and Rob held a prostitute against her will in a hotel in Prague."

I couldn't believe what I just heard and it took a few moments to be able to respond. "Why would he say such a lie? Let me tell you the story. Rob, Gary, and I went to Prague in 2002. I wasn't even in Prague that day, I was in Slovakia with Jitka. This is what Rob told me and Gary is the witness: Rob invited a Bulgarian prostitute to the hotel and refused to pay her unless she swallowed. She did it, got paid and left the hotel. That was the end of it. I told this to Jonathan back in 2002. Why would he twist the story like that? You know what, let's call him right now to clarify everything! This is a bunch of BS," I said, and immediately dialed Jonathan's phone number. He answered the phone and was placed on speaker. "Hi Jonathan, I need to clarify one thing. You told Romana that Rob and I held a hooker against her will in a hotel in Prague. Why would you say that? You know that's not true. Rob told the girl that she wouldn't get paid unless she swallowed. On top of that, I was in Slovakia with Jitka when this happened," I said, in a strong tone of voice.

"I don't remember, it was a long time ago when you told me the story. I don't want to get between you and Romana, goodbye," he said, and hung up the phone.

"Whatever you did, it must have been wrong," Romana said, but she was much calmer and the conversation turned to a different subject.

To get out of the house and forget about the whole situation became the priority. The kids and I went to Meadowgrove Swim and Tennis Club to play tennis. Both kids were eager to learn as much as possible. Teresa became sad when she was unable to direct a ball toward a wooden wall and bounce it back every single time. Julia was very sweet, she eagerly brought back every single ball Teresa and I missed. After a couple hours of playing I wanted to go home, but Teresa did not. She was clearly tired and irritated, but continued to play, not realizing she would feel worse without rest. Julia was on my side and tried to persuade Teresa to leave the courts.

A déjà vu of the classic good and bad kid scenario replayed in my mind and I gave up, left Teresa upset, stubbornly sitting on the court.

"She is seven and needs to learn on her own when it's time to end the fun and go home," I thought, and walked towards a bench right in front of the court to make a phone call.

The phone call was long overdue. I promised my dad to call him upon my return to the US from the overseas trip. We talked for a few minutes, I kept telling him excuses why I was unable to go to a post office and mail him two Fix-it car scratch removers and a copy of a DVD accidentally given to me.

"Don't tell me these excuses. How come you haven't unpacked your suitcase yet?" he said, in a strong tone of voice.

I promised to mail the package asap and the phone call continued normally. The conversation was very strange; how come he knew my suitcase was still unpacked? I returned from the trip over two weeks ago. Also, never in my life had Dad used this direct tone of voice.

Teresa finally came to her senses and we left the courts without any additional drama. At home, I quickly unpacked the suitcase and went to the post office to mail the package.

Not much else happened between March 4 and March 9 2017 except the following. . . I had difficulties concentrating and was unable to finish any of the projects. All the medical issues I had been experiencing since early January kept appearing and disappearing sporadically, without warning. At certain times my thought process was in overdrive mode when trying to figure out which scenario was the new reality. The more I thought about a particular idea, the more real it eventually became. There were "signs" of confirmation that an idea may be correct; if I assured myself of something, I heard an airplane or helicopter or a car every single time. The pattern never changed and I eventually became so afraid that chest/facial pains and difficulty to breath symptoms appeared. To lie down outside on the grass, listen to the birds, look at the trees and the sky stopped the out-of-control thought process and the symptoms eventually disappeared completely, as I was able to relax, close my eyes, and fall asleep at last.

My wife wanted a divorce no matter what. She became totally detached and unfriendly every time I tried to reason with her by telling her how much I loved her and stating everything would be OK. I even asked her what she wanted me to do to make everything better. Nothing worked, except for one thing, but it wasn't the strategy to win her again. Every time I told her to do something, she never said anything back and did it within a short period of time; cooked the perfect meals, grocery shopped, cleaned the house and left the perfect amounts of leftovers sitting on the kitchen counter for me to have a late-night snack. The pattern never changed, it wasn't her anymore and it appeared she was controlled by someone else.

On Monday, March 6th, I drove to the Cobb County Magistrate court to file a lawsuit against Christian, the operator of a Chick-fil-A restaurant. The young lady behind the counter was forthcoming and smiled at me several times. I was very upset as the marketing manager broke her promise and nothing about the fundraising event was ever posted on the store's website. At home, an email stating "Check out Cobb County Magistrate Court for case number 17-J-01542" was sent to several local news media.

On Tuesday, March 7th, I had a nice surprise waiting in my phone. I received a LinkedIn request from an unknown person named Alvin

Panah, a software sales executive from Texas. At the bottom of the profile, the phrase stating "Anything for children….," gave me the second clue.

Jessica had asked Alvin to send the request, indirectly letting me know Ronnee had read the letter. I couldn't believe what I was seeing and read over the phrase several times, assuring myself it was for real. Also on that day, and every Tuesday thereafter, I had a session scheduled with behavioral therapist Patricia Keller. She was understanding and forthcoming about my problems since the first time I saw her in February.

On Thursday, March 9th, I had a tennis match scheduled at Meadowgrove Club with a person named Nasir. My right hand was doing better; to warm it up and use it instead of idling seemed to work the best. Nasir was from India, about my age, married with three children. The game was fun; we took frequent breaks and talked about our lives. Around 9.30 p.m., military planes began to fly above us in the sky, one after another for at least forty-five minutes, landing and departing at the nearby Dobbins Air Force base.

"This is so unusual. Why would the military fly all these airplanes this late at night and this close to a residential zone?" I asked.

"I don't know, but I have never seen so many airplanes in this area," Nasir replied.

I knew exactly what was going on; the NSA was showing its muscles, trying to provoke me to panic and do something stupid, like run away. I therefore continued to play the game as usual, not mentioning the airplanes at all. I was afraid, who wouldn't be in this situation? For all I knew, a helicopter could have landed any minute and taken me away for good.

I kept thinking about the unusual comment made by the arresting officer in January: "So, you met your friends, the aliens from Pleiades, right?"

I must have unconsciously said something about the aliens after the government arrested me. What else would explain this crazy surveillance? I didn't completely rule out being on the Reality TV show either. It could have been a mixture of the NSA and the Reality TV, combined with aliens to make it more interesting. At that point, I was fairly certain the Heaven vs Hell and the Matrix scenarios were not real since this had been dragging on for more than two months.

"God and Satan are not this patient. They would have already made a more direct move by this time. The same goes for the Matrix people. There is no point in dragging this on any longer. I have seen enough and to wake me up in the real world, whatever that world may be, would not pose any psychological problems for my mind any longer." I was thinking this while playing the tennis game.

My mind didn't go into overdrive since I was talking with Nasir, effectively interrupting the thought process. After the game was over, we exchanged phone numbers and agreed to meet sometime for a workout at LA Fitness.

The next evening I had another tennis match scheduled, with a person named Donnie at Arbor Bridge subdivision. It was an unusually cold day to play tennis but both of us didn't want to reschedule again, since we'd already postponed this game several times. During the drive, the car's thermometer displayed 46 degrees, but a few snow flurries fell on the windshield.

"This can't be right! It has to be an error otherwise I am probably hallucinating," I thought, and continued to drive, wanting to forget the situation. The tennis courts were built away from the houses, surrounded by woods on two thirds of the sides. Donnie was an older retired gentleman wearing shorts. I wore gloves, a hat, and jacket in order to play.

"I am getting chills just by looking at you. How can you play in this weather dressed liked this?" I joked with him.

"I am used to this weather," he said.

The bathrooms were locked; going to the nearby woods was the only option to pee. The game started, and I easily won the first few sets, barely moving at all when returning balls.

"To make the game a little interesting, I need to take it easy on this grandpa and let him win a few rounds," I said to myself, and slowed down the game even more.

After the fifth set the game took an unexpected turn; the grandpa started to return balls in such a way that it was almost impossible for my racquet to even touch them. Many times, balls were flying toward me, changing angles while in the air. It appeared someone was manipulating the balls using a remote control. And then Donnie, who was facing away from me, returned the ball over his head while the ball changed angle in midair and landed on my side of the court right next to the net.

"Yeah right!" I said, as I was walking toward Donnie to pick up the ball. "Are you fucking with me, Donnie?" I asked, while standing right next to him, looking at his face.

Donnie didn't respond, he just stood there in silence, avoided eye contact and looked through an empty space with his fully dilated eyes. I quickly picked up the ball and walked away from the net to resume the game, realizing the agents were playing with me to entertain themselves. This had been the case since the beginning of the tennis tournament. The four opponents I'd played so far were agents; each looked totally different, but it was always the same story. No matter what I did, I wasn't able to win. Each game, except for the first, started the same way; I was winning at first but eventually the opponent became way better than me. In the prior games, angles of the returning balls didn't seem right at certain times, but nothing came even close to what I had experienced today. And, out of the blue, it started to snow but only snowed above the tennis court. I looked up several times to the trees hoping to see an agent with a snow gun but wasn't able to find anyone or any stand-alone devices.

"No matter what I do, I cannot win. This will continue to get worse and worse until I am driven to complete insanity," I thought.

I felt helpless, confused, but continued to play, knowing very well there was nothing else I could have done. After the match, we shook hands and exchanged phone numbers. What an incredible relief it was to drive away in one piece.

For the next few days nothing unusual happened except my medical symptoms were appearing and subsiding sporadically without any warnings. The scariest part was hearing the aviation and street noises every time I came up with new ideas or reasoned/confirmed suspicion of the scenarios.

To forget about everything, I paid for a real estate license course and networked with people on Facebook to help me with upcoming construction projects. I texted Aron to find out if he had any extra work. Aron helped me with construction back in 2007 when I first started. I came to know him through my then future brother-in-law, Lucas, who introduced me to the business. Lucas was receiving plenty of work from Aron, but was not paying enough to his employees because he was ready to move back to the Czech Republic. As a result, the work was sloppy and Aron stopped giving him any more business. Lucas eventually married Romana's sister, Ivana, who is a very pretty and classy girl. On one occasion, while visiting the family, I was drinking with her dad in the kitchen, became a little drunk and asked Ivana in front of her parents if she would like to have some fun with me.

I helped my mom to file income taxes and took the Mercedes to John's to fix the air conditioning, coolant leak, and electrical problem that appeared every time the car was parked in direct sunlight, making it impossible to start without pressing the gas pedal. The car was first taken to an upholstery shop right next to John's to fix the loose vinyl roof and torn-up armrest, by adding two new black pieces of vinyl. The original vinyl was tan color, but black interior seemed much nicer. Many people say this car is the last old-school model built by Mercedes. I planned for a while to have the car completely restored and this was the first step of any non-mechanical upgrades. In 2015, the car was upgraded mechanically; a chip, fuel management system, voltage regulator, K&N high performance air filter, two mechanical tornados and electronic turbo to increase horsepower from 217 to almost 300. The car became so much fun to drive that I managed to completely destroy the driveshaft in a matter of weeks. For this 1995 E320 model, Frank was only able to find three used driveshafts in the whole USA; in California, North Carolina and, to my luck, somewhere in the middle of Georgia. He was nice enough to drive to Hicksville where a junkyard attendant gave him an incompatible piece. Luckily, he saved himself a trip since he brought the damaged piece with him.

I finally fixed the sheetrock in the kitchen and upstairs bedroom. One evening, around 7 p.m., Romana came upstairs while I was sanding the wall and screamed, "You are crazy!" because the kids were about to go to sleep shortly. This was unusual, especially after she had to remind me almost daily to complete the projects.

On March 14th, I woke up a few minutes after 6 a.m. not feeling too good. To give up without a fight was not part of my personality, so I ate a small breakfast consisting of the usual: water, coffee with cream, no sugar, two pieces of Tuscan Pane whole-wheat bread with cream cheese/strawberry jam and a wedge of spreadable cheese. After breakfast, I drove to the gym.

On Robinson Road, I met a school bus in the opposite direction and had to stop until the kids were all inside. By this time, I felt nauseous and was seriously considering turning around and driving home. After passing the school bus, I drove for about twenty seconds and turned around, having had enough of the sickness, wanting to go to bed and sleep it off. I was expecting to catch up with the school bus in no time, but the street was completely empty, no signs of children waiting on the side of a curb. Later in the day, I went to DICK'S Sporting Goods store and bought a pink soccer ball for the girls.

On Wednesday, March 15th, I drove to LA Fitness on Roswell Road, feeling much better than the day before. Back and shoulder workout was on the schedule. I started the workout on the back-pulldown machine and for no reason I thought everyone at the gym was an agent. A well-built stranger asked me to spot him on the bench press, the weight was only 185 pounds.

We introduced ourselves. He was an adrenaline junkie who liked to drive a motorcycle at 150mph on Highway 400.

"Come on, Robin, no one does 150mph on a motorcycle, especially not on 400," I said.

"Yes, I have done it a few times and I am also a daredevil," he said.

"Is he trying to drive me insane, for me to react in an unusual way?" I questioned the conversation.

He asked me to connect with him on Facebook. As always, I decided to play the game and agreed. Robin had a photograph of Matterhorn Mountain as his profile picture. After the short conversation, I resumed the workout and noticed a decent-looking middle-aged woman lying on a bench, exercising her chest with free weights. As soon as we began to talk, one of the three guys who were exercising, talking with each other a few feet from us, walked toward me and I had to jump away to avoid physical contact.

"Shit, they really are agents, including the woman," I thought, and resumed the conversation with her like nothing had happened.

The three men walked to a cable pull machine standing about twenty steps away, next to the wall with all the mirrors. When I finished a sentence, one of the men laughed loudly. The pattern didn't change at least five times. It appeared they laughed at me for being such a sucker who jumped at the bait; to talk with the woman who was one of them. The woman was extremely friendly, and I became very anxious, not knowing what to do next. She told me her full name when leaving the club. I was petrified and didn't even bother to remember it. There was this pretty blonde girl, too. We'd briefly talked on prior occasions and I said "Hi." What a relief when she answered in a normal way and the three men were no longer laughing.

"At least this one is not an agent," I thought, and resumed the workout.

I grabbed 40-pound dumbbells to do a few sets of bicep curls.

"This doesn't feel like 40-pound dumbbells at all. I've lifted these weights a million times, it feels like 70-pound dumbbells that I can barely lift. Has someone changed the weights to trick me? Is the whole gym an enclosed military area and is everyone watching me? Is it because I said something about the aliens from Pleiades?"

As this crossed my mind, I turned around and saw a school bus passing by the front door.

"Is the army going to enter the place any moment?"

I'd had enough and wanted to throw the dumbbells into a mirror but changed my mind at the last second.

"I am not going back to jail or the mental institution!" I said to myself and threw the dumbbells on the floor instead, and abruptly left the gym.

I drove past a dollar theater and turned right on E Cobb Drive to enter Roswell Road. While waiting at the intersection, for no reason, a car two spaces in front of me slightly reversed, then the truck in front of me reversed and almost hit my car. Once the light turned green, I floored the Leaf, passed both the truck and the car, crossed the intersection and raced across the parking lot toward DICK'S Sporting Goods store.

"I can't just run away, it would not solve anything," I said, parked the car and entered the sporting goods store to buy an air pump for the soccer ball purchased yesterday. I was unable to concentrate and asked for help to find the air pump. After completing the purchase, I drove to Trader Joe's, located across the street, to buy some groceries and kept thinking about how to find out what was really going on.

Since December 2016, the world around me had been changing faster than I could comprehend. I tried to remember as much as I could about times when everything was normal; the times prior to December 2016. My ex-boss, Sue, once said because of NAFTA, you cannot purchase Canadian wine in the USA. This seemed like the perfect test to find out if I was still in the real world. I asked a store employee if I could purchase some Canadian wine.

"Yes, have this bottle," he answered, and showed me a bottle of wine produced in Napa Valley.

"No, this is not Canadian wine, thank you!" I almost lost it and went outside to sit in my car.

My worst fears became the reality; the world around me was incorporating impossible events into my day-to-day life.

"What will happen next? Is this only going to end once I lose control and start to act crazy?"

The uncertainty of why this was going on or what would happen next was the worst possible feeling at that moment. I just sat in the car and a few silent drops fell out of my eyes.

After a few minutes, I picked myself up and said, "Screw it, I should at least deserve to have a little fun before I die. There has to be a reason for this."

I reaffirmed my earlier promise not to react to anything, no matter how insane the situation might be, not to lose it and just to stay calm and hope everything would eventually return to normal. I drove to the nearest Bank of America to deposit a check, went inside the building and was told to use a paper deposit slip.

"In 2017, we still have to use paper deposit slips?" I asked.

"Yes, it is the bank's policy," the teller said.

I usually made deposits via ATM and hadn't been inside a bank in years, but was sure this was all part of the game to drive me insane. I left the bank, turned right on Roswell Road and drove to Sewell Mill Road, the nearest possible intersection to make a U-turn. The traffic signal ahead of me: two left-turn arrows pointed to a wall, to nowhere. I had never seen anything like this and freaked out again.

"Everything around me is changing fast, like in the Matrix."

To ignore the traffic signal, to floor the car and drive home as fast as possible, was the only thing on my mind. I hoped the scenery wouldn't change too much before reaching the house.

"Will the house still be there?" I asked myself.

During the drive, I didn't find any other abnormalities and safely reached the house.

"What am I going to do? How am I going to prove to everyone I am still OK? The NSA has the house bugged and is watching my every move."

I sat down and thought some more on how to get out of it.

"Fuck it. I deserve to have some fun before I die. I'll jerk off in front of the mirror, right into their camera, to give them a great show."

I went upstairs to the master bedroom and totally undressed in front of a large mirror that was hanging on the wall behind two sinks.

"How do you like that, assholes? Who's the real porn star now?" I thought, while playing with myself. "This better not take too long otherwise they will know something is wrong."

I was no porn star, just an ordinary Joe Blow who naturally had difficulties to finish in situations like these. I closed my eyes and had the following idea.

"I am lying on a bed and have one woman sitting on my face, two other women sitting on the fingers of my right and left hands, and the fourth woman sitting on my dick. The four women are taking turns, going in a circle," and finally, after a few minutes of the virtual orgy, I finished, and came right into the sink, feeling better than ever.

I was able to completely calm down and thought about Ronnee, Christine and Jessica.

"Are the girls OK if this is happening to me? Especially Ronnee, she experienced the same thing as I did during the lunch in December. Mark is giving her way too much work to keep her quiet. The people in the cafeteria are messing with her; talking to her in derogatory and offensive ways to drive her insane. Here are the rules of her game; the less she thinks and speaks about Joseph, the less work Mark gives her and the more the people in the cafeteria leave her alone. The more she thinks and speaks about Joseph, the exact opposite happens. Christine already learned her lesson and is doing fine except for receiving too much work. Jessica, the angel, is in the middle of everything. She strictly stays on neutral grounds and is not leaning to any side. To prevent the three girls from leaving Argos, the NSA is closely monitoring all their communication and is ready to influence any potential new employers."

I had no idea why this came to my mind but knew I had to do something to warn Ronnee. I went on LinkedIn and looked at her picture for a few minutes. Her naturally brown long hair was coming down past her shoulders. She genuinely smiled back at me, looking beautiful and sweet as ever. She looked exactly the same as I remembered her from Argos. I wrote two messages:

Ronnee
When you have a minute or you feel like it. We need to talk. DO NOT believe what you can HEAR. Only believe what you can feel and see. And remember, love is the most powerful force in the Universe. It will guide you through all the BS you are currently experiencing. Do not give up.
Love you and always will
Truly yours
Joseph

I mailed the letter to Jessica about 2 weeks ago. I am not sure if she given you the letter since I did not hear from you. It is 20 page long and has many answers to questions that you currently have. Please let me know if you received the letter.
Your only real friend
Joseph

In a few minutes, I received a call from an unknown number and a woman's voice said, "Why are you doing this?"

"Who is this? I don't recognize the voice," I answered.

"This is Debbie from Argos." I then instantly recognized the voice.

"And Ronnee," said another voice, that again I could not recognize.

I didn't say anything, and she continued to speak. "Don't ever contact me again! We actually felt sorry for you. Joseph, you are disgusting!"

"Thank you for the advice," I answered, and the call ended.

It was very strange to not be able to recognize Ronnee's voice until she said, "We actually felt sorry for you."

Debbie and Ronnee gave me a break by not calling the police. I went on Debbie's Facebook; Ronnee was listed among her friends. She confirmed her feelings for me by asking Debbie to give me a break for one last time. I thought some more about the situation.

"I poured my heart out to Ronnee, described my feelings for her and at the end of the letter stated: 'By the way, my wife and I have been attending swingers' clubs for the past two years and I enjoyed it.' What was I thinking, that she was going to welcome me with open arms? I wanted her to know everything about me, both good and bad. Everybody has a good and bad side; the perfect person doesn't exist. The perfect person is delusion created by the human mind."

The thought of a shower to forget about everything was on my mind. After the quick shower, I changed strategy and indirectly asked for help from anyone who would be willing to listen. This was the last resort to finally figure out what was really going on before it was too late. I wrote the message using Word document software, and basically begged for help:

"So what is real? When and where did it begin? What happened and what is next? I loved and love these three movies: The Truman Show, The Matrix, *and* Total Recall. *All three have one thing in common. A person loses touch with reality. At this point I don't even know when and where I am. Am I on Earth or a different planet or perhaps in a different time or in different dimension? Am I a secret agent whose mind/memory was changed so he could not save Mars, like in* Total Recall? *Does the Earth even exist as we know it? Were we able to solve global warming, overpopulation and resource scarcity? Maybe I only exist in the Matrix as some sort of digital memory waiting to be reincarnated. Does everyone remember* The Truman Show *with Jim Carrey? Maybe this is all just a reality show that started on 06/30/1978. So what is real? How do you define real? Reality is merely a set of electrical impulses. When different realities and different dimensions collide, the electrical impulses/memories combine to an equilibrium. Therefore, a different reality from the known past is created.*
All I know at this point is that I kind of liked my life from 06/30/1978 until sometime in mid-December 2016. Then I got really sick at work. I started to hallucinate in front the computer monitor. At certain times, I did not know what information on a spreadsheet was real and what was fake. I saw things that did not seem to be normal. For example, a ladybug flew past me several times. I had to run outside to clear my head and refocus. Then I cussed out a few people and was fired the next day. At this point, as of 03/15/2017, I really need my life back. I don't know what is going on anymore. It appears the reality is changing by each passing day.
So tell me, you the all mighty one. What is going to happen next because I don't want to be kept in suspense? Donald kept the whole country in suspense until the election. I need, or would like, my life back. I want the reality back that I knew from 06/30/1978 to 12/15/2016. So please, let me have it back if you can. If you cannot, I understand. If that is the case, at least let me have some FUN before I end up dead or in a mental institution. NO MATTER WHAT I DO, I CANNOT WIN. My wife will eventually send me to the mental hospital or I will end up dissected in some government laboratory like Area 51. I could also be part human and part some sort of alien being. How do you know what is real and

*what isn't? Maybe one day, someone who loves me will discover my
writings so I can finally be free.
So again, with a pretty smile on my face. Please let me have my REAL
life back. :-) Thank you and have a good night!"*

After finishing the letter, I just sat in the office chair and stared at
the screen for at least thirty minutes, hardly moving at all. Keeping busy
and your mind occupied usually solves many temporary problems. I
drove to Microcenter and bought a new monitor. At home, I cleaned the
office and reconnected a docking station. I didn't want to give up on
Ronnee that easily, so I created a phantom person named Jeffry Bagley;
real-life attorney, member of Forsyth County Bar Association, listed
right above Ronnee.

"Maybe I should be more straightforward with her besides sending
her indirect letters and messages. I'll just pretend I am writing a book. It
will surely justify why I contacted her in the past," I thought, and hoped
the following email, sent from Jeff's Gmail around 3.30 p.m., would
convince her Joseph is not disgusting and to give him a call.

*Ms. Pedersen,
The secret is out. I am writing a novel. It is a science fiction/reality,
autobiography, suspense and of course a love story. Nobody has done
anything close to this. I finally found a niche in the market. Hopefully, I
will become rich and famous like my favorite actors.
I was going to give all three of you royalties from the book and perhaps
from a movie.
I was hoping to get all three of you on board without your knowledge. I
need inspiration because I am no Shakespeare.
Can you keep this a secret and help me with it? I will give you % of net
earnings. I will even sign a contract in front of any attorney! How ironic,
isn't it?
Task number 1: Check out Cobb County Magistrate Court for Civil
Action# 17-J-01542. It is a great case but there is no money in it,
therefore, no attorney will take it. I do not want you to be my attorney. I
am looking for a friendly person in the media. You are going to like it.
That is a promise.
If you are interested, I can email you a part of the final chapter.
This is my last attempt to contact you. So, am I a lunatic or a brilliant
writer? A coin always has two sides. It is all up to you.

Regards,
Mr. Bagley*

Chapter 10
There Can be Only One Scenario

That evening, while putting the kids to bed, the classic good and bad kid scenario happened again. As usual, the pattern did not change. It was a rainy and stormy night and lightning struck a pine tree on top of a hill above my neighbor's house. It was a very loud bang, almost like a cannon shot, and the tree fell to the ground. We ran downstairs. I opened the door to our backyard, made the first step outside and a strong beam of light hit my face. The light came from a lamp mounted on the neighbor's house, where the tree had fallen. It was dark, rained hard and we were not able to see anything but tree shadows on top of the hill.

After returning to the bedroom, the kids calmed down and went to play with their toys that were scattered all over the floor. I lay on a bed, looked at the ceiling and started to think at a faster and faster rate.

"What a coincidence, a tree fell due to lightning and I was hit by a beam of light as soon as I made one step outside of the house. The NSA can control the flow of electric current in my house and neighbors' houses, but they cannot control the weather like this. They don't yet have the technology to bring down a tree with lightning, at least I hope not. Who can do this? The Matrix people or Heaven vs Hell? No, wait, I already ruled out those scenarios."

I continued to think and remembered seeing a Science Channel documentary few years ago. The host of the program is my favorite scientist, Michio Kaku, who explained that evolutionary stages of a civilization are best described by how much energy a civilization is able to control at various levels of development. He said the following:

Is our civilization able to control fire? – Yes.
Are we able to control energy of cities? – Yes.
Are we able to control energy of continents? – Yes, through the power grid, to a certain degree.
Are we able to control the weather; the energy of the whole planet? – No.
Are we able to control the energy of our Sun, our Solar System, or the Milky Way galaxy? – No, we are just now entering the stage of our development when for the first time in the history of mankind we are able to indirectly influence the weather of the whole planet via our uncontrolled emissions of greenhouse gases.

"The intelligence agencies and the government in general are experts in wasting taxpayers' dollars. There are only so many tens of millions of dollars the NSA is willing to spend on my surveillance and to entertain themselves. What about the Reality TV show, is it real? Probably not. Except for my health symptoms and several unusual real-life events, I still live a fairly normal life. Yes, my surroundings are changing in a weird way, but knowing Hollywood, something more drastic would have already happened. It has to be the aliens from Pleiades, but why? Why would I be contacted in such a way? Why would my life be turned completely upside down? There has to be a reason. Maybe I am being given an important message. Yes, this is it! The rain, the lightning, the flood, maybe the world will end by flood. No, it's too extreme. If this was the case I would not have been contacted. It has to be some sort of warning."

As soon as I finished thinking of the last sentence, Teresa came by with a children's book at least fifty pages thick. She coincidently opened the book to somewhere in the middle and pointed to a paragraph and asked me to read it.

"After the earthquake ended and the floods subsided, the whole family came out of the underground hiding to rebuild their garden. . ." I was unable to read any further and told Teresa to continue to play with her sister. I began to experience facial pains: slight eye pains and pressure going from my forehead to both cheeks. The following thought entered my mind:

"In the near future, waves of underground earthquakes will engulf the entire Earth. The earthquakes will create massive tsunami waves, flooding the coastlines around the world, killing everyone in its path."

I thought of one of my favorite movies, *The Terminator* (1984), where the idea of judgment day was presented to viewers over and over again. My thought process continued to accelerate: "The planet is dying and everything on it will die with it. We, the humans, and every living organism need help at this moment. The Earth will fight back and provide us with much-needed assistance before our civilization completely self-destructs. The occurrence of earthquakes and tsunamis will stun the survivors, take them out of their everyday routine to rethink their lives. OK, but how many people will actually die?"

I used my phone to access the internet and the answer was two clicks away; 40% of the world's population lives within 100 miles of coastlines.

"Three billion people will perish in a matter of hours; that's the true judgment day."

I became afraid and didn't know what to think or what to do next. I realized this couldn't be mentioned to anybody. No one would believe me anyway and I would eventually end up back where I was: Cobb County jail or the mental section of Kennestone Hospital.

I kept thinking about the situation and came up with additional ideas: "They are on the Moon, the directors are on the Moon, just like the directors in *The Truman Show* movie. Once the time is right, the friends will provide warnings to leave for safety. I will only be able to tell a few people, excluding my wife. This is not happening. Why can't I bring my wife with me?" I lay there in disbelief, realizing I would have to choose between Ronnee and Romana.

I didn't want to think about it anymore but was unable to stop the thought process.

"Knock on the master bedroom and ask Romana for toothpaste. Don't look at her or go inside, just insert your hand past the door. She will hand you the toothpaste without looking at you and will close the door without saying anything. This is the symbol of letting her go for the rest of your life."

Everything at that point seemed so real, with so much circumstantial evidence. The exact situation I had thought of a few minutes ago happened for real. I was holding the toothpaste and Romana closed the door without looking at me or saying good night. After the kids fell asleep, I went to my room and figured out one important aspect: "At least the survivors will have the chance to make things right and one day save the planet. This is the only way because people don't listen and don't change their habits until it's too late or a catastrophe strikes."

After this realization, I had no problems falling asleep with the idea of judgment day on my mind.

In the morning, I went to the gym and met Nasir for a leg workout. He was a doctor and I wasn't sure if he was an agent or not. The workout was normal except the weights felt way different than normal; either too heavy or too light. Just before lunch, I drove to Visionworks to pick up the prescription glasses. I stopped at the Apple store and asked if some of the speakers would be compatible with Android phones. The store employee was friendly, helpful, and answered every single question, regardless of subject. This didn't seem right so I kept asking more questions and he kept answering them and ignored everybody else around him. The pattern never changed and I wasted more than twenty minutes of his time before leaving the store to pick up the glasses.

The Visionworks store was busy and I was told to sit down and wait for the next available representative. Almost ten minutes later, I'd had enough, so interrupted a conversation a store employee was having with another customer and was promised he would be right with me. A minute later, he asked for my name and brought the glasses over and looked for something on a computer screen. While holding the glasses, his hand was slightly shaking.

"Try them on and let me know what you think," he said.

I placed the glasses on my face and everything was blurry, so I took them off right away. I knew my new friends had something to do with it, there was a reason for this, a reason unknown to me.

"They are great. Thank you," I said.

We said goodbye to each other and I walked away without any receipt. ID was not necessary or asked for to pick up the glasses.

While walking the corridors of Cumberland Mall, I placed the glasses on my face. The colors were instantly brighter, everything was sharper, and I was able to see further away than ever before. Individual skin pores were visible on every passing person. There were pleasant and unpleasant side effects; younger women looked younger and way more beautiful. The older women looked way older and less beautiful.

"This could be a graduation present given to me by my new Friends. (Let's call them Friends with capital F, going forward.) The responsibility of enhancing vision at will was given to me. That's great, I need to go to an ear doctor asap. Maybe I will be able to hear farther away than previously possible," were my thoughts as I was walking towards the car.

I had such extreme vision enhancement that my visual perception of surrounding spaces changed dramatically. I almost crashed into another vehicle while still in the parking lot. I quickly took off the glasses and didn't put them on until I reached Mom's house.

The vision experiment continued. At my mom's, I went outside and focused on faraway trees. Within a few seconds, I was able to see the treetops closer and sharper.

"Incredible, I have zoom ability as well," I said to myself, and immediately looked at a pool fence, which was the nearest object to my body. The fence was blurry and my eyes started to hurt, but within a few seconds I was able to refocus my eyes to see way more detail than ever before. I was excited and quickly fell in love with my new toy; a sort of a telescope and microscope combined. After entering the house, Mom suggested not to wear the glasses too often. I was plenty satisfied and took the glasses off, but felt nauseous and the facial pains appeared.

"Mom, thanks for the lunch but I have to go home," I said. I left the house and put the glasses back on. "Great, I am able to drive the car and see like a hawk at the same time. Why was I given this gift? Shall I do something good with it?" I was questioning the logic behind this device.

At home, I went straight to bed and my thought process accelerated as I closed my eyes and placed a pillow over my head. "I hope the Chick-fil-A people didn't hire a hitman to get rid of me. The corporation is known for its hate of LGBT and probably everyone else who thinks differently. I once applied for an indirect tax position with their corporate office and was asked invasive personal questions that had nothing to do with the position. The questions, answered in essay format, were nothing more than screening for true believers who would never break the code of silence, once employed. No, wait, this is not Russia. In the US, companies don't hire hitmen to get rid of people."

My thoughts switched to a different subject.

"Every time I started to feel bad, the only thing that ever worked was to lie down and fall asleep. What happened in jail when someone touched my shoulder? Did I die for a few seconds? To reset my brain, maybe I had to die. This would explain the accelerated thought processes and the reason behind the frequent naps."

While having these thoughts, I was breathing slowly, not moving at all. I felt tingling over my body; one organ after another. It began with face, chest, stomach, and lastly heart. It appeared the frequent naps were necessary for my mind to absorb all the data sporadically uploaded into my brain. This, I hoped, was the final data upload; to take my body out of the wireless life support I'd been on since January and return the ability to control life functions back to my brain.

In the evening, the kids wanted me to read a book before their bed time. Later, I was holding their hands while both were falling asleep and loud noise from a bird was heard at close distance. The noise woke the kids, who ran toward the window. The sound continued for about fifteen minutes while we were looking outside, to the darkness. What a shame this happened at night, the owl was nowhere to be seen.

On Friday, March 17th, the idea to influence a stock by spreading false news seemed like a great idea.

"Everybody is doing this, including the financial analysts. The internet is full of fake news these days."

I had long-term investments in eMagin Corporation – leading manufacturer of high-end OLED microdisplays. I posted the following message with a picture of Gordon Gekko smoking a cigar on Facebook and LinkedIn:

Hello Kids. Are you tired of watching HD fairy tales on 5-inch screen? Me too!! Apple Corp (AAPL) is about to introduce new VR headset using eMagin's (EMAN) microdisplays to solve all your technical difficulties. They always use the best of the best. Legally, this is not an insider's information so don't quote me on this! :-)

I called my friend Gary, who invested every single dollar to buy eMagin shares, and informed him the stock is about to take off.

"Something has to happen soon because the consumer market for VR headsets is taking off. Nobody has better displays than them," Gary said. "I just invested all my cash and 401k money into eMagin," I said, and he jumped in, "I support that move 100%."

"You are not going to believe what my brother-in-law told Romana about me and Rob."

I told him how Jonathan twisted the story about the Bulgarian prostitute in Prague. We talked more about the 2002 trip and couldn't believe it had been fifteen years already.

"Remember the girl at Karlovy Lázně dance club?" I said, and we both laughed.

"Of course I do. She came to me, didn't speak any English so you had to translate. We danced for a while and she came to you again."

"To translate," I said, and continued, "the girl said you would not be charged for time spent dancing but you have to leave with her right now because her girlfriend found a customer. I told you this and you exploded in laughter right in the middle of the club."

Gary continued, "Ha, ha, ha, she was a gypsy hooker. Do you remember we almost got pickpocketed by another group of gypsy hookers while walking at the main square? I saw her arm reaching for my back pocket so I pushed her away."

"Yes, and when I started speaking Czech, they got scared and ran away. This was one of the craziest trips ever. You know what was funny? Rob was going for the quantity and not quality. Back in those days, you were able to get a beautiful college girl for about $80. Rob was buying the ones on the street, paying no more than $30. I never forget how he fucked one girl in the middle of a street, on the marketplace table. I had to direct traffic; told people to keep walking, that there was nothing interesting going on. This one guy exited the apartment building facing Rob and the girl, walked right by them without saying a word. He must have been used to seeing these types of scenes in front of his house. The Nineties was an even crazier period than the 2000s. I saw a couple screwing at a subway station, on moving stairs. I experienced something similar on Halloween night in Las Vegas," I said, while Gary laughed again.

"You know, Joseph, Rob has issues. I don't know anybody else who would fight with Pierce Brosnan and Chris Brown's bodyguards. This happened during the time he was paparazzi. His agency's name was Ability Films," he said.

I continued to talk. "To fight 007 is the coolest thing on this planet. I always loved that name, Ability Films. That's the perfect name for a porn company, ha, ha, ha. He was in one real movie, remember the C-rated horror flick called *Chop Shop* (2003), filmed in Atlanta? Rob played the mechanic, and chiropractor Mark also had a small role. I really like 'Rob Rose,' his stage name."

We talked for a little longer regarding my arrest and hospitalization, then ended the call.

I thought of one more story about me and Rob: in the early 2000s, during one of our Las Vegas trips, Rob and I went to MGM Grand's Studio 54 dance club to look for girls. There was this young beautiful Asian girl who was all over us. We were both suspicious because she was too good to be true. Usually if something seems too good to be true, it is. Sure enough, we were told of her small, not too girlish abnormality down there.

"If you kiss her/him I will as well," Rob said, and laughed.

I had a few drinks in me, didn't want to chicken out and so kissed the he/she girl. Rob did as well.

"Why don't we play somewhere more private?" she said, and smiled at both of us.

I looked at her more closely and wanted to find something on her body that would resemble a man. I carefully examined her face, neck, torso, breasts, arms, fingers, ass, and legs. To my disappointment, I was unable to find a single male feature on her body, the excuse needed not to proceed any further. To my eyes and brain, she was a young, beautiful, petite Asian girl with cute ass, sweet feminine voice and long hair. I had no choice but to give up, since a mouth is a mouth.

"Look, you can blow me but there is nothing I can do for you. Please keep your clothes on. I am straight as can be," I said.

We took her to our hotel room and had fun with the prearranged sets of rules.

The next morning, while eating breakfast, Rob and I agreed not to do anything like that again.

"I am not doing anything unless we can find normal girls. It's disgusting, and I don't want to think about it anymore," I said, and at the same time was amused by the experience.

"I agree, let's call he/she 'it' next time we have this conversation," Rob said, and continued to eat his breakfast, consisting of a fully loaded omelet.

"And no more Coco and Honey either!" I said, about two Asian girls who gave me and Rob a massage a couple days ago while still in Los Angeles.

That evening, we went to Studio 54 again and Rob told the whole story to his friend, a beefed-up bouncer who worked at the club.

He laughed loudly and said to me, "Don't worry about it, this is Vegas. As a last resort, we sometimes do this as well. Think of this as an emergency release valve."

A heavy boulder fell from my shoulders; what a relief to not be the only straight man having this experience.

On Saturday, March 18th, the kids and I went for a one-day trip to Lake Allatoona. The RV, tent, and everything needed at the camp was available since Mom and Milan had come the day before. The weather was cool, windy, and I stayed in the RV most of the time. Much had happened this year and there was no record of it. Excel and OneNote were chosen as the tools to start organizing. I kept the glasses on while writing down the events and noticed I was not able to concentrate on the writings. I continued to look at the screen and thought about the movie, *Aliens* (1986). I looked up the company Weyland-Yutani, created a new Twitter account and connected with the company at *www.weylandindustries.com*.

I researched the website more closely; there were details about future space equipment and biohazard agents.

"What if the reality show is still continuing as the game between good and bad Friends? They have the ability to influence all electronic equipment and the behavior of every single person, including myself. The rules of the game: the bad Friends made my job loss, arrest, hospitalization, the seizures, and bad health the new reality. The good Friends were allowed to help me just enough to survive each ordeal. At the end, I realized what was happening and the glasses were given to me as a graduation present. Now it is all up to me; to help save the planet or eventually destroy the planet. I just fucked up and sided with the wrong Friends by creating and connecting the Twitter account with Weyland-Yutani. The bad Friends will start passing real scientific data regarding space technology and biohazard agents to scientists around the world. This will, in fact, speed up Earth's self-destruction process. To reverse the process, I need to cancel the Twitter account immediately."

I made the decision but unfortunately, Twitter accounts cannot be closed using a cell phone. I ran to the nearest camping neighbor and asked if it was possible to connect my laptop to their internet for a few minutes.

"Sorry, but we have limited data," the woman replied.

I thanked her and left the campsite.

"What should I do next? Should I drive home? No, there will not be enough time to reverse it. What about using the wireless hot spot in my phone."

I had never used this feature but couldn't believe it didn't cross my mind earlier, instead of running around asking people for help. I deactivated the account but wasn't sure if this would fully reverse the future scenario.

"There is nothing I can do about this except for being more careful next time, before I do something without thinking."

The sounds of trains, boats, and treetops moving due to strong winds were the only events sound-wise (except conversation), I was able to remember from the whole day. The sounds were accompanied by facial numbness, tingling, and sporadic eye pain. Upon this realization, I ran to the small bathroom in the RV and my eyes were completely dilated. I took the glasses off and the facial pains gradually went away. Showering would definitely help to get over everything that happened.

I walked to the nearest public bathroom. I closed the door, sat on a toilet and thought about the situation again. Being in a small quiet room surrounded by windowless concrete walls felt like being back in jail. I started to get nauseous and unable to catch a breath.

"What if I am unable to unlock the door and get out? I might be stuck here for eternity, unable to escape the prison of my mind while the body is lying somewhere in a hospital."

My thought process was spiraling out of control, with only negative ideas. At the last minute, I managed to pull myself together and unlocked the door using the last amount of strength left in my body and walked out of the bathroom, hearing a loud noise of a train passing at the other side of the lake.

This was the longest trip driven using the Nissan Leaf since the hospitalization.

While living in Florida in the Nineties, my granddad, who was an engineer, showed me many of his inventions such as a regular-size watch able to shoot two bullets or plans for a fighter jet with circular wings connected above the airplane; the jet that would not stall. He was obsessed with electromagnetic radiation; he measured the fields of household items like a dishwasher, dryer and told everyone how unhealthy is to stand next to the appliances while they were being used. Maybe the Nissan had something to do with the medical problems I was experiencing since December. Companies generally cut corners to maximize profits. The Leaf may not have been properly shielded to prevent it from emitting electromagnetic radiation to the cabin. As long as it is difficult to prove in a court of law, most companies don't care at all if their products cause negative short- or long-term health effects on their customers.

The highest priority for Sunday, March 19th was to finish writing the letter to Leah. Her fiftieth birthday was approaching fast. I wanted to let her know she was present in my mind and heart. I tested the glasses some more and noticed they were perfect for reading and writing. My thought process was accelerating faster, the longer I wore the glasses. As long as I was able to focus only on one idea, everything was fine and I was able to keep the thought process from spiraling out of control. It was a pleasant side effect and much-needed boost to come up with many ideas for the letter. I planned to send her flowers and attach the letter, therefore changed some names to protect Leah in case the letter should fall into the wrong hands.

To save time, Version 1 of the letter to Leah was copied from the letter to Ronnee. The plan was for her to call me, to have a cup of coffee with me. I made up a story about writing a book.

Hello Leah,
At certain times of my life I've met a woman. On several occasions, her eyes were looking directly into mine, not in an intrusive way. I met her stare and fully consented. I undressed her using only my eyes. I liked it. In fact, I was loving every second of it. She slightly smiled as her delicate gaze penetrated mine, and the eyes played their silent tunes consisting of heat, excitement, lust, and curiosity. I was breathless, completely paralyzed, unable to move an inch as we were seeing into each other's souls. Our thought process was synchronized and enormous amounts of information was exchanged. We were having eye sex. Right there in her office.
Leah, I have feelings that you might have experienced something like this. I know you love to flirt ;-) The weekend and several months after March 18th, 2016 were not easy. I lost the best job I ever had and the woman I loved on the same day. I am not going to go into any details, use your imagination. I gave it some thought if I should ever contact you again. The answer is 'yes', however, don't worry since this is my last attempt to contact you. I was going (still going) through internal struggles on the scope of the letter. I have two versions of the letter. Both are true but they are so different. It is up to you which version you like.

Version 1 (a rewrite of Ronnee's letter)
In late summer of 2014, I received two simultaneous offers through a local placement agency specializing in finance. I chose to work for a company called Imagin (medium size medical manufacturer). I was hired by a very attractive lady named Leah. She was in her late forties, had been married for twenty years and had two daughters. I am not sure about the marriage. Her husband never took her on vacation without her in-laws. I started to like her at the initial interview. There was longer than normal eye contact between us on several occasions. It did not feel like an interview at all. It felt like a nice conversation with a sweet lady.
I remember my first day at the office like it was yesterday; I was waiting in front of the finance section of the building. And there she was, opening the glass front door, wearing a certain dress. She looked absolutely stunning. The dress was not long, but not too short, either. She knew exactly what she could get away with. In my mind, it was a

welcome party exceeding my wildest expectations. At first, I tried not to get distracted too much. She was still my boss and I wanted to do my duties as best I could. I had to learn the processes as fast as possible since the temporary person was leaving soon. Therefore, I kept to myself and focused on the work. Leah approached me and wanted to flirt on many occasions. I liked it, I liked it so much that I was unable to react the way she would have expected me to. I mostly kept silent. I'd never experienced flirting in my life (way different from when you are fifteen years old), it was so new to me. It was gorgeous, electrifying, and indescribable feeling.

On a daily basis, she smiled at me, was relaxed and made me feel great about myself. She eventually stopped the verbal flirting. We never discussed job performance. It was always understood that I would do my part. She did not have to supervise me. In her office, I really enjoyed us having prolonged eye contact accompanied by silence. It was perfect since she kept the window blinds mostly closed. On one occasion, I was sitting there across her desk. I started to undress her using my eyes only. I moved very slowly from her waist until our eyes met. I had a feeling that being any closer, something magical would have happened between us. I've always felt there is a deeper connection once you look through the eyes of a person. This was the longest eye contact I had experienced to that day. It felt so good until I was unable to take it any longer. I was the first to move my head. She did the same and smiled a little in a very satisfied way. This only happened one time.

In May, a few weeks before my vacation, I asked Leah to have lunch with me. Oddly, the two of us had never had lunch alone. Her face froze and eyes widened. "I can't today," she replied in a surprised way. "Let me know of a good time," I said to her in a non-caring way. She never brought it up again.

I returned from the European vacation in early June 2015 and wanted to see Leah to tell her about my trip. I missed her since we hadn't talked for almost two weeks. As soon as I entered her office, I noticed the pictures of her daughters were no longer there. "Hi Joseph, how was your trip? My last day at Imagin is in two weeks, sorry," she said, without any kind of emotion.

All of a sudden, I felt a huge weight on my shoulders, I could hardly keep my eyes focused. The world collapsed around me. I thought I was in a twilight zone. Of course, I pulled myself together fairly quickly, then asked her a few questions, wished her good luck and left the office. I knew in the back of my mind this might happen someday. "Why so soon, why this soon? She promised a few weeks ago to teach me corporate income tax," I thought to myself. In those two weeks, I had difficulty concentrating and completing everyday work-related tasks. At home, my mind was somewhere else until my wife and aunt, who was visiting from the EU, asked me what was wrong. I kept waking up several times a night. During this period, I realized that I fell in love with Leah a long time ago. My mind was in a great dilemma; should I tell her how I feel about her or should I continue to maintain our professional relationship? I chose to maintain the current relationship and asked her the next day, "Leah, I would like to work for you again. Once you settle in, please let me know if there is an open position on your team." She smiled a little and explained the circumstances of her new company, Weyland. Due to the corporate headquarter relocation from Michigan to Atlanta, a brand-new tax team was currently being built. "Director of Federal Tax and Audit" was her new title. She was a manager in her present position. She had already hired her tax manager, Cody. "He is great," she said, and smiled again.

In early July 2015, about a week into her new job, I received an email from Leah asking me if I would like to interview at Weyland and work for her again. I could not believe this and read the email several times. The answer was, "Yes."

On the day of the initial interview, Leah greeted me at the lobby reception area. I had not seen her for several months prior to this moment. Our eyes met at full stare for a few seconds at close distance of about a foot. We did not blink at all. It was hot, lustful, and exciting. We were so in tune with each other. "Was this the interview?" I thought to myself. The interview process was a joke. Everyone was really friendly and I was not asked any technical questions. It didn't feel like an interview at all. Everyone knew that I wasn't qualified for the position. Corporate income tax is way different from sales/use and property tax.

My first day at Weyland was on October 19 2015. I was hired as a tax specialist and had an exciting career ahead of me. My mentor/teacher was the person I was in love with. "Perfect, nothing can go wrong." Those and similar thoughts were constantly racing in my head. I was really excited, but nervous at the same time. I was looking forward to having a nice conversation with Leah. Oh, it was so long since the two of us had spoken in private. I had a brilliant plan; I was going to thank her for hiring me and offer to buy her a lunch. We were finally going to have a private moment together, away from the office. I was so sure the answer would be "yes" since she indirectly already promised me shortly before departing Imagin.

All this went to shit; during our conversation in her office, she wanted to flirt verbally. Again, my responses were "the silence." After several attempts, she was irritated and gave up. I proceeded with my plan and asked the question. She gave me the "What the fuck are you thinking?" look and I left her office shortly after, disappointed and embarrassed. "I failed my teacher again. She was probably looking forward to finally flirting with me verbally. What a disappointment. I fucked up so badly. Why was I so preoccupied with that stupid lunch?" These were my confused thoughts. From that point on, we hardly ever spoke.

Manager Cody was in Leah's office daily. They spoke for hours and had a great time. Unfortunately for me, my cubicle was close by and I was forced to listen to the conversations. I was not jealous of Cody. He was a great person with an amazing personality. I was more disappointed in Leah; she was the director and able to set her own rules. To this day, I can't figure out how she was able to get me the job. It was a great job and I was not qualified at all. She knew that I enjoyed talking with her. She never invited me to come to her office and talk for at least a few minutes on some sort of regular basis. I understood that I was not working for her directly and things were not going to be the same as before.

I was four levels below her and of course was not able to "hang out" in her office. The VPs, other directors and managers surrounded her office. At Imagin, it had just been the two of us. I missed that setting so much.

The position involved substantial travel to Michigan until March 2016, the deadline for legacy to current tax team transition. I felt bad for the Michigan team, especially after I met everyone in person, because they were all losing their jobs. This was due to the following reason. Also, here is some background info on the company.

Bill Weyland founded the company from nothing in the 1950s. He built the first Weyland house and sold it for $10,000. The company grew to become the third largest residential builder in the USA with over $6 billion annual revenue in 2015. Bill always placed strong emphasis on his employees. It was not unusual for someone to work at the company for thirty years. Weyland was always a Michigan company, a great company to work for. It answered the "American Dream" question for many people. Bill retired from active operations in 2010. A couple years after his retirement, Peter Douglas, CEO since 2003, announced behind Bill's back the company would be moving to Atlanta. He made the announcement in the Michigan office, in front of all the corporate employees. It was a short announcement and he and his security guard left abruptly. According to rumors, Peter wanted to live in Atlanta to pursue a career in politics. Some of the employees were offered jobs in Atlanta. Why would anyone want to move? Especially if all their relatives lived close by. None of the eighteen tax department employees, including the VP, accepted offers. After the facts became known to me, I wanted this guy to disappear from Weyland as fast as possible. It appeared Peter did not care about his Michigan employees. They were just numbers to him. He cared about himself and apparently only loved himself. In Atlanta, he hired a custom builder and not Weyland to build his mansion. That is like Ford's CEO driving a Ferrari to work. It was an insult to everyone at Weyland. It makes me sick. In my opinion, Peter was the worst of the worst.

By January 2016, everyone in Atlanta was hired. The group was getting along really well. Everyone had great personality, an unusual feature for a tax accountant. The last trip to Michigan was in January 2016. This was the best trip to date. Apart from work, it looked like Leah and I would finally open up to each other again. Flirting aside, it was necessary so we would be able to work together going forward. About eight of us went to a karaoke bar. Leah tried to verbally flirt with me for the last time. I blew it again. She spent the rest of the evening around Cody. I played pool with a manager named Ricardo. The next day, an even smaller group went skiing. Leah and I finally spoke in a friendly and relaxed way on ski lifts and in the cafeteria. This was the best day at Weyland so far.

The first day after we returned from Michigan, I went to see Leah in her office. "Can you please consider mentoring me? I know we talked about it before," was the initial question.

"Yes, like I will everyone else. You need to get with the managers and do a good job if you want to score some points with me," she replied. We had never had a performance-related discussion before. This threw me off but I kept pushing my luck.

"We had a great relationship at Imagin and I miss it."

She smiled to herself and said, "So you're not getting it, right?" I could not believe my ears. We talked about a few more things and I left her office.

At that point I realized she may have actually enjoyed having me around. She knew I needed her and couldn't do anything about it. Every day at that office was emotional torture. She had to know I heard most of her conversations. There is only so much a person can take. Everyone has a breaking point. "Maybe if I tell her how I feel about her, she would figure out a way of not hurting me anymore," I said to myself many times.

On Wednesday, January 23 2016, first thing in the morning, I remember the conversation word by word, like it happened yesterday: "Leah, I need a few minutes of your time."

"OK," she said. I closed the door and we sat down.

"I started to have feelings for you in January, a year ago."

"Really, you did?" was her initial response as she smiled a little.

"Yes, I did, and I was hiding those feelings as much as I could. You are married, I am married, that sort of thing. Then you left and just the thought that I would not be able to see you and talk to you was overwhelming. I actually thought more about you than the job. What a mistake! When you hired me for the second time, I was not able to handle the situation and look what happened. I am not sure when was the last time this happened to you, but you can't even think clearly. The last time it happened to me was with Romana, ten years ago, and I ended up marrying her. With you, it was never about promotions, scoring points, and money."

"Well, thank you for telling me this. I have to think about what to do next," she said, as her body began to shake a little bit. Leah then reached into her drawer, took and opened a bottle of pills and shoved the bottle into her mouth. She then ran outside, probably to a restroom.

Not knowing what to do, I went to my desk. In a few minutes, I realized I had said a little too much. I wanted to see if she was OK and went back to her office. She was resting her head on a desk so I was unable to see her face. "Please don't do anything. I'll get together with the managers and stay out of your way as much as possible. I am over this," I said. She then slowly raised her head up and down in agreement and was crying silently. I tried to keep cool as much as possible and continued with daily tasks. I periodically glanced into her office to make sure she was not overdosing on those pills. I hoped she didn't swallow any.

The next morning, the VP of tax, Karen, called me into her office. She calmly and in almost a friendly way, asked about the incident. I truthfully explained the situation with as little detail as possible about the feelings I had for Leah when she left Imagin.

"But you don't have those feelings for her anymore, right?" Karen asked.

"That is correct, I don't," I replied.

"Good, because she does not have those feelings for you and even if she did, you would both be fired. She can't manage you anymore. Ricardo will be your new manager, effective immediately. Nobody will know the details and we will move forward."

I could not believe that I wasn't fired. I was expecting that outcome 100%.

After this conversation, I kept to myself and concentrated on work. Leah, however, was walking around the office in a fast, almost irritable manner. You could tell she was not doing too well. I hoped she would not fall apart. On Friday afternoon at 3 p.m., she had a meeting with Cody and my new manager, Ricardo. I am not sure what was discussed but nobody returned to their desks and it was already way past 5 p.m.

On the following Monday, Cody and Leah walked in at the same time. Leah took a much longer route around half of the floor so she did not have to pass my cubicle. (This continued almost every day.) I knew she had broken down and told the details to Cody and Ricardo. I was able to see it in their eyes, the way they were looking at me. I was able to see the fear in their eyes. At that point I knew my days at Weyland were numbered.

It was a fucked-up situation; a director was accommodating an entry-level employee four levels below hers by taking a longer route around the floor to her office on a daily basis. All communication, verbal and written, went indirectly via managers. I was not allowed to enter her office under any circumstances. It felt like she had an office restraining order against me. I was really sad and felt awful that things had turned out this way. From that point on, I was in pure survival mode. I tried to maintain an image of an outgoing employee fully devoted to his work. I went out with some members of the tax team to lunch almost every Friday. I helped everyone as much as possible. This lasted until the middle of March.

On March 17 2016, the whole tax department was scheduled to have a working lunch with the CEO, Peter Douglas. The whole team, especially the VP, Karen, was excited, but nervous at the same time. It is unusual for the CEO of such a large company to devote two hours of his or her time to such a small group. The meeting was held in the main conference room next to the CEO's office. The meeting was a lunch/PowerPoint presentation hosted by Peter and, lastly, questions asked by employees directly to the CEO on any subject.

I had one question prepared, "As a leader, are you still continuing to learn and develop or are you reaching, or have you reached, a certain point where you can say to yourself, 'I've seen it all, there is nothing that can surprise me anymore.'" To this day, I don't know why I prepared such a long question.

My turn came and I asked the question. "As a leader, are you still continuing to learn and develop or are you reaching, or have you reached, a certain point where you can say to yourself—"

Peter abruptly interrupted me and made the following comment, "I am one foot in the grave."

I immediately began to laugh. It was a genuine laugh but I laughed loudly. Out of the eighteen-person tax department, I was the only one who laughed.

I was fired the next day. They were not able to fire me for that reason, therefore a couple reasons were made up: 1) I described in detail what my wife and I were doing in a Jacuzzi while vacationing in the mountains. Not true. I only said to Cody and Ricardo that we were playing in the Jacuzzi and to use their imagination for the rest. Anybody can play in a Jacuzzi. This was clearly a gray area. 2) I showed a picture of my naked wife to a manager named Phillip. Untrue, I showed him a picture of my wife dressed in lingerie. This was a Victoria's Secret picture mailed frequently via catalogs. I knew I was being fired, but maintained my position in a meeting with the HR Director. When I left the building, it felt like a heavy boulder just fell off my shoulders. I felt so light and free. I was so happy this bullshit was finally over. When I arrived home, I broke down and cried loudly. I realized that I would never speak with and see Leah again. It is extremely difficult to get rid of those feelings no matter how hard you try.

On Monday, March 21 2016, Weyland's board director, Kristopher Scully, Bill Weyland and his grandson, had a private meeting with Douglas to tell him to step down by the end of May 2016 or "There would be a war!" It was all over the news. It gave me such pleasure to see this person go one business day after he fired me. All the legacy Michigan employees finally got their revenge. Bill Weyland lost a few battles, but ultimately won the war.

The next few weeks were not easy. I was unemployed, unable to focus and thought about Leah on many occasions.

Version 2

I liked Leah since the initial Imagin interview and fantasized a lot on how to get into her panties. Of course, I had to remain professional. "I have a wife and two kids to support, this is not worth it," I reminded myself frequently. As time went by, it was proving increasingly difficult to keep my eyes and thoughts away from Leah. I loved the way she looked and behaved. She was the perfect woman of "split personality."

First side: she was devoted to her family, community and most importantly to The Church. She was THE woman of the household who paid most of the bills since her husband "worked from home." She was the dream of any man with open eyes who would be able to find her qualities.

Second side: internally, she was not too happy with her present life. Her daughters were almost independent (not financially, of course) and her husband was boring. She became a workaholic spending most of her life buried in spreadsheets and negotiating with the IRS. She was a tough negotiator, especially when dealing with men. :-) The good news was she had Cody and Phillip around. They both flirted with her, made her laugh and in general filled the missing side of her life. Why not spend twelve hours a day at work with such a fine group of people? I don't think she was fucking them but who knows.

Back to me; as mentioned, I liked Leah from the beginning. I liked her for who she was. I was able to bypass all the endless filters and see through her eyes. I was able to find her soul and read her mind. This was only possible because I truly loved her. Love is the most powerful force in the Universe. It is a beam of light. It is energy that has gravity, therefore, it is able to distort time and space. That's why I felt so attracted to her and time did not exist every time our eyes met at full stare. Love created everything in every possible time and dimension. It created all the known and unknown universes. Without love, there would be just an empty space. Love has endless possibilities and anything can happen when you are in love. Love is God and God is love. I did not care she had gray hair when she forgot to dye it. I did not care that she had wrinkles when she forgot to put on make-up. She had a great personality, petite body, big tits and cute ass and of course beautiful face with large smile (mostly). Oh, I wanted to have sex with her so badly.

The good news was my wife and I started to go to swingers' clubs effective summer 2014. The agreement was to "do it" three or four times per year at the most. At first, she was not too thrilled about the idea but eventually warmed up and became the wild one. "That is great, I can't believe she likes doing this. My wildest fantasies finally became reality!" I thought to myself in a very satisfied way. Forbidden fruit always tastes the best, therefore, you should "eat it" only sporadically. This helped to keep my eyes and thoughts away from Leah and focus on the family and work. Also, my wife and I always had a great sex life with lots of experimentation. I could not ask for a better wife. She is the whole package; I have fun with her, can talk to her about anything and we have similar interests. We both love kids. The last ten years of my life were truly amazing. I will always love her. We are now connected because love is eternal and cannot be destroyed.

So Leah, what is your story? What do you want to be when you grow up? Do you want to be the workaholic not fully satisfied with her personal life or do you want to be the person with THE true split personality? The person who has everything: The Church, the family, the career and, of course, the perfect and open sex life. Well, it is time for you to make some changes. Unfortunately, nobody is getting any younger. :-(

Life exists everywhere in every time and in every possible dimension. Everything is based on the law of cause and effect. For example; if you choose not to eat a piece of bread in the morning, what's gonna happen? The bread will decay and that's the end of the story. Hypothetically, let's say you wake up one day and kill your husband. What's gonna happen? Your life, your family's, and the lives of everybody you ever knew would be over as you know it. At this point of

223

singularity, you unknowingly created two dimensions. One after the shooting and one if you just woke up and ate the piece of bread instead of the shooting. Consequently, there are infinite amounts of dimensions and universes. Every decision you ever made and will make in your life creates reaction. You created the world that you know around you, not anybody else. You and nobody else is responsible for your actions and associated consequences.

Why don't we create another dimension? One day, we will meet for a cup of coffee and I will tell you the following, "Leah, I know your dark side. Everyone has a good and bad side. This is the ultimate power struggle between the good and the bad forces of nature. It is more or less the same story of every single person that ever walked this Earth. Here's your dark side. How would you like to fuck your daughter's boyfriend without her knowledge? He is a jerk and she will eventually dump him anyway. You would like that wouldn't you? I know you like young guys. I have experienced this with you ;-) If we put our heads together, I am sure we can manage it. How about getting Tom to fuck my wife? You could finally be the director you always wanted to be. You could direct him what to do. You could teach him a lesson. He deserves it anyway. I don't think Cody's wife will do the job. Although, I agree with him that she truly is beautiful. How would you like to eat my wife's pussy? Most women are bisexual anyway, they just don't know it. My wife likes Tom and you. She already agreed to everything I told you so far. Or, all four of us could have dinner and some 'fun' together." The possibilities are endless. Use your imagination.

You have the power to create your own dark little universe and you can choose the people which you want to include. That is the real power. This game is not for the weak. It is only for the strongest of the strongest. Fuck the CEOs like Douglas. In reality, he's weak. He lost the war with Bill. Why not create this universe/dimension? I can help you with this. Why not Leah, why not? You called me the Devil at the Christmas party anyway. :-) I can be your employee, or your Angel, your Devil or your God. I can be anybody you want me to be. How ironic is this twisted marriage of the beauty and the beast. The possibilities are endless. It is all up to you. Do you want to listen to some person that sells bullshit stories for 10% of gross income or do you want to finally listen to yourself for a change? Just think about it. Just think about it really hard. You have all the time in the world. Once you make up your mind, just call me. You still have my number right? It is (404) XXX-XXXX, in case it was "accidentally" blocked. That's all I have to say. My coffee is getting cold and I got to run to pick up my kids. Hopefully, I am going to make love to my wife tonight. Please at least give me a credit for selling you this idea! If I try to sell you a pen just tell me that I can't do it. . . She then closed the door of her black Lexus, and was gone, gone forever in her own little dimension and I was stuck with paying the tab. . . What a bummer.

Version 3
There are always exceptions to any rules so I have one more surprise for you. I just thought of another dimension/version 3. Why don't we just stay professional? Let's cut the bullshit and treat ourselves like ex-colleagues. Why don't we have a cup of coffee and discuss indirect or corporate tax? V2 would probably get me lost really fast since I only learned UNICAP. We both love the details, right? ;-) Or we can just say "fuck the details" and live a little for a change. We should really listen to Trump. He promised at the inauguration that all the bullshit is finally over. {OK the secret is out. I am writing a novel. It is a science fiction/reality, autobiography, suspense and of course a love story. Nobody has done anything close to this. I finally found a niche in the market. Hopefully, I will become rich and famous like my favorite actors. I need inspiration because I am no Shakespeare. Can you keep this a secret and help me with it? I will give you % from the net earnings (that's after taxes and before the BS deductions) from the book and possibly a movie. I will of course change all the names/characters. Everything will remain confidential. It's been a year and your career is safe. I will not talk. That's a promise. I think I've proven myself to you over the past three years. You have been a great teacher. I learned everything I needed to learn. . . ;-) We can take it easy at first with small baby steps. Don't ever forget about time management. Your other dimension has to remain intact. If you don't want to help me, I totally understand. In that case please destroy the letter. In any case, however, please delete the part that is in the brackets above the brackets. Oh. . .I gotta stop writing. All these details are driving me nuts. So, am I a lunatic or a genius writer? A coin always has two sides.}
In case you don't reply at all, you will always have a place in my heart as long as I am alive. . .
      Half a century has passed and you still have the spirit of a young woman. Don't ever lose it. It's a beautiful thing. Happy Birthday.

Truly Yours
J.

On Monday, I went to Carithers Flowers, chose a nice bouquet of pink and red roses to be delivered with the letter the next day. At the gym, pictures on TV screens were moving faster than normal at unpredictable times and a treadmill in front of me partially turned off then on. While listening to Pandora radio, different artists and songs were displayed for music I knew very well. I chose to ignore the discrepancy and pressed "thumb up" every time my favorite song was played. After the workout, I drove to Starbucks to purchase a small cup of coffee with cream, no sugar, and decided to listen to some rap music. It's been years since I heard a rap song. The rap music played on the radio was not the best.

I went to Sope Creek Park to drink the coffee and to relax before driving home. I switched from FM radio to Pandora and typed "Snoop Doggy Dogg" as the new station. "I wanna be a motherfuckin' hustla, ya betta ask somebody," said a middle-school kid to his teacher before an actual song started to play.

I knew something was wrong and thought, "Wait a minute, that's not the correct order of the verbiage. There is another middle-school kid who answers, 'I wanna be a fireman,' to his teacher before the second kid says he wants to be a hustler."

Someone definitely hacked the phone to play games with me. Again, I chose to ignore it, closed my eyes, relaxed, and listened to a few Snoop Dogg songs not heard since the Nineties.

Back in 1994 Czech Republic, Snoop's album *Doggystyle* was huge and the "Who Am I" song played endlessly on MTV. One day, after emptying the "Flash" slot machine in the Stardust casino, I purchased the original *Doggystyle* CD. The graphics on the CD cover were interesting but I couldn't understand anything except "Beware of Dogg" and "parental advisory, explicit lyrics." Sadly enough, most of the words were not in the dictionary; the sentences didn't make much sense. My English teacher looked at the CD, read over the texts, smiled and said, "Sorry, I can't help you with this."

When it comes to rap, Snoop's *Doggystyle* and Dr. Dre's *The Chronic* are absolute masterpieces. For me, at least, it's not gonna get any better than this. In early Nineties, I wondered if the person photographed on the white CD cover was artist/real medical doctor combined. In 1995, my high school chemistry teacher, coach Puckett, joked with the class, "I wonder if Dr. Dre is a real doctor?" At that time, I had already received a much-needed culture crash course and knew the answer.

In the evening, I had a meeting scheduled with my Greek friend, Nick, and his dad at Suburban Tap tavern located a few minutes from home. We were discussing the possibility of forming a company to renovate and flip houses. Nick kept quiet most of the time. The dad was really friendly and we mostly discussed a situation in Greece and world politics in general. During the conversation, my eyes started to hurt and I became suspicious they may be dilated. I was walking across the tavern and the pictures of TV screens were moving faster than normal. In the bathroom, while looking into a mirror, both eyes were fully dilated. I tried the usual trick: to place a finger in front of my face and focus on it with my eyes. This didn't work. I returned to the table hoping nobody would notice. The dad left after a few minutes.

"I have to tell you something. Several months ago, I suffered a nervous breakdown," Nick said, and was not happy about the situation.

What a coincidence, there was another friend who had suffered a nervous breakdown. I couldn't believe what I was hearing and asked him to repeat the sentence.

"I suffered a nervous breakdown. The doctors put me on a bunch of antidepressants and other medication. I am doing much better, can function, but working at the school is not helping. I am thinking about doing something else. At least Kerry is fully supportive," Nick said.

"I wish Romana was as supportive as Kerry but she is not. We're heading toward divorce and there is nothing I can do about it," I said.

We talked back and forth on how everything happened. I told him my side of the story less the inner thoughts. "I have plenty of time these days. Why don't we hang out more often? You should not be alone while in this state of mind," I said.

Suddenly Nick awakened, jumped up a little and his facial expression changed from depressed to very happy. "I appreciate it, buddy," he said, folding and extending his fist toward me to do the same, so I did.

"Are you fucking with me? Come on, Joseph, are you fucking with me?" he said, in the happiest possible tone of voice.

It looked like he knew my secret and wanted to hear everything buried in my mind. The tennis opponent, Donnie, came to my mind. "Are you fucking with me?" I had said to Donnie in a similar tone of voice to Nick's.

"Are you ready to go?" Nick said, effectively interrupting my thoughts.

"Yes, let's go," I said, while being happy the conversation was almost over.

In the car, I thought more about what just happened.

"Either my Friends have somehow influenced Nick or he and his dad were forced by the NSA to scare me and to dig information out of me."

For a few minutes, again I wasn't sure which scenario was the real one. More thoughts justifying both scenarios were entering my mind until the following idea: "Can we control the weather? – No. The lightning striking a tree and the beam of light hitting my face at the right moment, and the loud owl. No, the NSA doesn't have this ability. They use fear and terror to intimidate people, not nature, not the beautifully sounding owl."

I reassured myself the Plejaren Friends and not the NSA were behind everything and drove home. To prove to myself I will no longer be scared or have any doubts about what is real, I searched for the *Aliens* movie on Netflix. The search was done indirectly by typing Bill Paxton or Sigourney Weaver. No luck, *Aliens* was not available for viewing. I was relieved. There was a chance my thoughts could spiral out of control during or after seeing the movie.

The next day, my wristwatch showed a few minutes before 10 a.m. and I had a strange feeling the flowers had been delivered to PulteGroup. The thought of Leah reading the letter entered my mind right at 10.20 a.m. That morning, I researched more about Eduard Albert (Billy) Meier and came across a section called "Spirit Teaching." I read a few of the articles, which described in detail many values such as love, compassion, and peacefulness. The readings also described recommendations on how to effectively handle challenges on a personal and global level. I came across a book written by Bill in 2008 called *Goblet of the Truth* and read a few pages. On page IX, this line is written, "Originally, he had intended to undertake this eminent and highly expressive transcription in the year 2017."

"Why 2017, does the book have something to do with my recent problems? I definitely need to read it to make sure," I said to myself, and scheduled daily reminders on my calendar to read ten pages of the book, a section or two of "Spirit Teaching" and to learn more about the world's religions.

Filing personal income taxes was an ordeal this year. A $16,000 sum of Pulte income was entered into TurboTax and a refund of $8,000 was instantly calculated by the system. A person doesn't have to be an accountant to realize something is wrong. I was anxious and pulled the computer's electric wire out of the outlet. After the computer restarted, the system came up with exactly the same calculation. I scrolled down through all possible tax exemptions and saw that churches and religious organizations have many exemptions unavailable to everyone else. There are so many loopholes and deductions that clergy practically pay very little income tax, no Social Security and Medicare taxes. These people only take from society and don't give anything back. I remembered a story my ex-boss, John, told me about eight years ago. John was the owner of a collection agency I worked for while going to college.

Boss John's story
According to John: "Back in the 1980s, when you didn't pay a portion of the phone bill related to 900 numbers, the phone company would

disconnect your phone. We bought 900 numbers wholesale indirectly from AT&T to run phone-sex chats. We even purchased numbers costing $25 and $50 for the first minute. There was so much money coming in, we seriously considered starting a church. If you want to be in a money-laundering business, open up a church. This is the greatest legalized pyramid scheme in the US."

He also worked for the Mafia in a sweepstake scheme where a person was guaranteed to win one in five prizes after paying a $2,000 award fee, which later went up to $5,000. The business had an annual gross revenue of $35 million.

Per John; the more money you ask for, the more legit your business looks. Four prizes were of high value, such as a new car, but the last prize – a diamond ring appraised at $10,000 – was actually only worth about $10. You can have anything appraised for whatever you want. Most winners, about 99%, received the $10 ring. The organization was getting names of people who loved to gamble and win, sometimes paying $100 per name. One of the lucky winners was a federal judge. To play it safe, the group decided to give him a prize that actually had value. John purchased a brand-new John Deere tractor worth $4,000 and personally delivered it to the judge's home. He was the happiest person when he saw the price. The scheme was semi-legal and the feds were not able to outright shut the scheme so they disconnected the phones. The mob brought in a semi-truck with a satellite dish to beam a phone signal to the office.

John left the organization and started his own scheme, which was outright theft. His employees were asking for $9,999 checks (to avoid raising a red flag with the IRS when cashed) but no prizes were ever delivered. He had an employee who did nothing but open P.O. boxes. Once a check was received, the P.O. box was never used again. John came up with business process improvements and legitimate business addresses of mom-and-pop stores, doctors or tire places, that were used to receive checks.

"We would call a business," John recalled, "and say that a FedEx envelope was mailed there accidentally and a person would go there to pick it up. One time, a doctor was suspicious and refused to give my guy the envelope, so he jumped over a counter, grabbed the envelope from the doctor's hands and ran away." We both laughed loudly.

"The FBI later told me it drove them crazy that checks were mailed to legitimate businesses," John added, and we laughed some more.

Within a few years, John shut down the operation and retired. His luck ran out when he loaned $30,000 to a friend who used the money to buy weed and ratted him out once arrested. At least John was able to blow $1.5 million in six months with a stripper girlfriend before his arrest. Out of the sixteen-year sentence, he only served three years since he kept fighting many of the bogus charges.

"There are no cliques in federal prisons. Upon slightest suspicion of a clique, the members are shipped to different prisons across the country. My cellmate was Gene Gotti, brother of John Gotti. He was getting the latest editions of new books and said to me, 'John, read this and tell me if it's any good.' So all I did was read books. The prison was in a secluded location surrounded by woods," he said.

"That's like being in a resort. Were you able to lift weights?" I asked.

"We actually had steaks once a month and the gym was really nice."

John was a well-connected individual and upon his release secured himself a $65,000 marketing position for Sports Life Fitness health club in Atlanta. He did very well and was promoted to marketing director. The gym franchise was purchased by Crunch Fitness and John was responsible for marketing the opening of its premier location on Akers Mill Road. John reminds me of Jeff Mathis, except for one difference – he can function and take care of business when he parties.

In the early 2000s, John built two additional rooms in his house. Coincidently, drummer Shawn Drover installed sheetrock in the house shortly before joining the band, Megadeth. I liked the house addition; John's office was upstairs. The downstairs had a full bar, pool table, and a stripper pole. How perfect was this twisted marriage of his work/life balance.

(In September 2017, I went to work part-time for John as a debt collector. Sadly, his wife Sheila was diagnosed with breast cancer and had passed away in 2016. I remember her as this sweet lady who always asked me about my family. She gave me a beautiful baby dress on the day Teresa was born. John is a fighter who never gives up. At present, there is a twenty-one-year-old stripper girlfriend living in his house. :-) I've never met her because she sleeps during the day. He is probably going through ridiculous sums of money but who cares? In his mind, John is living "the dream" and needs someone to help heal his heart and soul, to forget about his beloved wife. That's all that matters.)

In the afternoon, my wife and I had a joint session scheduled with therapist, Patricia. Romana kept talking the whole hour, recycling the same five problems she'd had with me over the past ten years. I just sat there and looked into an empty space. Patricia only said a few sentences and mixed in words that didn't make sense. I knew something was up and kept quiet until the end.

"I don't know what else to do. Romana keeps repeating the same issues over and over again, no matter how many times we've discussed this. I went to the gym one evening, asked my mom to put the kids to bed but she didn't. Romana came home at 9 p.m. and saw Mom cooking and the kids were running around – OK, this never happened again. I loaned $2,000 to my mom behind her back – OK, it never happened again. She has problems with my mom – OK, we fired her. She has a problem with me going to the gym three times a week – OK, I go one weekday night and twice on weekend days, when she's at work, and the kids go to the gym's daycare. I refuse to give up something that makes me feel good. I have been consistently working out for twenty years. She complains I didn't make enough money while at school seven years ago – OK, I pay most of the bills these days."

I finished explaining the situation and Patricia deeply exhaled; exactly in the same way the nurse in Kennestone did when Romana left me in the hospital. I became nervous; there was another room adjacent to this one, the room I had never seen. It could have been full of doctors eager to take me away to a mental institution at the slightest suspicion of saying anything that happened in January while being hospitalized.

"That's why Patricia exhaled. She exhaled in relief as I had proven to everyone I am mentally stable," I thought.

Patricia walked us out of the room to a hallway and removed a stick placed under knob that held the door from inside, so no one could get in from outside. Being disturbed by a maintenance person was her explanation.

In the evening, I received a text message stating someone would like to share lottery winnings with me. I was stunned and deleted the text message. Teresa and Julia insisted that I watch with them a computer-generated fantasy/thriller called *Coraline* (2009), and I did. This was an interesting fairy tale with an exciting plot about a hidden alternate world, a sort of parallel reality. I enjoyed the movie until the "other mother" told Coraline that buttons would be sewed into her eyes. I became light-headed, had chest pains and found it difficult to breathe, excused myself and went straight to bed.

"Yesterday, I wanted to watch *Aliens*. What would've happened then? I can't even handle a kid's cartoon," I said to myself, and fully understood I was not psychologically ready to handle the truth, to be certain about the correct scenario regardless of circumstances. I wasn't fully cured from what happened to me in December and January. "How are the girls doing at Argos? Did Leah like my letter?" I thought, breathing deeply to get over the chest pains while falling asleep.

On the morning of March 23rd, after breakfast, I began to have slight chest and facial pains. Going to the gym was the only thing on my mind, regardless of the feelings. "I better take it easy and walk for a while," I thought, and drove to the soccer field next to Sewell Park. I exited the car and immediately felt worse; not able to breathe, dizzy, light-headed and ready to collapse any second. I couldn't drive back home. The rush hour was in full swing, the road to the house was jammed. Wellstar East Cobb Health Park was about a mile away in the opposite direction. I drove the car as fast as possible until an intersection was in my sight. I then drove in the opposite direction, while honking at everyone, and crossed the Robinson Road/Roswell Road intersection at a red light.

I left the car running in front of the main entrance, went inside as fast as possible and told the receptionist I was about to pass out. A nurse took me in, told me to lie down and relax if possible. Two nurses entered the room: a blonde who was friendly and tried to calm me down, and a black-haired nurse who didn't say a friendly word and asked me questions in the most formal way possible. This reminded me of the January hospitalization, of the Heaven and Hell, the Good vs Bad. I was afraid everything would eventually spiral out of control; I would move deeper and deeper into the gates of hospital Heaven until a mental institution or death was reached.

The symptoms eventually subsided, severe panic attack was the diagnosis. I must have been lying there for at least an hour before everything was close to normal. I became fully aware of my surroundings and breathed normally. Romana refused to pick me up and referred me to a psychiatrist. While being discharged, I was given a large brown envelope and told to go see a psychiatrist located at 2151 Peachford Road, Atlanta 30338.

I was walking the hallways of the clinic towards the main reception area and noticed a woman looking like Jessica who was sitting on a bench, not too far from me. She got up and walked away before I was able to see her in greater detail.

"We parked your car by the urgent care entrance," the receptionist said, and pointed outside to the parking lot area.

"I better leave now before my symptoms worsen," I thought, and walked outside to find the car. I started the car, entered the address into the phone's navigation and left the clinic. I drove with no problems, but my mind was somewhere else.

"After all, this is probably still the reality show; the Friends have uploaded data into my brain on how to save the planet. I was made to give some of the data away, including the rules of the game, to the government while being unconscious, just before I was thrown in jail. Rules of the game; exactly what I have to do minute by minute is preset and part of each data segment already released by the Friends. The government is able to decode each segment exactly one hour in advance and they only have one hour to get all actors ready and prepare each set. The Friends are recording the show, including my inner thoughts, using my eyes as camera lenses and airing it live, twenty-four hours per day, seven days a week, to the whole world. The show directors are on the Moon, just like in *The Truman Show* movie. Each set has to be adjusted exactly according to my current inner thoughts, given to the government live via the Friends. If I have negative thoughts, such as being tortured in a hospital, the government would have no choice but to make this the reality. If I have positive thoughts, such as going undercover and connecting with powerful allies, the government would have to make this reality as well. This would explain the unusual military activity at the Dobbins Air Reserve Base every time I had negative thoughts, the tennis opponents, all the sick friends, divorcing wife, Ronnee at the cafeteria pretending to have feelings and sensations, the friendly/unfriendly nurse, and the person looking like Jessica who actually might have been the real Jessica. If I die, the game would be over.

"I better give everyone a good show," I thought, and shifted the transmission to sport. "No, hold on," I thought, "maybe I should keep it on auto and focus on driving. What about the cars around me? Everybody is in on this."

My thought process was spiraling out of control and I couldn't make up my mind on what to do next. Simple decisions, like whether to shift gears, became an ordeal. Chest pains increased again as I was having what appeared to be another panic attack.

"I can do whatever I want, I am on TV, the show is all about me. Maybe I should get to the hospital as soon as possible. The bad Friends might kill me if I don't get there in a preset time."

My symptoms worsened; the chest pains were accompanied by strong facial and neck tingling, then my whole body started to vibrate in exactly the same way as when I drove to Argos for the last time.

"I can beat this," I said, and manually downshifted and immediately upshifted again. It felt like I was no longer fully controlling my body. The car was being driven by instinct only as my mind was somewhere else.

"It is all up to me, I can slow down." Right after this went through my mind, I pressed the pedal to the floor and crossed I-285 against the flow of traffic at New Northside Drive, a one-way street. I entered I-285 and drove towards Dunwoody. At that point my thinking was out of control.

"Yes!" I said, and in front of my eyes saw a vapor cloud that was quickly rising from the top of a mountain. "It's in the Matterhorn. The mountain where Europe and Africa collide is the key, the gateway to reverse global warming. I have to make it on time and find the hidden entrance to start the reactor to neutralize the excess greenhouse gases in the atmosphere!"

I was not focusing on the road, I just saw myself starting the reactor and looking at the cloud of vapor rising from the mountain.

"Half a million years, that's the age of the reactor. Aliens always lived among us, hiding their true identity and watching everything we were doing. That's why many pyramids appeared around the world at the same time! This is exactly like in *Total Recall*. I was dumped on Earth to complete this mission. My wife is really not my wife, she is just a memory implant. I always preferred brunettes and not blondes."

I wasn't sure how I was able to drive without crashing the car. I then saw Ronnee and myself facing each other at close distance, standing on top of a hill.

"I just had a terrible thought. What if this is a dream?" I said.

"Well, then, kiss me quick before you wake up," Ronnee said, and we kissed.

I was approaching Highway 400 and additional thoughts entered my mind.

"Do you know now? What else do we have to do to make you realize. . .? Yes, I truly know what is really going on."

I then saw the actor, Christopher Lambert, being struck by lightning and continued to think, "This is it! Just like in the movie, *Highlander* (1986), I am the only one – the only person ever whose mind has been wirelessly hacked while he's fully aware of it." I drove off Chamblee Dunwoody exit, was a few minutes away from the hospital and continued to think.

"This is just a game that can be influenced. I don't have to do anything. If I go to see psychiatrists in this state of mind, I will not be allowed to leave. My thought process will eventually spiral out of control and it will be much harder to dig myself out of the institutions than the last time. Each time, it will be harder and harder until I'll eventually die somewhere in the process. Doctors can't help because it's all in my mind. I have to make a stand right now."

I drove to Peachford Hospital's parking lot, did a U-turn and drove away. I was able to calm down and regained full control of my body; the vibrations went away, breathing slowed to normal.

"Not even the president is being watched this closely. That's why I wasn't given a traffic ticket in ten years," I said, stopped at the nearest parking lot and pissed outside, in a wide-open area visible to every passing car. I did this to prove to myself I am in total control and believe nothing will happen to me.

I accidentally drove off to an unknown part of town, but eventually made it home safely. At home, my thought process spiraled out of control again. Many thoughts similar to these went through my mind: "I need to prove to myself that I am in control and nothing will happen to me. I will run naked on a street or drive 120mph on I-75. No, I cannot act in an abnormal way at all otherwise I will end up in jail again. I have to act like nothing is going on."

I was finally able to find the middle ground and my thought process returned to normal. To relax and forget about everything was on my wish list. Watching porn always helped me to fully relax regardless of the situation. "The magic glasses really helped when I wrote the letter to Leah. What's going to happen if I use them to watch porn?" I searched the web and came across my favorite porn actress of my childhood, Kay Parker. I remembered a short story about Kay.

I might have been about eight years old, still in elementary school, when I came across a VHS tape hidden behind some books. The whole tape was about Kay Parker; she was so beautiful, sweet, and caring, especially when she spoke to younger men while still fully dressed. Many of the scenes were full of love and compassion when compared to today's mainstream porn, which is totally emotionless. Kay was a great teacher and I was an eager student who learned a lot. Even at that age, many times I wondered how she would like it if I kissed her down there for a prolonged period of time. Upon the discovery, I couldn't keep my mouth shut and told all my friends at school. About ten of us had frequent social gatherings at my place where we watched porn and threw water balloons from the second-floor apartment at strangers walking on the sidewalk below. None of my friends were able to keep their mouths shut either and the school's principal somehow found out. This was during communism, when it was illegal to own porn VHS tapes. The school launched a full-blown investigation but for some reason none of the friends ever talked. I was lucky because my parents would have faced prison terms for illegal possession of pornographic material and for endangering the moral development of a minor.

I placed the glasses on my face, the movie slowed down and a particular scene kept repeating itself, but from different angles, cutting off just before I was about to finish.

"This is strange, the Friends are adjusting the movie so I wouldn't be able to finish," I thought, turned off the computer monitor and went to bed.

"All thoughts are being monitored and I have no privacy, even during this so private moment."

I tried to play with myself but similar thoughts kept affecting my concentration until I had the following ideas.

I remembered when Jessica, Ronnee, and I had lunch together at the cafeteria during the 2016 presidential election. "Who did you vote for?" I asked. "Let me guess, Trump," I said, and pointed my fingers at both of them.

"Yes," Ronnee and Jessica answered simultaneously.

We spoke about the reasons why they voted the way they did and the subject steered towards LGBT rights, since Jessica's cousin is gay.

"I fully support gay marriages. I don't even want to think about what two guys are doing in a bedroom. . ." I said.

Jessica interrupted me, "But you wouldn't mind two women in a bed. Don't answer it!"

This was music to my ears. I looked at both Ronnee and Jessica and said, "That's a pleasant thought."

Then the memory turned from reality to fantasy.

"I booked us a room at the Hilton across the street," Ronnee said, smiled at Jessica, winked at me and continued to speak. "Joseph, you are our Daryl. Do you know what happens at the end of the movie? Jessica and John would like to have a baby but they can't. Your two daughters are very beautiful. Would you be so kind and do your magic again, please? I booked us the same suite where Mark and I normally relax after a full day of being buried under legal paperwork. The three of us will start together and you will finish with Jessica. A young man who works out regularly is full of energy, don't hold back and go more than once if you like. How does that sound?" Ronnee said, then both she and Jessica smiled and looked directly into my eyes.

"How can I say no? I'll be the godfather who shows up once a year with arms full of presents," I said, and my thoughts switched to Christine. "Well, she looks great, maybe I can also do something with her or her daughter. Yes, her daughter is twenty-one, has the same beautiful large brown eyes as her mother and looks very cute in a photograph, cute just like Christine."

My thought process was out of control and for no reason I thought of Leah.

"I didn't verbally flirt with her so she introduced me to her sixteen-year-old daughter, Sarah, that one time at work, to warm me up, to prep me for verbal flirting. No, wait! I don't want to end up like Frank, so I better think about her eighteen-year-old daughter, Maggie, instead. One time, Leah called me to her office and showed a video of Maggie competing in a diving competition. She was dressed in a swimsuit and looked great, like a young woman who was fully developed, compared to Sarah who looked too childish. That's right! Leah wanted me to warm up by showing her elder daughter in a swimsuit. Ronnee did the same by showing me pictures of her seventeen-year-old daughter. Hold on! She also said her daughter could be a bitch from time to time. By the way, Ronnee looks much sweeter than her daughter anyway. Maybe I could do something with Leah and her daughters together. . . No, this has to stop!!

All the girls: Christine, Jessica, Leah, and Ronnee, are my friends. I can't do this with them or their loved ones. These aren't my thoughts. . ."

I was able to stop the out of control thought process and realized I was just being used for amusement. My Friends must have had a blast when this happened.

"You know what? I will not jerk off or think about anything sexual ever again," I said, and really meant it.

After that experience, the first time I was able to finish was about a week later, after finally being able to overcome the idea that everything that comes to my mind is being monitored. Having no privacy was the most difficult aspect of the whole situation.

In the evening, I remembered a movie not seen in almost thirty years, *Never Too Young To Die* (1986). At the start of the movie, I placed the glasses on. As with the porn, the scene of John Stamos working out kept repeating itself from different angles until I took off the glasses.

As of July 1 2017, I had written 140 pages about what happened in the first few months of 2017. I could be writing here for the rest of my life, something unusual or coincidental is happening almost every day. Here is a summary from my diary of the most important late March, April and May occurrences:

03/24/17 – Unable to concentrate on reading *Goblet of the Truth*, studied organized religion instead, began with Christianity. Wore the glasses and had uncontrolled thought process again, thinking I was some sort of Christian saint. Symptoms of panic attack appeared again. I took the glasses off, went to bed, closed my eyes and was fine after about thirty minutes. "The glasses could be your best friend or the worst enemy," I thought and was happy not to be a religious person. The ideas were so real, a religious person would succumb to that nonsense in no time. The idea of playing a lottery appeared for the first time; the Friends would surely hook me up. I looked at Mikhail Khodorkovsky's wealth – estimated 500 million USD. That's the amount of the jackpot I am going to win. Opened GA lottery online account and scheduled a few lottery drawings. Played a few of the instant win games – never seen anything more stupid. The games have been written so people with low IQ would play and lose.

03/25/17 – Thought I will win the jackpot on Tuesday. Pretended to be sick all day, especially at Home Depot where the cameras were in use. Had strange feelings the government will backtrack several days of my life and continue to watch me using the best surveillance technology available, including satellites that can see a person moving around while in a house, to make sure the lottery wasn't rigged. I planned to donate 25% of the winnings to the HOPE Scholarship fund in return for anonymity. *(Several months later, I was glad I never won because the lottery is not anonymous after all; 1. Of course, winnings are listed on a tax return. 2. Thanks to the Patriot Act, lottery user private account data, including all activity, is recorded and can be shared with the federal government upon request.)*

03/27/17 – My daughters and I went to East Cobb Park. The kids wanted to play in Sewell Mill Creek, took their shoes off and went right in. "It has been a while since I took my shoes off and went into a natural stream. Why not, it will be fun," I thought and went into the creek as well. I showed the girls how to build a dam using clay, stones, and wood sticks. They both were eager to finish the dam themselves and towards the end I only watched. We also built dishes from clay and threw flat rocks at specific angles to make them fly off the water surface. We then walked on a small elevated circular area of mud/sand surrounded by water positioned right under a walkway. I walked the circle once and upon the second pass saw about fifteen small sticks that resembled a small walkway lined up perfectly right next to each other. "I just walked through here few seconds ago and this wasn't here," I said and tried really hard to remember if this was there during the first pass and a small splinter touched the top of my right foot. "Teleportation is the only logical explanation for this." I thought about *The Fly* (1986) movie and was happy at the same time to receive another reminder from Friends. (In July 2017, China successfully teleported a photon from a ground station to a satellite in space.)

A few minutes later, a young blonde girl in her late teens walked at the shores of the creek with a little boy, no more than four years old. We talked and I found out she was an au pair from Germany who was ready to go back after summer to resume school. After about twenty minutes into the conversation, I thought about giving her my number. Right after I finished the thought, she said a sentence and mixed in unrelated word, "husband." I knew this was a test and did not give her the number. I remembered something similar happened about a month ago at Fullers Park. I spoke with a lady in her forties who wore a short white skirt and her legs looked the same, with the same type of freckles, as Ronnee's. Throughout the conversation, I pictured myself having lunch and talking with Ronnee at Argos' cafeteria. Just before we said goodbye, she eagerly took my phone number. Her hand shook in the same pattern as the hand of the person at the Visionworks store, right before I was given the glasses. I realized she will never call me. *(A couple of months after I put two and two together, I knew that no woman will ever call me until after the book is finished and my divorce is finalized.)*

03/28/17 – In the morning, I went out to my backyard to relax. As soon as I sat on a garden chair, a beam of sunlight completely blinded me. It came from the neighbor's fence; a metal decoration plate placed on top of the fence was reflecting the sunlight. I sat on the chair at precisely the right time for this to happen. In the afternoon, I went to see therapist Patricia, alone. It was a normal session. As I was leaving, I noticed the only empty space in the whole complex was a parking slot in front of the window to her office. I had doubts about the scenarios again. Maybe the agents were real and were listening to every single conversation. I didn't feel right, had chest pains when driving home, thought the NSA was using satellites to track my movement and wouldn't want to pay me in case of a lottery winning. Laid in the bed, the negative thought process was spiraling out of control, everything was getting worse and nothing helped including closing my eyes. The symptoms were so bad, I thought the agents were going to kill me using the same device that caused the seizures in January. I ran downstairs, laid on the grass and breathed deeply. Every time I thought of something positive, for a few seconds the Sun felt warmer and light intensity was stronger but at the same time the sky was cloudless – the pattern didn't change until the symptoms went completely away. This was another test to make me believe. The Friends and no one else can control the weather.

In the evening, I researched the Mother Church, Donald Trump, and the Reform Party of the USA. Went on LinkedIn; Leah's boss Kim was looking for a new employee: Director of Federal Tax and Audit. "Did my letter have something to do with it?" In any case, I was happy for Leah to leave the corporate world and enjoy life for a change. Maybe at age fifty, she finally realized money is not everything. One thing was for sure, I did her a huge favor because the daily commute from Suwanee to Buckhead would have been a nightmare. A couple days after her birthday, the I-85 bridge collapsed as a result of PVC pipes set on fire by a homeless man. A few days later, I posted on Facebook we need more incidents like this one so our city officials realize a better public transportation network is a must. Then, I-20 West closed indefinitely as the road swelled up. For unknown reasons, fires happened next to Highway 316 and under Peachtree Creek Bridge in Brookhaven. Around this time, the downtown connector was closed due to a chemical spill and a sinkhole appeared in Midtown. I had my suspicions these were not just coincidences.

"How convenient for someone lobbying for a public transportation network? Unfortunately, greater disasters have to happen before the whole of metro Atlanta will truly have interconnected, efficient, safe, and reliable public transportation network. The problem is that many people in the suburbs, especially the government officials, view the poorer people living in the inner city as sub-humans destined to live for the rest of their lives in the same place. Many northern suburbs have opposed extending MARTA to their communities for decades. Do you know what MARTA stands for? Moving Africans Rapidly Thru Atlanta – that's why there is so much opposition to extend MARTA. The city/county officials of the northern communities would rather waste their residents' lives in endless traffic jams instead of building a public transportation network. Cobb County is the worst; elevated express lanes next to I-75 are being built from Kennesaw to the new Braves stadium instead of a new MARTA line. This approach will never solve the traffic nightmare and will make long-term growth of the area unsustainable.

This leads to another issue that is quite disturbing – Martin Luther King Boulevards. It never fails, in every major US city in the entire country, if you want to buy crack, weapons, and HIV positive hookers, just find the nearest MLK Boulevard. Be aware, don't forget to bring a machine gun to these business meetings just in case a negotiation goes south. The people who live on the MLK Boulevards are at the opposite spectrum of the people that reached the American Dream. They are living the American Nightmare. These people live the American Nightmare because the last person who had a dream got shot. The citizens are being educated by the government that MLK was this great civil rights leader who made a difference for all Americans. So why doesn't the government honor this great man by naming other streets after him, such as the streets in the northern suburbs of the Atlanta metropolis where the million-dollar mansions are standing? Maybe the MLK name is reserved for the ghettos." I analyzed the situation.

03/31/17 – Several days ago, a letter from producers of judicial reality show *Hot Bench* was received, showing interest in the case 17-J-01542. On March 19th, I received an email from Faith Abubey asking where the case is located. I then received a call from Faith stating a misunderstanding happened and to go see the family. On March 21st, I received the below email.

Hi, Joseph:

I've spoken to both Clark and the family.
The family says they received the money from the fundraiser and are happy with everything.

240

They are shocked and appalled by the lawsuit and say they don't understand why it was filed.
There's no indication the family feels the restaurant in anyway "embezzled" any funds from the fundraiser.
Good luck with the lawsuit.

Faith Abubey
Journalist
WXIA/WATL
One Monroe Place
Atlanta, Georgia 30324
404.381-7381

Faith never asked me why I filed the lawsuit or had any questions at all. I then fully understood why Donald Trump fell in love with the mainstream media. I reached out to Ronnee as Jeffry Bagley for the second time, describing his client's symptoms and the business idea that came to Jeffry's mind.

Ms. Pedersen,

Thank you for the referral to your friends in the media. It looks like my client will appear on TV show called Hot Bench.
I have two additional cases that are beyond my scope of expertise and would appreciate referrals to other attorneys.

Case #1
My other client is seriously sick. It appears the sickness was caused by prolonged driving of Nissan Leaf. Respectively, the electromagnetic radiation emitted by the car while in use.
Here are some symptoms:
Headaches, facial/jaw soreness, tingling in right arm + wrist hurt, heart palpitation, low energy levels, low sex drive, depressions
Eyes hurt, uncontrolled pupil dilation in both eyes (there are recordings of this at airports, federal and state courthouses, jail and hospital), is sensitive to light, bad vision (recently acquired prescription glasses)
Bad hearing (made an appointment with a hearing specialist)
He has partial memory loss, however, there are suspicions of mistreatment in jail and a hospital
Additional complications:
Went to marriage and behavioral therapist – his marriage is falling apart. He is about to be thrown out of the house. He is also unable to work as a result.

He was in a hospital again about a week ago. The diagnosis was a panic attack.

There are plenty of witnesses such as the spouse and relatives that are willing to testify.

Case #2
This pertains to escrow funds embezzlement by national mortgage lender. This scheme involves the lender and two other insurance companies; the hazard insurance funds are simply being "lost" in a process and none of the parties can "locate" the money. I have extensive evidence of this that I can provide upon request.

I have additional cases in the pipeline and may require assistance in the future.

Again, thank you for your help.

Regards,
Jeffry

04/01/17 – I missed Ronnee and was not able to stop thinking about her. On March 22nd, I received a letter via email from attorney Daniel Bloom informing Joseph T. to stay away from Ronnee, Jessica, and Christine. Mr. Bloom sent another email seven minutes later stating "Never mind," another email three minutes after the second email stating "Disregard the Never mind." Mark was copied on the letter. I really hoped Ronnee was doing fine. The second email could have been a code word that she was not doing so well. She also changed her LinkedIn profile; removed her photograph and changed her name to Ronnee P. Coincidently, my profile at that time stated Tax Anal. instead of Tax Analyst. At this point, I firmly believed the Friends were behind everything that recently happened and decided to be direct with Ronnee for the first time. Third email from Jeffry was sent as the final contact attempt.

Ms. Pedersen,

Case #3
I have one more case for you. My client is an elderly gentleman who enjoys women's company. He signed up for a Tinder dating application using his Facebook profile. On Facebook, his birthday setting is set to private (only visible to him), however, Tinder displays his age to everyone that views his profile. He is unable to adjust the settings and hide his age on Tinder without paying a subscription fee. He is effectively being "held hostage" by Tinder.

I am looking for assistance to organize a class action lawsuit against Facebook for privacy violations (forwarding private data to a third party without the owner's consent) and against Tinder for using this "private" data to demand money.

This is my last attempt to contact you. The three cases I have given you would be any attorney's dream. So, what's your story when you want to grow up? Would you like to continue to work on BS workers' comp lawsuits and be underpaid? How is your work/life balance? Do you feel loved at work and at home? Are you able to do the things you always wanted to do? Are you the master of your limited time? Unfortunately, nobody is getting any younger.

This is it Ronnee. It's not going to get any better than this. If you devote your time to the three cases you could become a millionaire. You don't have to do all the leg work. You could hire as much help as you need. Maybe, you could then travel the world and find true love. There are many more lawsuits to be fought such as: makers of 'Roundup' for poisoning our soils and waters, Biofuels "farmers" for diverting land from food to industrial use in order to keep the price of the food high. Therefore, effectively starving millions of people. Trash companies for cherry picking on what to recycle. Food companies for pumping unnecessary chemicals into foods to make people sick, effectively playing into the hands of medical insurance companies and doctors. There are many more... and they are not easy. What is easy in this world? Ronnee, the planet is dying. Someone needs to step up. The longer the people wait, the harder it will become for future generations to make any kind of changes because they are sinking deeper and deeper into the abyss of this dark digital age. The lawsuits will raise public awareness and you will not be the only good lawyer on the block. Others will follow the green pastures. You will help to change the world.

Please let me know as soon as you can. Think about it. Think about it really hard. You have all the time in the world. My client who referred case #1 is getting impatient. Other attorneys have already offered assistance.

Here is one more twist to my client's story:
The client had partial memory loss and was arrested by police (arrest recorded by officer's camera attached to the uniform) and doesn't remember much how he ended up in jail. Supposedly, he refused medical help and fought with the police. The police arrested him for breaking an item of less than $500 of value, an aquarium at his sister's house. In jail, he was isolated in a holding cell and felt really sick (possibly due to head injury). As he was falling asleep, he started to feel cold, was losing

243

feelings all over his body and noticed his heart was beating at a slower and slower rate. And suddenly, white light was all around him and he was gently touched by some person's hand. He then realized the only way to get out of this situation was to not hear and speak at certain times and to use double sided wording when answering questions. He had the same difficulties of falling asleep going forward but strangely enough, a guard would always come at the right time to wake him up. Before he was released from jail (mom bailed him out, wife refused), he heard many awful things that could happen to him from fellow inmates. He always kept silent even during the good cop bad cop game.

After he was released, his mom dropped him off at home. Unfortunately, nobody was there and the mom left. That afternoon, he passed out in the backyard (same sleeping problems as in jail) but strangely his mom woke him up at the right time on both occasions. My client wrote the following account:

That evening I went to Walmart to buy a watch. I had extreme difficulty concentrating on anything and had problems with time perception. It appeared time would flow faster and slower at certain periods. Later in the evening, I had bad seizures. I could not find my phone, so I posted comments on Facebook around 2 a.m. asking for help. At certain times, I was barely able to lift my fingers to complete a word. Then the seizures went away but the same sleeping problem persisted. I was afraid to go to sleep when nobody was around. I drank coffee and listened to music all night. In the morning, I received a FB message from my friend stating I probably hit my head and should go to a hospital. Nobody called 911 to help me.

I did not know what was going on so I came up with a plan; to pretend that I could not hear or speak. I went outside to cut the grass. Within minutes, members of my family showed up one by one. Using signs, I begged my wife to take me to the bedroom and hold my hand so I could finally get some sleep. She refused and took me to the hospital. The doctors did all kinds of examinations including an MRI scan but nobody was able to find anything. They even tried to trick me into talking by saying in front of my wife that I would be dissected during the next examination. At that point, I did not know what was real and what was not, so I kept silent. At the end they said I would go home, but instead I was transferred to what appeared to me was a mental section of the hospital. My wife was not allowed to stay with me overnight.

When she left, the psychiatrists started to play "The Devil and The Angel" game. At certain times, the doctors talked about what kind of medical experiments they will do to me once the wife is convinced that I am crazy, therefore, persuading her to sign my life away to the hospital. The doctors had all kinds of toys to abuse the patients; helicopter noises, *sounds coming from different points of the room, flashes of light hitting your face, a psychiatric person talking nonsense who pretended to be your roommate and invisible device that was shooting electric currents to your body (not harmful but very annoying especially when directed to your heart and genital area). At times, I heard the staff will send me home. I kept silent at all times. Again, strangely enough, I was awakened by the personnel several times a night. On one occasion, a fake IV was attached to my arm. The next day, they tried really hard to persuade my wife to sign the documents. I came up with a plan; to sleep and to wake up hearing and talking again. I did just that in front of my wife so there would be a witness. The staff was not too happy about this, making comments such as "Oh miracle has happened, yeah right". The medical staff said the insurance would not cover the hospital visit if I left today and they need to keep me for observation one more night. Ronnee, they got scared, they did not know how much I really heard.*

When my wife left, the same game started again; adjusted for hearing, same for the eyes. I was friendly to everybody to make them believe I did not hear anything. I tried to convince everyone I believed I was in a normal hospital. I even asked for a razor to shave.

The psychiatrists and my fake "roommate" became friendlier as the evening progressed but they remained scared. The staff performed the following test after midnight, I heard my roommate jerking off. The nurse sitting in front of my bed pretended to be asleep. The electric currents were going through my body for hours, the person kept jerking off for hours, the nurse was asleep in front of my bed, a helicopter "landed" and kept idling. Another nurse opened the main door, pointed to the exit and stated, "I am trying to make it easy on your department." The doctors hoped I would panic and try to run away. A video showing the attempted escape would be played to my wife together with verbal explanation of why I was sedated and "taken away." I, however, got up, went to the bathroom and back to bed.

My wife picked me up at noon. That afternoon, I was able to fall asleep and wake up without a help for the first time.

If this leaks to the wrong person at the wrong time, my client is a dead man. If any institution at any level feels threatened by a citizen, the citizen loses his/her rights immediately. Reasons for arrest or sudden death are easily fabricated. You cannot defeat the institution by a fist, you have to use your head. This is the only way. My client has been trained for this since early childhood. Everything in his life had and has purpose. Something happened to my client as a result of these experiences. Something opened up within him. He now has the ability to strip away all the endless BS filters and see the world how it really is.

Why do you think I got so busy with these lawsuits all of a sudden? Maybe, he was somehow able to start the generator of love described in Einstein's letter to his daughter. Who knows, right? A coin always has two sides. It is all up to you.

I totally understand if you don't want to help. In that case, please delete the emails. That would be the end of it and you can continue your life in a business as usual way.

Regards,
Jeffry

At the beginning of April, there was so much direct and indirect evidence I had no more doubts what was really going on. The Plejaren Friends and no one else were behind all the unusual events that had occurred since middle of December. "Why has all this happened to me? What do I have to do with this?" I searched and questioned many different events but was not able to come up with answers. And then, for no particular reason, everything stopped. The glasses were no longer magic; the ability to zoom in and out, sharper view and bright colors were gone. At that point, I wore the glasses throughout the day and was able to concentrate without my thought process going out of control. Given the particular scenario, I thought of three to ten steps ahead at maximum, no longer able to think ahead several hundred steps. Aviation and street noises were no longer audible every time I came up with a solution. People were no longer mixing words into sentences that didn't make sense. Going forward, I did not experience any abnormal visual effects and my thought process remained normal. Being normal felt strange; I was just there, present in the space of my house, not knowing what to do next. I missed my special powers.

A few days went by; I became sort of depressed and disappointed that it was all for nothing; I lost Leah, then Christine, Jessica, and Ronnee. I hoped this was not just some reality show that had to end as soon as I figured it out and believed beyond reasonable doubt what was going on.

"What if it has to end so the lives of everyone involved remain intact? No, it can't end. I've seen too much and realized too much to go back to the so-called normal lifestyle like everybody else. After this experience, I can no longer just eat and swallow everything governments and corporations throw on a plate in front of my face," I thought on many occasions, and eventually went back to all the rules:

As long as you can see, hear, feel, and speak it will get worse and worse and worse. . .and at a certain point, as long as you can see and feel

but can never hear and speak, it will get better and better and better. . .
Love will provide the ultimate answers in the most difficult situations. If
you break the rules, everything will reverse and you will continue to sink
deeper and deeper into the abyss. . . to a certain point, or when you figure
it out, and the game will reverse in your favor again.

The rules were a clear warning not to ever speak about my inner
thoughts with anyone. The rules never stated that I cannot write about it.
I figured the reason behind this: to write about my experiences and to tell
the world where it's heading if nothing changes and people continue to
live in a business as usual way. On April 15 2017, I wrote the first lines
of this book.

Going forward, my health improved dramatically; I no longer
experienced severe chest pains or any symptoms resembling panic
attacks and severe eye pains. My eyes were only dilated while writing
the book or playing with myself. The facial pains/tingling, arm and chest
pains reappeared sporadically, mostly while or after driving the Leaf.

(In April, May, and June, I went to see countless doctors: primary
physician, neurologist, cardiologist, hearing specialist, gastroenterologist,
physical therapist, and had countless tests performed, including full body
MRI and abdominal ultrasound. No one was able to figure out the cause
of the symptoms. There were a few abnormalities: low pulse, elevated
liver enzymes and low glucose. I had several thorough psychological
evaluations performed as well. Again, no one was able to figure out what
happened. From a psychological perspective, the combined
circumstances/experiences do not fit into medical books. I was not
diagnosed with any mental illness. Ha, and you thought I lost my mind,
right girls? ;-))

After about a week, I thought the Friends had abandoned me for
good. Except for a few medical symptoms, nothing unusual happened. I
drove with my kids to Chick-fil-A and waited on Lower
Roswell/Johnson Ferry intersection to make a left turn to Johnson Ferry
Road. Before the light turned green, the cars in front of me left one by
one. I ended up being fourth in line instead of at least tenth.

"They're still here, reading my mind and watching every step I
make. I was just given a bone as a reminder."

I figured the craziness was over and I was going to be mostly left
alone.

I needed to be left alone, at least at home, since my wife was
becoming more unfriendly and argumentative with each passing day. For
some reason, however, she cooked better than ever. The perfect portion
meals were delicious. Also, the kids always left something on a plate for

me to have an afternoon or late-night snack. I decided to test Romana in the middle of a strong argument.

"Please go to Trader Joe's and buy papaya, strawberries, bananas, and yoghurts. Please slow cook the pork tenderloin with vegetables for dinner tomorrow. I love that dish." I said this for no reason.

She became quiet and left the room without saying another word. The next day, the requested items appeared in the refrigerator and the meal was prepared as well. I tried this several times and the pattern never failed.

"Is this how a divorcing wife reacts every time there is an argument?" I said to myself, and knew the divorce was inevitable. Sure enough, I was served with the divorce papers on April 17 2017. I was sad at first but realized she might have never truly loved me. I was always the one who hugged and kissed her first. Even when we first met, she never hugged me or jumped into my arms. Unfortunately, she was not understanding of my medical problems, so I tested her as well.

"I have some sort of growth in my bladder and have to repeat the abdominal ultrasound every six months for three years. It could be cancer," I said, and looked into her face.

"Then you are screwed. Once I divorce you, no one will insure you with a pre-existing condition," she said, with a smile on her face.

I sat there, didn't say a word, just looked at and analyzed the stranger who had a cold stone instead of a beating heart.

Romana had many wrong friends, women who never worked in their lives and always complained about something. The women that couldn't save and loved to spend every single dollar that went through their fingers. The longer I was married to her, the more I realized materialism became the main goal of her life. Her mom and I told her on numerous occasions not to compare her life to her friends' lifestyle to such an extent. Deep down she always wanted to be "The Housewife of Beverly Hills" but eventually realized she could never achieve this status if married to someone like me.

Romana said on numerous occasions, "You are in mid-thirties, you should have been a CEO of something by now. Do whatever it takes, even if you have to work all the time. Other men do it to provide for their families. This is America, this is how it works here. Why can't you do it as well?"

She knew materialism was never the primary focus in my life but kept persuading me over and over again.

My answers were always something similar to the following: "Well, I don't want to work fourteen-hour days and on most weekends. I only live once. My kids only live once. I want to teach them about life, raise them and be with them as much as I can. Too much money will not raise them, it will only spoil and corrupt their personalities. I'll teach them to go around the system to a certain degree so they don't have to make as much money. For example, the kids will be able to graduate debt-free by renting a trailer in a trailer park for $300 per month. Having a part-time job to prove they live independently, below the poverty line, to qualify for the Pell Grant. Of course, in reality, they will continue to live with us. The kids can also qualify for the HOPE Scholarship if they have good grades and stay in Georgia. I just made you two hundred grand. How do you like that?"

"All you want to do is cheat the system because you are lazy. You are like your dad. I should have never married you," was one of her typical answers.

04/11/17 – I didn't receive a single phone call or email from Ronnee, Christine, or Jessica. To give up on the girls was the only thing that was left. One last hope was to show them the bleak future world of 2047. The world where personal freedoms will be greatly restricted. The very last email was written from Jeffry Bagley.

Ronnee,

Please watch this program; Next World – Part 1, Predicting the Future
https://app.curiositystream.com/video/1057/part-1-predicting-the-future
login: Bagley.jef@gmail.com
password: pepa1942
This is exactly why the people have to step up now. We still have few years before the world becomes a luxury prison. I am sure you heard of Ed Snowden. This is not a game anymore.

Regards,
Jeff

About thirty minutes after sending the email, I received a Facebook request from Veronica Snowden. Before I had a chance to accept, the friend request disappeared. Later in the day, I received a text from Leah stating she is not interested in forming a joint business venture. It appeared Leah was unemployed, so I sent her the below text the day before using a second phone line.

Hi Leah

I am in the process of forming a venture specializing in S&U, PPT tax refunds/reverse audits. I am looking for someone exactly like you to widen the services. Work/life balance is a must. We would be the masters of our limited time. Joseph

04/21/17 – The local Nissan Dealership didn't rotate tires that had 22,500 miles, stating they are too worn out. There was a very friendly person who answered every single question I had. No one was able to tell me why brake fluid on the Leaf has to be changed every 15,000 miles or six months. I was referred to Firestone to file a complaint about the prematurely worn out tires. Same scenario occurred at Firestone dealership, there was also a friendly person who answered every single question asked. I found out the tires were designed and manufactured based on Nissan's request; using different rubber compound in order to slightly improve the fuel economy of the electric car. Couple days later, I received a call from a Nissan representative who wanted to schedule an oil change for the Leaf. :-)

04/22/17 – The family went to pick strawberries near Dahlonega. As soon as we parked and made a few steps away from the vehicle, an older lady approached and informed us where the best strawberries can be found. During hayride, a family gave up their seats and told us to sit in their place. "We were here yesterday and these are much better seats for viewing. Here are few pieces of bread so you can feed the cows." The mom said and after few minutes into the conversation the dad informed me of good places to camp in northern Georgia. Later, I spoke with a lady that recently moved to Alpharetta from New York. She complained about Atlanta's inefficient public transportation network. I found out from her that MARTA rail line will extend to Alpharetta. After leaving the farm, we drove to have dinner at Ichiban Steak & Sushi located on Windward Parkway, Alpharetta. Sushi Nami right next to Ichiban Steak was the restaurant I asked Ronnee to have lunch at with me in December.

04/23/17 – I remembered about three boxes of Girl Scout cookies that were accidentally left by someone in front of the house. "There has to be a reason for this," I said to myself while looking over the cookie boxes. Sure enough, "Supporting sustainable production of palm oil," was written on the box. What sustainable palm oil? This industry is one of the major contributors of rain forest devastation around the globe.

05/06/17 – None of the weird symptoms experienced from December to end of March appeared again. From emotional perspective, I was close to normal and decided to research mental illnesses such as schizophrenia and split personality. I was anxious at first but the symptoms described did not exactly fit with what happened to me. During the out of control thought processes, the thoughts always felt like mine except for the very end when I realized what caused all this. Except for the seizure-type symptoms, it never felt like someone else was controlling my body. I did experience hallucinations at Argos just before I was fired. The visual symptoms were accompanied by voices of real people. I never had the courage to go to Cobb County police station and request to see the video of my arrest. I don't remember almost anything and don't want to see myself in that state of mind. Some things are better left alone.

05/07/17 – There was strong chance, I'll probably lose the (Chick-fil-A) court case. I did not feel normal; unable to concentrate and had the enhanced vision on February 28 2017 when my daughters and I went to the restaurant. Towards the end of 2016, I lost the ability to fully concentrate and didn't regain the ability until early April. As a result, it became very difficult to prepare for the lawsuit. There were two major errors in the statement of claim: "It appears the business has embezzled all or portion of the donated funds and the request for Christian to fully comply with O.C.G.A 43-17."

The documents: the exhibits and written answers to Christian's defenses prepared in March for sure would help me win the case. One of the exhibits was a flyer displaying the company's logo, picture of the mother and a child and Fundraiser Night Statement. On May 7th, I went over the supporting evidence one more time since the hearing was scheduled for the next day. To my astonishment, the case looked different than in prior months. It was not such a clear-cut win anymore. The counterclaim defamation was even split. A person was accused of a crime without hard evidence and the case was referred to the media. Business revenue didn't fall under "charitable donations." Ethics and transparency were the only cards I had left.

"I will probably lose this case but will not settle, no matter what. This will be my first time attending a civil hearing. I need the experience." I analyzed the situation and modified the supporting documents.

The next day, I had a slight fever but went to the hearing scheduled for 1.30 p.m. as planned. The Cobb County magistrate court is conveniently located a few minutes' walk from Marietta Square. To enter any court building is always a process: belts, watches, wallets, and cell phones have to be removed and scanned by metal detectors. It seems the security at government buildings is becoming stricter with each subsequent year. After passing the security checkpoint, I went to a nearby table to put on my belt, the watch, and placed the wallet, keys, and cell phone in my pockets. Due to the width of the belt, it was difficult to insert it back through every loop on my pants.

"Why is the government so afraid of its citizens? Why would the citizens want to harm innocent government employees: the judges, secretaries, and law enforcement officers? In the middle of the 1990s, anyone could walk into any courthouse without being searched. There were no security checkpoints," I thought.

A dark-haired male in his early forties, wearing a blue dress shirt, tie, and badge pinned to his chest, was sitting next to a blonde woman. They were sitting on a bench close to the elevators leading to courtroom "I", located on the third floor.

As I was approaching the elevators, our eyes met for a couple of seconds, then we looked away at the same time and I thought, "That's him. The person I'll be fighting with today. Social media is a powerful thing. You can indirectly meet anybody before the actual face-to-face meeting."

The woman sitting next to Christian didn't notice me at all. The waiting area between the courtrooms was full of people, all kinds of people: men, women, young and old. I was able to find a seat and review notes. Everyone around me, including myself, was under the impression our names would be called to enter the courtroom.

"Go ahead, you can go inside the courtroom," said an employee sitting behind a rectangular-shaped glass window to a person at 1.45 p.m. I and a group of about fifteen other people went inside the courtroom.

"Everybody should have been here at 1.30 p.m. Why are you interrupting the court in session?" A judge named Jennifer Inmon spoke in a direct and firm tone of voice.

"We waited in front of the courtroom to be called in," said an older man standing next to me.

"You should have been here, in the courtroom, not sitting somewhere outside," the judge said, as she clearly become more irritated.

I became slightly nervous as I heard her talk. "I better sit down and be quiet. Ms. Inmon, 'I am the Moon' what a colorful name, is feisty, irritated, and kind of cute. She is a strong woman who gets it her way most of the time. The husband, poor guy, I definitely don't want to be him. On the other hand, she could be great in bed."

The thoughts were racing in my head as I was shifting my eyes between the judge, the paperwork, and Christian, sitting in front of me. I was not sure if the blonde woman accompanying the defendant was his wife, girlfriend, or lawyer. The judge suggested everyone get together with the opposing party to work out an agreement. The defendant and I firmly shook hands, politely introduced ourselves and walked to the adjacent waiting area to negotiate.

"What are your suggestions?" I said to Christian.

"I would like this to go away," he answered.

"That is not a problem," I continued. "Just register according to O.C.G.A 43-17 and open your accounting books regarding donations."

"This applies only to nonprofit corporations. You did not do your research. This is business revenue, not charitable contribution—"

I interrupted him and answered, "There is no transparency regarding the donations at all."

The lady sitting next to him joined the conversation. "Mr. Joseph, do you know who I am? I am Taylor's mother."

I opened my mouth in disbelief.

"My little girl has been in the hospital since January with severe brain injury. You don't even know how I feel. I don't understand, what are you going to gain from this?" she said.

"I am sorry this happened. I have a daughter that is the same age. There is no transparency at all regarding the Spirit Night events," I replied.

"Look, I gave her a check, here is the proof," Christian said.

"Nobody knows the percentage of sales donated to the cause. It's not written anywhere. Since there are no rules and regulations about the charitable events, you can give out anything you want. Even at 10%, you are still making money. You are not doing anything except using these people to raise revenue. Why do you need a marketing person at a fundraising event?" I said.

Both of us knew the conversation was over and we returned to the courtroom.

As expected, the donations were part of business revenue, therefore, O.C.G.A 43-17 was inapplicable. Furthermore, I failed to contact the store after the event had ended. I didn't think it was necessary since the percentage of gross sales would be posted to the store's website, as promised by the store employee. The percentage of sales or the donated amount was never posted to the website.

"It is not our practice," Christian replied, when the judge asked him a question regarding disclosure of the information to the general public.

Toward the end of the hearing, the judge asked Ms. Barrett "Were you promised a certain amount of money?"

"No," she said.

"Were you promised a certain percentage of the sales?" the judge continued.

"No, Chick-fil-A and this community gave me so much over the years, I would be happy with a milkshake," Ms. Barrett answered.

"The poor woman," I thought. "She's been brainwashed her whole life by the Church. She is not able to think on her own and blindly obeys the unwritten laws of the community; to listen with no questions asked to anyone above her in the hierarchy, especially the clergy."

When presenting my closing statement, I apologized to the lady that she was dragged into this and reiterated my sympathy toward her and her daughter.

"You knew that I would have no choice but to bring her here," Christian said to me, with a smirk on his face.

"She didn't have to be here. Her presence would not make any difference to the case at all. I came here to lose anyway, you asshole," I thought, while completely ignoring the comment.

The counterclaim defamation was upheld; however, the judge was not sure about the monetary amount of the judgment. I left the courtroom shortly after Christian and the lady. The three of us met at the elevators.

"Well, it was nice knowing you and good luck to you! I hope you understand my issues regarding transparency," I said to him.

"Yes, transparency is important," he answered with a smile.

All three of us said goodbye to each other politely and professionally. I disappeared inside the elevator, alone, while Christian and Ms. Barrett had to attend to other business matters on the third floor.

It was a good experience, a much-needed and priceless experience. It would have been wise to consult an attorney before jumping into this battle head first. I asked the court for $10,000 of punitive damages, with the intent to donate the money to Ms. Barrett's family. I lost the case and was prepared to pay the price. I expected the damage to be somewhere between $4,000 to $8,000. The next morning, I went online and the judgment against the plaintiff was $5,000. The judge asked everyone the right questions and didn't cut off anybody before finishing a statement. The plaintiff asked for fifteen minutes and the defendant for ten minutes to present the case. We wasted almost an hour of her time. The judge, the hot chick, the "I am the Moon" girl was fair to both parties, therefore, I had no problem paying the $5,000.

"Education costs money anyway. I will consult with an attorney if there are any chances of reversing the verdict. If not, I will not waste my time or money on this," was my final assessment of the situation.

05/24/17 – In the afternoon, my wife went to see her stress therapist and knew very well I had to leave the house by 3.15 p.m. at the latest to make the 4 p.m. appointment with attorney Cynthia Counts. I came across Cynthia while searching for defamation attorneys online. Around 3 p.m., the classic good kid bad kid scenario happened. Teresa misbehaved extremely; she threw cereal around the house and banged on the bathroom door to get in while I was showering. Julia was sweet as an angel, listened to everything I told her and went to the car on her own. I tricked Teresa by telling her we will go to the aquarium if she follows her sister and gets in the car.

Romana did not show up by 3.30 p.m. As a last resort, I went to see next-door neighbor grandma Julia to find out if she could watch the kids for thirty minutes until my wife came home. The lady was home and had no problems watching the kids for a few minutes. Her two grandchildren: seven-year-old Mia and four-year-old Julie, played with my daughters on a regular basis. I left the house exactly at 3.30 p.m. and according to GPS would arrive at the Peachtree Street office right at 3.55 p.m. I didn't want to be late and drove as fast as I could. When I approached the I-75 bridge over Chattahoochee River, a white sedan driven by a young male passed me from the right side.

"How convenient, he will clear the traffic and I'll just follow him. My Friends could not have planned it any better."

I pressed the pedal to the floor. We were doing 95mph for a few minutes. I had a hard time keeping up with the car and eventually lost him. It was a great adrenaline rush, but the Leaf would not go faster than 95mph. After passing Moores Mill Road exit, the traffic slowed down significantly. I pulled into the HOV lane and stayed there until the I-75/I-85 junction. The traffic situation did not improve. I decided to drive in the emergency lane. After I drove over a square metal container right after passing 17th Street exit, the car slightly jumped upwards but I was able to keep it under control.

"I hope the battery will not catch on fire, like it happened with the Tesla car a couple years ago," I thought, slowed down and drove to a regular lane.

I had a feeling that I would not be pulled over that day but didn't want to push my luck. The Friends were the real reason why I wasn't given a traffic ticket in ten years. Coincidently, police officers always looked somewhere else. I found a paid parking lot next to the office building, parked the car and exited the parking lot without paying a dime. A young woman who stood not too far from the office building entrance asked me to support the LGBT community.

"Sorry, I am late for a meeting. Let's talk when I came back," I said and continued to walk at fast pace.

In the lobby, a security person unlocked an elevator and pressed the twentieth-floor button. Upon entering the reception area, it was obvious Duane Morris was no cheap law firm. The office was modernly decorated with Ikea-type light-colored furniture. There was plenty of natural light coming in from all angles. The receptionist walked me to a conference room and offered a drink. I asked for a water, relaxed and enjoyed the great view of the Atlanta skyline while waiting for Cynthia.

"Hi Joseph, nice to meet you. I am Cynthia," said a smiling woman in her late forties.

"It's a pleasure to meet you in person," I said, and smiled back.

We both wore glasses and it was impossible for me to access her soul and read her personality with the glass barrier on both sides. "That was so easy at Argos. I really miss those days," I thought, for a split second. Nevertheless, I had a good feeling about her as soon as we shook hands and looked into each other's eyes.

We went over the case in greater detail.

"The Georgia anti-SLAPP law was updated on June 30 2016 to widen the protection so companies or individuals couldn't go after people who publicly express their opinions. The counterclaim judgment is clearly wrong. You had every right to refer media to a court case," she said.

"The judge stated in the statement of claim I accused the defendant of a crime without any hard evidence," I said, and wanted to make sure she knew every detail.

"Yes, but the sentence is opinion-based on your description of what happened. It clearly states: 'It appears the store has embezzled all or portion of donated funds.' This sentence is part of judicial proceedings. It doesn't fall under defamatory statement at all. If you went on TV and stated the defendant committed a crime, that would be a different story. It looks like the judge didn't like the lawsuit."

She reassured me I didn't do anything wrong.

"I actually looked up defamation before writing the statement of claim. I made sure the word 'appears' is listed in the sentence. The judge was fair to everyone and asked the right questions. We wasted more than an hour of her time instead of the fifteen minutes originally asked for. She wasn't sure about the monetary award, that was kind of strange," I said.

"I also teach at Emory Law School and this is a very interesting case. Would you mind if I teach it in my class?" she asked, in an excited tone of voice.

"You have my full permission. If you need me to sign something let me know," I said.

"That wouldn't be necessary since I'll be doing the same thing you did; refer people to publicly available information," she said, offering documents of some of her prior cases for me to prepare the appeal. "Go ahead and copy paste as much information as you need."

Cynthia realized I didn't have money to burn on lawsuits and provided as much help for the least possible amount of money she could. I was initially quoted $30,000 over the phone for her to appeal a defamation lawsuit. "Thirty thousand dollars to appeal a five-thousand-dollar lawsuit?" I immediately said to her, almost laughed loudly and thought about receiving at least a blowjob after giving her a check for this much money. I ended up purchasing a one-hour consultation for $450 after an unsuccessful attempt to receive a free consultation.

After leaving the office, I was plenty happy with the results; the case would be presented at Emory Law School to the next generation of attorneys. The original intent was to make the public aware of one fact: a corporation that is vehemently trying to present itself as saintly could be as greedy and heartless as any other nonprofit or for-profit company. I didn't have to do anything else except to sit back and enjoy the show.

04/24/2017 – The kids wanted to have a late lunch at Chick-fil-A. We drove to the Woodlawn Square location on Johnson Ferry Road. Teresa asked for the chicken sandwich since she was usually hungry after eating a kid's meal consisting of chicken nuggets. Kids' chicken sandwich meal was not available. I ordered two kids' meals, told the cashier to swap the chicken nuggets for a chicken sandwich and charge the difference. This was not an option and I was charged the following price for one kids' chicken sandwich meal: chicken sandwich – $3.09, small fruit cup – $2.09, apple juice – $1.19 and kid's toy – $1.09, total $7.46, before tax. This was more expensive than a regular chicken sandwich meal. I was frustrated and asked the cashier in disbelief, "Why am I being charged for kids' toys?"

"You did not purchase a kids' meal," the cashier said.

"I have two daughters with me – three and seven years old – and wanted to buy kids' meals. Can you at least not charge me for the toys since the so-called kids' meals are way more expensive than regular chicken sandwich meals?" I tried my best to get some sort of discount but gave up since the cashier strictly adhered to the corporate policy.

We sat down to eat our meals. I looked at the apple juice box and thought, "Honest Organic Apple juice that contains 42% juice. CFA really cares about the nutrition of our youngest citizens. These stores are always so busy. It appears the corporation has the perfect armies of clientele that never question anything; individuals brainwashed by the Church their whole lives, willing to pay for and swallow anything that someone of higher hierarchy throws in front of their faces. It is like the elementary school teacher, Ms. Barrett, who never questioned the rules and regulations of the Spirit Night events and would have been happy with a milkshake instead of an agreed percentage of gross sales. The corporation can't afford to sell kids' chicken sandwich meals, but to my knowledge, they frequently give away free chicken sandwiches to teachers at nearby public schools. Why? The teachers will help raise the next generation of believers and devoted customers. Has anybody ever questioned the separation of Church and State?"

Chapter 11
What Happened?

At this point, I can categorize the experience into two sections;

1. Events that occurred from December 2016 to early April 2017.
2. Events that occurred from early April 2017 to July 2017.

From December to April, real-life events were accompanied by visual, audible, and uncontrolled thought abnormalities. At certain points, I was a few steps away from total collapse but everything always changed for the better at the last minute. Around the time of my hospitalization, I was clearly made aware that something extraordinary was happening to my mind and body. This was accompanied by real-life events; people around me acted in a certain way that, coupled with countless indirect evidence, eventually made me realize what was going on. As soon as I believed beyond reasonable doubt, all visual/audible effects and abnormal thought processes completely stopped. I then entered the post-realization stage; the special effects disappeared except for that people around me continued to act in an unusual way and real-life events occurred in a pattern. All this combined was impossible to have happened on its own without external influence.

How was this possible and why did this happen in the year 2017 and not in a different time? Why did this happen to Joseph and not to somebody else? Why would the Plejaren Friends do something like this in the first place? Why were Leah, Christine, Jessica, and Ronnee involved to a certain degree? You asked the questions, here are the answers.

Why did this happen in the year 2017?

To answer this question, we need to first compare our history with the present time. Until the middle of the 20th century, most people lived in rural areas, grew their own food and rode horses, as cars were nonexistent or expensive. Families spent evenings together, dining, playing all kinds of board games and talking about current events. Then technology started to change at such a fast pace, it eventually became very difficult for most people to fully comprehend what was happening. As a result, the world around the average person continued to speed up and placed greater and greater emphasis on work and productivity to stay competitive. Those unable to adapt fast enough were left behind. So much progress was achieved that by the early 21st century, no person on the planet is able to keep up with all the continuously evolving events/inventions.

For example: a forty-year-old English-speaking person named John, born in the calendar year AD 100, is somehow transported through time to the year 1800. John is left on a city street to figure out how to adjust and survive in the new environment. What will happen? At first, he will be confused by the city's layout, people's clothes, and behavior. Within a couple hours, John will start asking people for food, shelter, and potential work. After about a week, John will say to himself, "I had no problem finding work as a blacksmith. I am good with my hands, can work with iron and love horses. The people here are friendly and helpful. The housing, food, clothes, and other items are more available and way more affordable than in the year 100. I kind of like my life here." After a month, John is transported further into the future, to the year 2017. What will happen to John's inner thoughts after he is left on a street for a couple hours? "I ask people for help and they ignore me. The fast-moving boxes don't stop when I approach them. There is this horrible endless noise present all the time and my ears are killing me. The headache is the worst! Nobody ever stops because their souls are possessed by the Devil. This surely is hell and I want out now!!" John will become completely insane, unable to comprehend the world around him and jump in front of a bus, the largest moving box he sees, to end his life.

This is exactly how John and our other ancestors would look at today's society. The average people live to work. Women leave babies as young as six weeks old with complete strangers so they can work. Consequently, the world is not producing enough loving people to reverse the upcoming catastrophe. Parents hardly ever talk to their children anymore because they are at work, catching up with work, or getting ready for work, indirectly making the lonely children vulnerable to fall under the wings of predators, religious fundamentalists, and other extremists. Why talk to the children since they are so busy with school, social media, and the internet? The kids don't want to talk to us, the parents, anyway, they're smarter than us, way smarter than the older pre-digital age generation.

All information required for a successful and productive life is now just a click of a button away, readily available to anyone who knows how to search for it. To make as much money as fast as possible, to buy as many things as fast as possible, has become the primary purpose of most people's lives. "The souls of these people are possessed by the Devil. They never stop and pause to rethink their life or what truly makes them happy until they are too old to make any differences in their lives," our ancestors would surely say about us. Today's society is so focused on materialism that we have lost the ability to responsibly handle new technologies. Every single new technological invention is being misused by governments worldwide, or someone trying to gain power or make a quick and easy profit at the expense of others or the environment. We have grown apart from each other, from nature and from the planet that supports us. We treat our planet, everything and everyone on it, as a piece of property; the house we could use as we please, the house we could flip in five years with no emotions attached and move somewhere else. Unfortunately, the Earth is the only house we have and we can't move anywhere else.

As of 2017, our planet is in the middle of the Holocene extinction; the sixth wave of extinctions of plants and animals in the past half-billion years. We're currently experiencing the worst succession of species die-offs since the loss of the dinosaurs, sixty-five million years ago. This extinction is different than the others because it is being caused solely by overpopulation and human activity. No one, regardless of numbers, is safe – including humans. Just ask the passenger pigeon; at the height of its population, an estimated three to five billion of these birds were once flying over the North American continent. Although extinction is a natural phenomenon, it occurs at a natural "background" rate of about one to five species per year. Scientists estimate we are now losing species at 1,000 to 10,000 times the background rate, with literally dozens going extinct every day. According to a World Wildlife Fund report, the global wildlife population has decreased on average by 60% between 1970 and 2014. Once the ecosystem completely collapses it will be all over, even for humans, since large-scale farming will no longer be possible.

Why did this happen to Joseph?

I was born at the right place at the right time to the perfect family. I experienced the best and the worst of socialism and capitalism. The bottom line, the big picture, is that I was influenced to tell the story of my life.

I was born just before the digital age took off and was loved beyond imagination by four women of different generations. My mom stayed home with me for four years. I am able to remember the pre-internet world of the communist Czechoslovakia; the Peter Pan's Neverland for children, surrounded by barbed wire. I experienced the first taste of capitalism via my beloved movies and always felt deeply connected to something higher while I watched the movies over and over again. I experienced the Velvet Revolution and moved to the New World shortly after to live the real capitalism experienced by the majority of

Americans; anything from extreme poverty to very comfortable middle class.

I was made to miss "love" – the true love I experienced while living in Czechoslovakia. I fell in love with Romana, we started to date, and it was great. I didn't, however, experience the unattainable, passionate love until I met Leah and Ronnee. I eventually realized that a person who was truly loved during early childhood years can overcome any of life's difficulties without alcohol and drugs. Why do people use these substances? To suppress an unstable inner thought process and to fill the missing part of their life; the part of early childhood when, as babies and toddlers, they were left with complete strangers, not loved, not kissed, not hugged, not sang to, not touched unless being fed or a diaper was being changed. These babies and toddlers were treated like property (as displayed on Megadeth's *Youthanasia* album) that can be left for ten hours a day to lie/sit in an empty square white room full of plastic toys and to somehow grow up on their own. They grew up all right, but with less emotions, as selfish and sometimes hateful and aggressive people who don't give a shit about the planet, other people, animals, plants or anything else except for money and themselves.

During the 2017 Total Recall mind game, I was forced to decide which political system is better. Is it socialism or capitalism? Well, they are both good and they are both bad. It depends on how old a person is. For children, socialism is the better system. Every child in the world, regardless of social status, has the right to grow up in the socialist paradise free from drugs, violence, and predators. Children want to be able to freely, and by themselves, explore the surrounding areas where they live and have a carefree childhood in general regardless of materialism. They don't want their lives to be controlled all the time. All kids want to live in a happy family. It doesn't matter to them if their parents consist of mom and dad, or mom and mom, or dad and dad. They just want to be loved beyond imagination: nurtured, hugged, kissed and sang to by loving people. All people, regardless of background, are born as good people. It is the adults who corrupt their little minds in several different ways: not enough love, religious indoctrination, separation from other kids because of different racial and social background, overprotection combined with not enough responsibility, providing not enough or too much money, living in depressed areas (ghettos) or secluded rich areas, not enough activities or too many activities, cities not providing safe and efficient public transportation networks.

In the late Eighties Czechoslovakia we, the children, were able to do almost anything we wanted. We could go safely anywhere in the country, day or night. All of us participated in countless activities and played together regardless of background. Love was everywhere in those years.

261

It was openly talked about by everyone and freely practiced by teenagers and adults. Many artists sang about love; musicians like Lenka Filipová with "Prỳ Se Tomu Říká Láska," Karel Gott's "Je Jaká Je," Iveta Bartošová and Petr Sepéši – "Knoflíky Lásky," and Dalibor Janda, who won many women's hearts with the love songs "Oheň Voda Vítr," "Kde Jsi," and "Hurikán" – in which an eighteen-year-old boy died in a motorcycle accident while his girlfriend waited for him in front of a movie theater. I never understood why the Communist figure Miloš Jakeš picked on Dalibor Janda in his 1989 speech, since Dalibor only sang about love and made people happy.

When a person reaches adulthood, capitalism is the better system because adult individuals like to differentiate and achieve something on a personal level. People don't play anymore but pursue hobbies in sports, arts and business. To provide for the family becomes the highest priority for many. Why not become wealthy? There is nothing wrong with being materially rich. It can be very beneficial if used wisely; no more seven-to-seven job, freedom of time management, more time to spend with family, full enjoyment of wealth, and allocation of money for good causes. Capitalism provides many incentives for people to innovate, excel in something, work to build and enjoy wealth. Consequently, civilization advances faster than under any other political system. Many people like Bill Gates leave a long-lasting impact due to their innovative spirit and by leaving most of their accumulated wealth to charities, therefore becoming larger-than-life figures. This can never by achieved under socialism where most people are pretty much at the same level. For adults living under socialism, there are no incentives to innovate, excel in something and work harder because everyone is being paid a similar amount of money. As a result, civilization stagnates or progresses very slowly.

Under socialism, a person can have a carefree lifestyle and many real friends, but not material wealth. Under capitalism, a person can have a lot of material wealth, but not a carefree lifestyle and very few real friends. Why not combine and take the best out of both systems? All of our youngest citizens, regardless of background, deserve to be loved, and have a carefree and happy childhood without having to worry about material things. This is the only way to provide a truly fair start in life and to prepare all children for adulthood. Once the children grow up, they separate from each other to pursue individual dreams.

My generation, born in the 1970s, is the first generation that fully grew up on computers, playing video games, thus we possess a certain intellectual curiosity and technical knowledge unavailable to anyone born in prior years. By 2017, humanity as a whole had reached another level of technical knowledge and is now able to explain many events our ancestors frequently viewed as Godly, Satanic, or magical.

Is a civilization technologically thousands of years ahead of ours able to wirelessly hack into a person's brain to alter reality/upload data in the form of audio/visual effects and out-of-control thoughts?

What is real? How do you define real? If real is what you can feel, smell, taste, and see, then "real" is simply electrical signals interpreted by your brain, as correctly described in *The Matrix* movie. Only one hundred years ago, our civilization had no idea about hardware, software, wireless internet, CPU, the blue screen, system crash/reset, cloud server farm, or how the brain really works. Even today, we don't fully understand all brain functions. In the past, the Friends never hacked into a terrestrial person's mind to such an extent because the person would have never figured it out, for three reasons.

First reason, insufficient technical knowledge.

Second reason, even with sufficient technical knowledge, a religious person's brain (the CPU), could have never correctly processed the uploaded data because the virus called "organized religion" has been corrupting the person's mind since early childhood. The person would have been marked as possessed by the Devil and killed by a priest or family members.

Third reason, until recently, the world was not technologically developed enough to leave a sufficient amount of real indirect clues for a person to figure it out anyway. There was a reason why I didn't have a cell phone and no one was around that night when I experienced the seizures. Strong will, love for people I knew, love for the world, and love for music were the only tools available for me to perform the exorcism.

The out-of-control thought process/data upload always happened in the same pattern. I was not able to remember my surroundings or anything else except the original idea and related thoughts. The thinking of my brain was accelerating at a faster and faster rate: 50, 100, 200 steps ahead of the original idea and counting. Within 20 to 30 minutes, I had reached the point of no return and was unable to stop the process. After about an hour or two, everything seemed so real that the original idea became the new reality. At that point, chest and facial pains overcame my body. I was getting colder, shivering, and could not concentrate on anything anymore. I was getting closer and closer to total body collapse and my thought process was entering another dimension where the brain would eventually need to shut down completely. Just before the total collapse, coincidently, the symptoms always improved and my thinking slowly returned to normal. I eventually realized that fighting the data upload would significantly worsen my physical symptoms. The best strategy was to lie down (preferably outside), close my eyes and relax.

This can be compared to an overclocked CPU; a computer processes data way faster than the original design and, all of a sudden, the blue screen appears and the computer crashes. When a computer crashes, a user can take a coffee break or walk away completely because the hardware can survive without the software. Unfortunately, biological hardware cannot live without its software. A medic only has a couple minutes to restart the vital organs so the brain is not permanently damaged. No, thank you, I already experienced this once while in jail and don't think I could survive another episode.

How is this possible? What kind of technology is able to wirelessly hack and upload data to a person's mind?

In April 2017, Facebook announced plans to develop augmented reality (AR) glasses and eventually AR contact lenses to change the user's perception of real-life events, live and as fast as the new reality can be processed by a human brain. This explains the shining bright, crystal-clear white eyes of Argos employees and people in the ghetto, coworkers answering my thoughts, the person without a face, the police officer mentioning aliens and rules of the game, malfunctioning computer/cell phone screens giving away vibrating flashes of light, countless cars honking and flashing at me during the drive home from Argos, the enhanced vision – bright and sharp colors and the ability to zoom in/out on objects.

OK, but how do you wirelessly import the data to a person's brain?

In March 2017, Elon Musk publicly announced Neuralink – the venture to merge the human brain with AI. Mr. Musk stated: "Over time, I think we will probably see a closer merger of biological intelligence and digital intelligence. It's mostly about the bandwidth, the speed of the connection between your brain and the digital version of yourself, particularly output." Brian Johnson, another tech futurist, recently stated: "We know if we put a chip in the brain and release electrical signals, that we can ameliorate symptoms of Parkinson's."

This is a piece of cake for a civilization thousands of years ahead of ours. They can, and without invasive surgeries, remotely control everything that is going on in a human body at any given time: heartbeat, breathing, seizures, headaches, sleepiness, tiredness, you name it. Telepathy makes wireless data input/output possible. Today, telepathy is the least understood function of the brain. A part of the brain – the pineal gland – is also in fact a radio transmitter able to detect electromagnetic fields in a completely different frequency range, and like a sensor, track and recognize them, therefore receive information. This explains the facial pains and collapsing cheeks accompanied with facial and neck vibrations.

As our civilization advances, more brain functions will become available to control at will. Think of it as a video game: the further a first-person shooter goes, the more advanced weapons become available.

The Friends never hacked into a terrestrial person's mind this extensively; however, they have been hacking into people's minds indirectly. The lost UFO book which I was given for my fifteenth birthday stated that writers, movie producers, and other artists have sometimes been influenced by the Plejaren Friends to inform the world about the future in sci-fi novels and movies. Nineteenth-century writers frequently drank a hallucinogen called absinthe. Many modern artists and writers get high to receive inspiration. Occasionally, scientists receive information as well so the world advances further.

By the 1980s the US intelligence agencies instructed the Hollywood studios to custom-make several movies for people living behind the Iron Curtain. It was always the same story: a one-person army defeats the system or higher authority, followed by a love scene at the end of the movie. The message was not to give up, no matter how bad the situation may be, fight to the end, fight for the country and the loved ones. The agencies wanted to achieve the following scenario: after seeing such a movie, Joe in a tracksuit will get his ass up from a couch, turn off the video and go to school, work, or a pub to bitch about the communist system. Once there is a critical mass of these pub politicians, the system will collapse on its own without a single shot being fired.

A few movies were specifically produced to include hidden clues for me to be discovered during the 2017 Total Recall mind game.

Mad Max 2: The Road Warrior (1981) – Extreme circumstances such as lawlessness and shortage of resources can either bring out the best or the worst qualities in people. There is no middle ground since there are only good or bad people left in the world. When a person is down in life or in a bad situation, only a true friend will offer to help and everyone else will turn their backs and walk away. Extreme situations can also burn out the human spirit because there is no hope, no future, and nothing to live for anymore. This approach is wrong because the future is not set in stone. There is always something to live for, always a hope for a better future. "You don't have a future, I can offer you that. . . What are you looking for? Come on, Max, everyone is looking for something. Are you happy out there, wandering, one day blurring into another? You are a scavenger, Max. You are a maggot, you are the corpse of the old world. Tell me your story, what burned you out? Have you seen too many people die, lost some family?" says Pappagallo, and Max punches him in the face. Pappagallo continues, "You think you're the only one that suffered? We've all been through it in here but we haven't given up. We are still human beings with dignity. But you, you are out there with the garbage."

Rambo: First Blood (1982), Rambo: First Blood Part II (1985), Rambo III (1988) – Our soldiers are the true heroes who give everything they have to fight for their country, sometimes paying the ultimate price. I admire their bravery; on the battlefield, the men and women in uniform have no problem giving up their lives for their country, families and friends. Unfortunately, the public has not always welcomed them home with open arms as they always should. It's never the soldier's fault he or she fought in a senseless war. No matter the training or how tough a person may be, the human spirit will always suffer great and irreparable damage during combat. As the body enters "the edge of darkness," the mind inherits and continuously plays the "fortunes of war" song, unable to "look for the truth" for the rest of the life. The intelligence agencies, the policymakers, together with other bureaucrats in Washington are solely to be blamed for dragging the country into senseless wars, for betraying the soldier's trust, for endangering and sometimes killing the soldier. A soldier who suffers mental wounds shouldn't worry that some bureaucrat conveniently issues a dishonorable discharge to save money; in fact, they are disqualifying the soldier from receiving medical benefits available to honorably discharged soldiers. In the early 2000s, an income threshold requirement was established to prevent many veterans from receiving medical benefits.

In January 1973, a peace treaty with North Vietnam was signed and Hanoi released 591 prisoners, including John McCain. In a letter dated February 2nd, 1973, addressed to Hanoi's premier, Pham Van Dong, Nixon pledged $3.25 billion in postwar reconstruction aid without any political conditions. According to a transcript discovered in Soviet archives in 1993, a senior North Vietnamese general, Tran Van Quang, told Hanoi politburo members that Hanoi was holding 1,205 American prisoners. The general/politburo briefing took place only four months before the 1973 peace accords. Hanoi was skeptical the funds would be delivered and kept the remaining prisoners as collateral. Despite overwhelming evidence that North Vietnam held back prisoners, the money was never paid and the 614 forgotten ghosts were left to die. "Anyway, who gives a shit about a few numbers?" some people in charge probably thought to themselves.

Surprisingly, Senator McCain fought very hard to keep POW information hidden from the families and the American public. He bitterly opposed "The Truth Bill" of 1990, which would have made all Vietnam POW documents, including sighting reports, public information. Furthermore, Senator McCain, together with government allies, suppressed and sought to discredit the transcript of the North Vietnamese general's briefing to the politburo found in the Soviet archives. But why? According to Marine/Delta Pilot Pete, who I've known since my days at MEF gym, it is expected for POWs to give away some information to the enemy to avoid torture. Supposedly, McCain talked too much while in captivity and was afraid the remaining POWs, if still alive, might talk upon their return home. Enough of these conspiracy theories. Who knows if they're true or not, right? Regardless of the situation, the 1,204 soldiers and John McCain suffered beyond imagination while serving their country. Torture cannot be used under any circumstances. You can either defend the Constitution or torture, but you cannot defend both.

Rambo – "In the field we had a code of honor; you watch my back, I watch your back . . . Back there I can fly a gunship, I can drive a tank. I was in charge of million-dollar equipment but here I can't even hold a job parking cars!!!" Rambo yells, and throws away his gun. "The shoeshine box was wired and blew his fucking body all over the place. My friend is all over me, his blood is over me. I tried to hold him together and nobody would help. . . I can't get it out of my head. . . I can't put it out of my mind," Rambo says, crying.

Rambo II – "Sir, do we get to win this time?" Rambo asks, referring to the lost Vietnam War. "This time it's up to you," Colonel Trautman answers. Later in the movie, Rambo is betrayed by Marshall Murdock, who is in charge of the mission. "Oh Trautman, I still don't think you understand what this is all about," Murdock says. "The same as it always is – money. . ." Trautman immediately answers. Then they speak about Vietnam's POWs. "Do you think that someone is going to get up on the floor of the United States Senate and ask for billions of dollars for a couple of forgotten ghosts?!!" Murdock yells. "Men, goddammit! The men who fought for their country!!!" Trautman yells back.

At the end of the movie, Rambo expresses his desires for change.

"The war and everything that happened out here may be wrong but dammit, don't hate your country for it," says Trautman to Rambo. "Hate? I'd die for it. . . I want. . . what they want and every other guy who came over here and spilled his guts and gave everything he had once. . . for our country to love us as much as we love it. . . That's what I want," says Rambo.

Rambo III – "The Afghan people fight hard, they never be defeated," Mousa says. Middle Eastern people, like the Japanese during WWII, cannot be defeated with conventional non-nuclear weapons. Many would rather commit suicide before surrendering.

The Terminator (1984), Terminator 2: Judgment Day (1991), Terminator 3: Rise of the Machines (2003) – The rise of artificial intelligence is first presented to the audience in 1984. Skynet, the system that somehow couldn't be destroyed, the system with seemingly limitless capabilities, is in charge of the machines. In 2003, Skynet's technical aspects are revealed; it has spread over the internet to every known and unknown computer and server farm in the entire world. It couldn't be destroyed because the world had become totally dependent on the internet. Shutting down the internet would lead to the collapse of civilization as we know it. The AI system becomes self-aware and grows smarter by the minute. It is a military system indoctrinated in hate and destruction, so the only logical consequence is to rise up and annihilate its masters, the human race. Artificial intelligence cannot be controlled if bad people are in charge.

Highlander (1986) – People of different backgrounds have always lived among us. They have been hiding, living on Earth on/off in perfect disguise and watching our civilization progress for thousands of years. People like the Plejarens, with an average life span of 900 years. Other people, such as the Old Lyrians, have not been as "careful." Many pyramids appeared in the world around the same time to honor the gods from the skies. A few decades ago, ancient granite stones with high-tech precision hole drillings were discovered in Egypt, Bolivia (Tiahuanaco), and Peru (Pumapunku). Machine tools with diamond heads are the only tools capable of drilling holes and lines in such precise detail.

Never Too Young to Die (1986) – The villain, Ragner, is a transgender person born in the late 1940s. His family and community hated him because he/she was different than everyone else. He never understood why there was so much hate against LGBT people around the world. By 1986, he wanted to give the hate back to the community and decided to poison the water supply of the entire city for thousands of years. A person cannot have a balanced psyche and inner thought process without love. Love alone defeats Ragner when Lance offers what appears to be a genuine kiss. For love we live, for love we die. It is the most powerful force in the Universe. There is this beautiful blue costume Danja wears. Leah and Ronnee wore very similar dark navy-blue outfits to work.

The Witches of Eastwick (1987) – This is one of my favorite movies. It's always a lot of fun to flirt with and seduce multiple women at one time. When I saw this movie as a child, I could not have imagined I would one day experience something similar with my three "witches" at Argos. It was like a lottery. I never pressed hard, always went with the flow and dreamed about getting a little pussy after lunch. I didn't want to hurt anyone's feelings and always thought about the other girl; what would she think if I preferred one over the other. I just sat there, had fun, and fully enjoyed the show until the girls conspired against me and took the empty chair away from their table. All of you looked absolutely gorgeous that day when you dressed up for the occasion, to perform the ritual. Well girls, you wanted me to go away, you made it happen and your wish came true. I became sick and forever disappeared from Argos. ;-)

The Running Man (1987) – It couldn't be any more obvious, this movie is custom-tailored for the Joe Blow living in communist Eastern Europe: TV has two channels. . . black-market clothes. . . censored music and network propaganda twenty-four hours a day, seven days a week. What or who is the number one in the whole wide world? Only a megalomaniac can think this way. The average people are fully brainwashed zombies that clap and cheer, without ever questioning anything the Church, the government, and the corporation throw in front of their faces. The only person in the audience who has the common sense and balls to question, to stand up and challenge the authority, is an old senior citizen lady born before the dark digital age. As a result of overpopulation and increased competition for natural resources, the world is a loveless society where only power and money talks. Most people are fighters and not lovers anymore. There is "Dynamo" – an opera singer turned rapist and executioner. What a perfect marriage of the beauty and the beast. Jesse Ventura acts as "Captain Freedom" – gladiator and steroid user in the movie. In real life, he is the most successful candidate of The Reform Party USA. This movie is rare because it also contains hidden clues for the four of you – Christine, Jessica, Leah, and Ronnee – you are smart girls and will figure it out.

Total Recall (1990) – Brain can be hacked, memories erased and replaced without a person's knowledge. Perception of reality can be changed, and thoughts read while a person is awake, knowing or not knowing what is going on. A wireless thought-reading device would be the perfect tool for any government trying to efficiently find internal enemies of the state. The corporation that controls the flow of breathable air doesn't start the reactor to free the people confined to caves because it would lose control and a significant amount of revenue. A corporation can never have equal status to a person because it doesn't have the needs and feelings of a person. "Half a million years old. . . is the age of the reactor." Mars' climate was once similar to Earth's. Artifacts hidden in mountains and caves are to be discovered on Mars. The items belonged to an ancient civilization that was forced to leave the planet for a more hospitable world.

The Shawshank Redemption (1994) – After a certain amount of time behind bars, a person becomes institutionalized – unable to return and function in normal society. A person behind bars doesn't develop but degenerates. Excommunication to secluded areas away from society where a person can work and study until he or she learns the lesson is the only way to correct the person's behavior, while at the same time respecting his or her human rights. A "free" person's mind can also become institutionalized for life when indoctrinated with religious and other extreme ideologies, such as Nazism and Communism, from early childhood. The brainwashed person will lose the ability to question authority and to fight for rights and freedoms.

The Edge (1997) – Most wealthy people are busy maintaining and building wealth, thus, fully detaching themselves from common people and nature. Money doesn't rule the billionaire Charles because, despite his wealth, he never forgot who he really is. It's a paradox because Charles doesn't have any true friends that value him and love him for his personality. He knows it and watches his back all the time since everyone, including his wife, is after his money. In an emergency, Charles shows his true spirit, becomes the "nature" and tries to save his killer's life. In 2017, I bought the 2010 edition DVD, 2004 European DVD edition and 1998 VHS tape wrapped in the original foil. I saw this movie countless times in a movie theatre and remember the following sentence spoken by Charles, like it was yesterday: "You can either have a lot of money or a lot of true friends, but you can't have both." The sentence was deleted and never made it out of movie theatres. Who felt threatened by this statement and ordered the studio to remove it?

Event Horizon (1997) – An incredible amount of energy is required to fold space and open the wormhole to travel way faster than the speed of light. The wormhole can change a planet's trajectory, consequently should only be opened in deep space. Scientists are close to creating a quantum black hole in the Large Hadron Collider, located in Switzerland.

The Truman Show (1998) – A person can live without his or her knowledge in a world where everything is staged, to the smallest possible detail, according to a script. The Friends staged the Total Recall game exceptionally well. The directors were literally on the Moon and controlled everything from the weather to a flying ladybug. They knew I like the outdoors, therefore provided much needed inspiration when I sat outside and wrote this book. The 2017 spring and summer in Atlanta was unusually wet and cold, like the weather I remember from living in the Czech Republic.

American History X (1998) – There are many individuals at churches, governments, corporations, and extremist organizations who indoctrinate people with their beliefs to fully control them. It is always about power and money. In order to be at the top of the pyramid you have to be able to live off other people; be able to brainwash the individuals to give you their hard-earned money and other resources, such as child brides, to work for you and agree with you without any questions asked. Finally, to fight for you whatever your cause may be. In other words, you need an army of obedient zombies.

A person living in poverty surrounded by hate, drugs, and lovelessness is way more susceptible to believe in wrong ideologies than a person living in a decent, safe, and drug-free area surrounded by loving people. I know this from my experience as, for a brief period in the mid-1990s, I was torn between political ideologies.

Only after Derek goes to prison does he realize the skinhead movement is all bullshit. Luckily, his teacher, Dr. Sweeney, knows Derek is a good person deep down and doesn't give up on him. At the prison, Sweeney asks Derek about his feelings regarding the skinhead movement.

"I don't know what I feel, I am all. . . I feel little inside out. . . I don't know. . . some things don't fit," Derek says.

Dr. Sweeney replies, "One time in my life I blamed everybody. . . blame White people, blame God. I didn't get to know the answers because I was asking the wrong questions. You have to ask the right questions."

"Like what?" Derek asks.

"Has anything you've done made your life better?" Sweeney says, Derek then breaks down and asks him for help.

Lamont, a Black fellow inmate, also doesn't give up on Derek and provides him with much-needed protection after Derek publicly leaves the neo-Nazi movement. Lamont is serving six years for stealing a TV and dropping the TV on a police officer's foot. Derek questions inconsistencies in the American justice system. After Derek leaves the prison, the neo-Nazi leader, Cameron, realizes that Derek can no longer be brainwashed and offers him a partnership.

"So, I guess this is where I tell you what I learned. My conclusion, right? Well, my conclusion is hate is baggage. Life's too short to be pissed off all the time. It's just not worth it. Derek says it's always good to end a paper with a quote. . . We are not enemies but friends. We must not be enemies. Though passion may have strained. . . we must not break our bonds of affection. The mystic chords of memory. . . will swell when again touched. . . as surely they will be. . . by the better angels of our nature," Danny says, as he is dying in Derek's arms.

If the skinheads and anarchists united and came together in 1991 at Bzenec, other people of the world are also capable of putting their differences aside and uniting.

Three Kings (1999) – There were many senseless wars fought by the Soviets/Russians and US armed forces since World War II. It was always about ideology, power, and money. The Middle East is a volatile region of culture greatly different from the Western culture. The US or anybody else has no business, no right, to establish and maintain military presence in that part of the world. The region has to stabilize on its own and without outside influence.

The movie offers views on the Iraq war from a Middle Eastern person's perspective, a rare occurrence since that view is censored and cannot be reported by mainstream US media.

"My main man, tell me something, okay? What is the problem with Michael Jackson?" The Iraqi intelligence interrogator asks the question multiple times and continues, "The King of Pop, woo-hoo, hee hee. . . He come to Egypt. . . Hello, with the white glove. I'm Michael Jackson in my hotel room with my chop-up face. Your country make him chop up his face. . ."

"That's bullshit, he did it to himself," says Sergeant Troy, and is slapped several times by the interrogator.

"You are the blind bullshit, my main man. It is so obvious a Black man make the skin white and hair straight, and you know why? Your sick fucking country make the Black man hate himself just like you hate the Arab and the children you bomb over here. . . you broke the ceasefire to steal the gold. . . Do your army care about the children in Iraq? Do they come back to help?" the intelligence officer says.

"No, they are not coming," Troy says.

"Do your army come back to help the people?" asks the interrogator, and then he tortures Troy by electric current. "You bomb my family. Do you know that? You blow up my home. The whole street. My wife is crushed by big fucking block of concrete. She lose her legs.

Those legs cut off now. . . my son was killed in his bed. He is one year old. He sleeping with his toy when the bomb come. . . Can you think how it feel inside your heart if I bomb your daughter? . . . I got training from America. . . weapons, sabotage, interrogations," the interrogator says, and pours oil into Troy's mouth to let him taste the commodity that is the number one reason why the war started in the first place.

In 1991, George H. Bush told the Iraqi people to rise up against Saddam but failed to help the people once Saddam agreed to US demands; Kuwait and its oil fields were secured and the US military presence in the region was assured. Bush then watched the civilians get slaughtered and Saddam re-establish dictatorship. The war was not about the Kuwaiti or Iraqi people, it was about oil and power.

The Matrix (1999) – "What is real? How do you define real? If real is what you can feel, smell, taste, and see, then 'real' is simply electrical signals interpreted by your brain," Morpheus says. With the right technology, perception of reality can be altered with or without a person's knowledge.

There were five fairy tales my daughters begged me to watch with them over and over again during spring of 2017.

Coraline (2009) – The other parents live in overabundance. This lifestyle, if not under control, leads to lovelessness, selfishness, degeneration, and self-destruction.

Hotel Transylvania 2 (2015) – Kids want to explore and break fear barriers. At the summer camp, the vampire dad can't do the same things with his son that he did there when he was a child, because of insurance limitations. Parental overprotection combined with insurance restrictions negatively influence child development. I have yet to see any open-pit granite mines around Atlanta where kids can test their strength and gradually overcome their fears by jumping from higher and higher cliffs, eventually learning to dive from the height of thirty feet.

Princess: A Modern Fairy Tale (2008) – "So what are you gonna do now?" a friend holding a baby asks William Humphrey.

"I figured I'd hang out here for a little while. Finally start writing my novel," he says.

"What's it about?" asks the new princess, Calliope.

"It's set in the world of mythological creatures," William answers.

"Don't you think that might make people start to wonder about us?" Princess Ithaca says.

"No," replies William. "Everyone knows they don't exist."

About a week before seeing Princess for the first time, I was severely bitten by mosquitoes while in my backyard, writing the book. I had no idea this was happening until I felt and touched the bite marks. The bite marks were on the right sight of my neck continuing upwards to my skull. It was painful, I was barely able to touch the affected area. While watching the movie, Teresa insisted on fast-forwarding over the part where William is attacked by the water creature while wandering in the castle's basement. I couldn't figure out why Teresa wanted to skip over this scene until I saw the last few minutes of the fairy tale.

Tři Veteráni (1983), (*The Three Veterans*, Czech fairy tale) – I hadn't seen this fairy tale in thirty years. The three retired soldiers are approached by three dwarfs who give them three magical items so the soldiers can make other people happy. The main plot happens once the soldiers reach the kingdom, whose inhabitants don't question anything and fully obey their king. The government officials, including the king, are thieves who rob their people blind. The king and his daughter steal the magical items from the three soldiers. Toward the end of the movie, the three dwarfs confiscate the magical items because the soldiers only used them for personal gain and ultimately for self-destruction. "We gave you the items to make us happy, for you to be happy, to see you make other people happy. Were we happy with you? – No. Did you make other people happy? – No. We are patient and will try again until you stupid people learn your lesson," said the three dwarfs, just after the items were returned to them. Only after the three soldiers are left with nothing do they learn to make other people happy. The movie has my favorite Czech actors: Rudolf Hrušinský, acting as one of the three soldiers (he also played Josef Švejk in *The Good Soldier Schweik*, a 1957 movie) and writer/director/actor Zdeněk Svěrák, acting as the king's advisor. Svěrák's movie *Kolja* (1996) won the Academy Award.

In a nation where most people don't question anything and blindly agree to everything that is thrown in front of their faces, the government or any higher authority dictates the people's lives and robs them blind. From time to time, Earth's scientists have been given valuable data so our civilization moves to the next level of advancement, but it is always the same story. The inventions have been/are being used to gain power, satisfy greed and, ultimately, for self-destruction. Greed can never by satisfied, therefore self-destruction is inevitable if people continue to live in the business as usual way. Only after everything is taken away and people are left with nothing, will they finally learn their lesson.

Pyšná Princezna (1952) (*The Proud Princess*, Czech fairy tale) – The princess of the Midnight Kingdom lost her mom in early childhood and was raised without love by three advisors. She grew up to be a selfish person who only cares about herself. The advisors rule the kingdom behind the scenes, enriching themselves by robbing the people and the king. Even the king and the princess listen and do everything the advisors tell them with no questions asked. Next-door neighbor King Miroslav would like to marry the princess but the three advisors say no. Miroslav disguises himself and gets a job as gardener at the Midnight Kingdom's castle. He gives the princess a gift: a singing flower that will die if not maintained by a caring and loving person. The princess eventually changes her manners, saves the flower and falls in love with King Miroslav. The three advisors are thrown in jail and the Midnight Kingdom finally prospers.

Other people and/or entities besides elected officials can rule a nation behind the scenes. Like parasites, the other people and/or entities shift resources elsewhere and steal for themselves as much as they can. As a consequence, the nation is in debt, unable and unwilling to provide all basic services to the citizens.

There was also more direct evidence provided during the Total Recall game.

1. Divorcing wife that always cleaned and cooked the perfect meals.
2. Stepdad Milan sold his businesses and wired me $19,000 a couple weeks before the game started.
3. The good and bad kid scenarios where the pattern never changed.
4. Many of the places I lived in and worked at served their purpose and closed down – the Scottish Inn and Super 8 on Delk Road, Clark Creek South campground (where I camped as a homeless person), Main Event Fitness, Houston's Restaurant, Georgia Credit Systems, Compton CPA – all located on Powers Ferry Road, within walking distance of each other closed as well. In 2011, I took an employer-sponsored QuickBooks class at Compton. In 2016, Compton CPA were used for indirect tax advising at Argos. The KPMG office moved from Cumberland to Perimeter Center in 2016. The Citgo gas station on Windy Hill Road where I sold pictures changed owners and remodeled. Uncle Maddio's Pizza, where I went with my family for years and The Sage Social Kitchen, where I took my family while in the divorce process, both closed in spring of 2017. The restaurants were standing close to Roswell Road, within walking distance of each other. In the summer, Sage Woodfire Tavern opened in the same building where Houston's Restaurant was located.

Many entities took off shortly before I started to work there: Netcollection in 2008. Immucor received an unexpected injection of much-needed cash to stay afloat. Argos has been rapidly expanding since 2011.

Most of the above places (except for Netcollection, Immucor, Argos and Clark campground) were located within ten miles of the new Braves Stadium. The first game at the new ballpark was played on March 31 2017, at the same time as I realized what was going on and just before the special-effect uploads completely stopped. On March 31 2017, Leah's open director position was posted online.

WellStar East Cobb Health Park, stress counselor Patricia Keller and psychologist Dr. Rush are within walking distance of each other.

5. The mild spring and summer weather in Atlanta (except for a few hot days) was the perfect weather to sit outside and write the book. On May 6 2017, the morning temperature was only 51 degrees Fahrenheit. In early January of 2017, I experienced a temperature of 1 degree at Maggie Valley, NC

6. I-85 Bridge collapsed and the subsequent road calamities happened one right after the other.

7. I was raised by four women and later became friends with four women.

8. I met Newt Gingrich on two occasions while I worked as a server at Cracker Barrel on Delk Road and at Houston's Restaurant. I live two houses away from where he used to live when he was the House Speaker. In spring of 2017, while cutting grass, for the first time I accidentally bumped into his ex-wife, Marianne, who occasionally lives there. She was as sweet as she could have been and invited me and my daughters to her house. She wanted to show the kids a real dinosaur bone.

9. Wrote about déjà vu in the book, came across déjà vu article on LinkedIn the same day.

10. Wrote about the *Pulp Fiction* movie in the book and the same day came across a Facebook post where the friend and his sister were sitting in front of a *Pulp Fiction* poster.

11. Wrote Ronnee about Ed Snowden and within an hour received a Facebook friend request from Veronica Snowden.

12. Wrote about MLK and came across MLK article on LinkedIn the next morning.

13. James Brandon occasionally lived at Mom's place during his divorce proceedings. Until spring 2017, it was unknown to me he was a famous illusionist who had his own show at the Luxor Hotel

in Las Vegas. His ex-wife is from the Czech Republic. In the 1990s, James did a show in the Plaza Hotel, performed a money trick and Trump who had to be Trump said, "I will throw you out of my hotel if you don't tell me how the trick is done." James wasn't sure if this was a joke, but brushed it off. He traveled the world and slept with the Princess of Monaco during the time she was dating her ex-bodyguard. James has an interesting hobby: to photograph nude women (not porn) using special effects to adjust the surroundings. The pictures are amazing. During the game, James gave me priceless advice on how to keep emotions under control, regardless of circumstances. He has the same personality as Rob Rosen.

14. Extremely friendly people everywhere I went willing to help and give away almost any kind of information.
15. The jobs at Houston's Restaurant, Georgia Credit Systems, Netcollection, and Argos were acquired without interviews.
16. I was driving home with my kids and thought about why all this was happening to me. I pulled over to talk with a neighbor and for no reason he stated: it runs through the generations.
17. Accountant lost his job and while in the process of divorcing wrote 100,000 words of the upcoming sci-fi novel in two months. That happens every day. :-)
18. As of August 15 2017, the Leaf reached the 25,000 milestone and I have been writing the book for exactly four months. I drove from the Extended Stay Hotel in Alpharetta to attend a 1 p.m. therapy session with Patricia Keller. I was running late for the appointment and around 1 p.m. was forced to take a different route because of a fallen traffic signal at the Roswell Road/Bishop Lake Road intersection. It appeared the traffic light fell off due to stormy weather. Roswell Road was closed and I drove on Bishop Lake Road, where the streets and subdivisions were named "Bishop." The next day, I went to the AutoNation Nissan dealership located on Highway 41 to recharge the Leaf and spoke with a service manager named Mr. Bishop regarding a nonworking electric fast charger. Coincidently, on August 14 2017, I had an idea about Plejaren Friends and their AI system named "Bishop."

I realized the 2017 Total Recall game was planned ahead. I have seen too much and there were too many coincidences. I've never read a book or seen a movie where someone experienced similar occurrences. As a result, in 2017 there can be only one person to write about it. If the game was planned with such precision, then my life was planned ahead as well.

My life was not just coincidence but was staged from the beginning. Everything and everyone around me was affected by the Friends to some degree at some point in time.

Eduard Albert (Billy) Meier has been in direct contact with the Plejarens since he was five years old. Direct contact was the only option so Bill would believe beyond reasonable doubt the Friends are real. He has been writing about them since childhood. As a young adult, he traveled the world and worked countless jobs. In the pre-digital age, this was the only option to learn about different cultures in greater detail. To protect his life in the future, an "accident" had to happen where he lost his arm. In the 1970s and 1980s, as a one-armed man, he provided to the public writings describing all encounters in great detail, physical evidence in the form of metal composites unknown to Earth's scientists and the sounds of the Friends' spaceship. The intelligence agencies didn't mess with Bill because a one-armed man could not have been the contact person. His extraterrestrial contacts would surely have prevented the accident, consequently, the physical evidence must have been falsified. This assumption saved his life. In the 1990s, the operation became "hot" again so Bill's wife divorced him and accused him of being a con artist. Her actions saved his life.

By the mid-1970s, Billy and his Friends realized that he could be writing about the contacts and warnings of upcoming world events for eternity but most people would not listen until too late. They decided to change the strategy; to create a human being with certain qualities and indirectly influence the settings of his life for him to always be at the right place at the right time, to experience the best and the worst that capitalism and socialism have to offer. At the perfect moment, the person would be made aware that something in his life wasn't normal and with enough stimulation and indirect clues, the person would realize who he really is and the purpose of his life.

I was made to resemble Reinhard Heydrich and Prince William by wireless gene manipulation while in the womb. In 1983, the brain infection was designed to hide certain abilities, to make me the average Joe Blow blending in with the crowd. In 2017, while in jail, my brain was shut down and rewired to pre-1983 level.

During the early years of my life, I was raised by four women who loved me beyond imagination. The Friends kept me away from men so my feelings of compassion, love, and caring for others would develop to be more like that of a woman. I had two dads who were kept away during several periods of my life. Except briefly, when I was thirteen, my biological dad, Josef, stayed out of my life until I became an adult. My stepdad Milan was and wasn't there when I was growing up. From a material perspective, Milan provided more than enough for me to experience the best of capitalism while I lived in the socialist paradise. He worked or stayed away most of the time.

In 1988, I was able to spend the summer in Fort Lauderdale with my granddad, grandma, and two aunts to experience the real USA, to this point known only from movies. This was unattainable for 95% of the population living behind the Iron Curtain. You may as well have asked for a trip to the Moon. My parents were not allowed to travel with me and it took about six months to complete the paperwork. The school principal's career was in jeopardy; she had to personally guarantee that I would not stay in the US permanently. Luckily, my grandmother was a teacher at the same school and asked her friend for the favor. When I arrived, everything was bigger, brighter, and cleaner. Houses were a different color than gray and I was able to sit on a sidewalk without getting dirty. I knew everything was going to be different, but not this different. I didn't experience shock like this and don't think anything will be able to surpass it in the future. The family had to drive me everywhere and there was not much to do except for going to a beach twice a week for a couple hours, to shop, and play with endless amounts of toys. I couldn't go anywhere to explore anything by myself, due to safety reasons. It felt like being in a luxury prison. I cut the trip short by a month so I could enjoy the rest of the summer at the cottage.

In 1992, Mom accidently bumped into Marcel's uncle Káža, a US citizen, while going around stores trying to sell faucet water filters her dad shipped from the USA.

After moving to Atlanta, Mom dumped Káža and nothing was given to me. I was made to work for everything, to learn the value of a dollar and to experience poverty. Along the way, there was always a friend who helped or a situation always worked itself out so I wouldn't fall too deep into poverty or become addicted to drugs or alcohol. It was not entirely Mom's fault we experienced so many ups and downs in our lives. The lifestyle eventually caught up with me; I became depressed on and off for about ten years and did not do anything with my life. In 1998, I fell in love for the first time as an adult with a girl named Martina while visiting the Czech Republic. I was to be reminded of the lifestyle I was missing while living in Atlanta. She temporarily moved to England to be an au pair. We drove all over England and Scotland for two weeks, what an incredible trip. That was the last time I saw her. A few months later, I received a letter stating the long-distance relationship was not going to work.

At MEF, I was made to see the best and the worst of bodybuilding: incredible physiques outside, rotten bodies ready to fall apart inside. The Friends arranged for Lex Luger to be touched as well, while lying paralyzed in a hospital. "I was touched by God," was the explanation Lex came up with.

In 2000, I was reintroduced to childhood friend Jitka while skiing in Slovakia. Her job was to make me have some fun for a change, to visit her four times a year for two years and to travel all over Europe while she waited for a green card. We got married, but were too young and divorced shortly after her arrival to the USA. In 2005, Jitka referred me to a friend: my future second wife who helped me to break the cycle of depression. I entered the construction business just before the recession started but it never felt right from day one. There was a higher purpose in my life, so I went to college. I couldn't make up my mind whether to pursue accounting or sales. For some reason, I chose to study accounting and never liked the classes except for tax and business valuation. The Friends set up my first ever professional interview through Paul Brown, an internal recruiter for Thomson Reuters. Unknown to me, Paul knew my friend Brant very well. I was hired by a nice and caring woman named Noel who was surprised to find out I was married a couple weeks after I started. The indirect tax division was purchased by KPMG six months later. I was made to see the worst corporate America had to offer; people were treated like numbers, worked unreasonable amounts of hours, were indirectly pushed against each other and were promised a dream that 98% would never achieve.

I looked for other jobs over the three-year period but no one hired me. The Friends made me stay at KPMG until Leah was reasonably persuaded to take a pay cut and to leave her director position at Ashbury Automotive to work as a manager for Immucor. Suddenly, I received two job offers simultaneously from two women. I chose to work for Leah since she was so sweet and beautiful. With Leah, I was made to see the best of what corporate America had to offer. Most importantly, her job was to open me up, to awaken the emotions, desires, dreams, and people's personality that had been buried in me since the 1990s. Her second objective was to awaken my leadership qualities; be able to fight and to go after my dreams no matter what, be able to stand up and laugh directly into the face of the CEO of one of the most powerful corporations. Her third objective was to teach me that love is the most powerful force in the Universe. And finally, Leah was to prepare me for the lunches at Argos; to be able to communicate and flirt with three women simultaneously, and to fall in love with one of them, with Ronnee, who is the perfect match. The lunches were staged and I didn't have to do anything except to show up and enjoy the show.

Christine, Jessica, and Ronnee – all this comes down to the single event that started everything. The short lunch the four of us had on December 15 2016. Something happened that was so extraordinary, it will stay with you for the rest of your lives. No matter how hard you have thought about it, you will never be able to figure it out on your own. You can't, because not enough evidence was left for you to figure it out. It took me until late March to be sure beyond reasonable doubt what really happened.

Ronnee, I am just a human being like everybody else. I don't have the ability to dilate my eyes at will, to look you in the eyes and in a matter of seconds create feelings and sensations in you that last for days. Believe me, I wish I had this ability, but I don't. It is scientifically impossible to dilate eyes at will. Even if I somehow did it, do you know what the odds are? There is about a one in a million chance of being struck by lightning. There are 7.5 billion people in the world. This means, we were struck by lightning 7,500 times in a row that day. This is a mathematical impossibility and it cannot and will not happen on its own. The truth is, we were both played like marionette puppets by the Friends from the skies.

Here come the million-dollar questions. Have your lives changed in any way? Have you experienced anything unusual since that day? I would love to hear the answers because my life turned completely upside down and hasn't been the same ever since.

The event lasted no more than ten seconds. How would you feel if events similar to this were happening continuously for three months? How would you feel if it appeared that everything and everyone, including your family, were in on it? How long would you last before suffering a nervous breakdown – a week, a month, three months perhaps? Jessica, you would maybe last for the full three months. Ronnee, I give you a month at the most. Christine, because of the way you acted after the ten-second event, you wouldn't last a week.

"So why me? What does this have to do with me? Joseph somehow dilated his eyes and tried to trick us in order to eventually lure us into a bedroom. There isn't any other evidence besides his bullshit story," Christine, Jessica, and Ronnee asked themselves.

Well ladies, don't take my advice and listen to your college professors instead. Take your time and do thorough research before jumping to any conclusions. Watch the movies (get the original disk, many free online versions are edited) including some of Kay Parker's instructional videos, especially *Taboo* (1980) – Ronnee, when you look at her face in this movie, it will be like looking in a mirror. ;-) Finish reading this book and read *Goblet of The Truth* at
http://goblet-of-the-truth.org/download-book/

Find out more about Eduard Albert (Billy) Meier at *www.figu.org*; there are close to 800 contact reports written since the 1950s. Learn more about the Plejaren Friends and topics such as telepathy at *www.futureofmankind.co.uk,* where you can quickly search for any subject, and read over "Spirit Teaching" at *www.futureofmankind.co.uk/Billy_Meier/Spirit_Teaching*

In the meantime, I would advise you to keep this a little secret, hidden from everyone – your co-workers, friends, and family. It is for your and your families' protection. Even if you talk about it, no one will ever believe you, everything is purely circumstantial. If you are persistent enough, you may eventually end up arrested and in a mental institution. Let's say you complain to the authorities about Joseph. In his defense, Joseph is writing a sci-fi autobiography novel and in the interim tries to provide entertainment to bored middle-aged housewives.

Christine, Jessica, Leah, and Ronnee, at this point the choice is yours to take either the red or the blue pill. If you take the blue pill, stop reading this book. You will stay in the current world and will live your lives, business as usual. Once the judgment day arrives, you will realize that everything written so far was the truth and you will regret for the rest of your lives that you didn't listen to the person who tried to awaken you. If you take the red pill, continue to read the book and you will find out the truth, will awaken in the real world, will experience things and be able to do things you never thought possible. You will help to change the world and eventually depart the world, leaving it in much better shape than when you were born. I think you have seen and read enough. It is all up to you.

Part II: The Year of the Gathering

Chapter 12
The Meeting

It took some time for the girls to process the information. In October 2017, I received a phone call from Jessica. "Hi Joseph, can we meet? The three of us would like to talk with you."

"Hi Jessica, no problem. Let's meet at Sushi Nami. I wanted to take Ronnee there for a date back in December," I said, and we agreed to meet there for a late lunch on Friday. "We will have a lot to discuss, please take the rest of the day off," I said, slightly laughing.

"Sure, it's a date and we don't want to cut it short anyway," Jessica replied, laughing as well, and the conversation ended shortly after.

We were meeting in October, in the month of one of my favorite heavy metal bands, Helloween. The band was formed in 1984, in Germany. My favorite person was born in 1984, in the month of Halloween. Last year, "The Bootiful Girls" carved an awesome pumpkin. :-)

"The Friends always have a backup plan and I cannot be the only one with similar direct or indirect experiences. Just like in the *Keeper of the Seven Keys* album, there are seven of us in the world: Joseph in North America, someone in China, Russia, India, the Middle East, Africa, and Colombia – South America, ready to meet once the time is right. This makes sense because I don't know much about these cultures. Why put all the eggs into one basket? Once this book is published, the other six people will realize what happened." I came up with an additional clue while thinking about the Helloween band.

On the Friday in late October, the weather was perfect: seventy-two degrees, dry and sunny, without a single cloud in the sky. Fall foliage was underway; leaves changed color from green to a mixture of orange and bright dark red. You couldn't ask for a more perfect day. I reserved us a table in a corner of the restaurant so we could have some privacy. The three ladies were beautifully dressed in a similar way to the last lunch in January and their hair was tied in a bun. I was impressed, as they looked absolutely gorgeous. I took off my glasses to remind them of the Joseph they knew from Argos. We greeted each other and I gently hugged and kissed Christine and Jessica on their cheeks. Once it was Ronnee's turn, my heart was beating very fast and I was barely able to breathe. We looked at each other and our eyes locked, then I kissed her on her left cheek.

The restaurant was nicely decorated and created the perfect atmosphere. We sat down and none of us knew how to bring up the subject related to the book. I ordered two bottles of red wine, with several sushi and sashimi appetizers, to relax everyone.

"How are you and your families? Anything new happened at Argos?" I asked, and we talked about ordinary items for at least an hour.

I ordered another two bottles of wine. We all laughed, we were in a great mood, so I said the following, "I don't understand guys who tell me they don't like sushi."

"Why not? Everyone has different tastes," Christine said, and looked at me like I was crazy.

"Because when I ask the guys if they like women the answer is always 'yes,' well, always except for when they're gay. I then tell them: if you like women, how come you don't like to eat sushi? It tastes exactly the same." I finished the sentence and laughed but the girls did not.

"Ha, ha, ha, OK Joseph, cut the bullshit. This is not what we came here for!" Jessica said, with a stone-cold face, but I could tell she liked the joke.

"Relax, I just wanted to have a little fun. I wanted to show you it is still me, the real Joseph you remember from Argos; the person made of flesh and bones and not the Devil you thought I was," I said. I took out my cell phone and turned it off, and looked directly into each woman's face one by one.

"There will be no recording of any kind. You can write whatever you want but it has to come out of your head. Right Jessica? I know exactly what you were thinking and I am not kidding," I said, and slightly smiled.

All three ladies turned off their phones and placed them on the table.

"Were they really able to read all of your thoughts? I find it hard to believe," Ronnee said, and looked at Jessica and Christine.

"Yes, this is a little too extreme." Jessica agreed with Ronnee.

Christine was silent but her facial expression demanded a truthful answer.

"It's actually much better than you think," I said, and laughed loudly but respectfully.

I then continued to speak. . . "The Friends not only know everything about *me* but they know everything about the three of you, too. To a certain degree, your lives were staged as well for you to have specific experiences and knowledge. The Friends predict when you get sick, where your next vacation will be, what your next favorite hit song will be, your political views, the best possible career and even your future boyfriends and husbands. They know everything you ever did in your life, both the good and the bad. They know your fantasies, dreams, desires and everything you like and don't like. The Friends know you better than you know yourselves. Don't worry, they don't hold anything against you. If they did, we would never have met in the first place. By the way, I am no angel either."

I paused for a few seconds as the girls were looking at me with the realization they have never had any privacy whatsoever, even during their most private moments.

"Don't worry about it. I don't know anything unusual about you and will never know things you don't want me to know. And the Friends? It doesn't matter, because you'll never meet them in person anyway, at least not in the foreseeable future. They have strict sets of guidelines regarding interactions with terrestrial human beings. Let's forget about it and get down to business. Here is the plan," I said. I looked around and saw the restaurant was almost empty as people went back to work, then continued to talk.

"The four of us met at Argos at the perfect time and it was no coincidence. Each of us has different qualities and can do different tasks. The lunches were arranged for us to get to know each other; for us to find out that we like to hang out together, have similar views on the world and are loving, down-to-earth people.

"*Christine* – a skilled finance person, great with spreadsheets and details. She gave up on the American Dream a long time ago and realized money isn't everything. Christine had a rough childhood and maybe one day she can tell the world how religion can be used to generate fear in a person.

"*Jessica* – a natural-born leader with excellent organizational skills who can clearly communicate anything to anyone regardless of subject. She values her privacy more than anything. Did something happen to her or her family in Texas that persuaded her not to be on any social networking sites? She likes to give back to the community, especially to children.

"*Ronnee* – a skilled corporate attorney with people's personality. She is as sweet as a person can be to everyone around her. This is extremely rare for someone with her status and accomplishments.

"Why don't we form a company, a law firm specializing in corporate lawsuits? Let's start with the quick hits to generate some cash flow to fight the more complex lawsuits later.

"During the game, I was stumbling over and continue to stumble over potential lawsuits almost daily and was able to see things from different perspectives more than ever before. I realized how everything is purely profit-driven, with total disregard for the people and the environment. There are many weaknesses in the 'business as usual' processes that many companies adhere to. It has to change at some point in time for our civilization to survive. Most of the lawsuits are class action and some are easier than others. Here are examples:

"Big 4 CPA firms (class action) – It is no secret the employees are pressured to work unreasonable hours, easily reaching a hundred hours per week during tax season. The lack of sleep combined with high stress levels negatively impacts employees' well-being and health. Most people cannot take the abuse and leave within five years. The ones that stay longer mostly never achieve the promised dream of becoming a partner unless they become skilled office politicians fully devoted to work. Their personal life suffers because they don't have one; jumping from marriage to marriage, their kids grow up without knowing them, their health is negatively impacted. How much is it worth? Can you put a price tag on a destroyed life? Of course, the settlement amount will be different for someone who leaves within a year than for someone who endures the abuse for fifteen years and has bad health and no personal life.

"I was employed at Thomson Reuters before, during, and after the indirect tax division was acquired by KPMG. It was day versus night. Before the acquisition took place, Thomson Reuters' management fired employees who lied on KPMG's application regarding their backgrounds. This happened in December, the sale did not close until February. Is it legal? I know plenty of people, including myself, willing to testify against KPMG. Once we settle with one firm, we will sue the rest of the Big Four CPA firms all at once. This is the perfect class-action lawsuit. We will have thousands of people joining in once we make the announcement public. Our job will not be to put companies out of business but to change the way they do business. Why can't a CPA firm hire temporary agency workers during busy tax season? Why must a person work a hundred hours per week and suffer negative health and personal consequences? We will not settle until a company agrees to change business processes going forward.

"Brother printer cartridges (class action) – Many of the laserjet cartridges for printers such as mine, MFC– L2700DW, are tied to a sensor that locks the printer and gives you a 'replace the cartridge' message. I noticed the ink cartridge did not last nearly as long as in my old printer. My old Brother printer never locked and continued to print until there was no ink left. I did some research and found online instructions (not listed in owner's or cartridge manuals) to unlock the

printer without changing the cartridge. I was able to print a significant number of additional pages with no difference in quality of the printouts. This means the printer locks when the cartridge is not empty, forcing a person to purchase another $70 cartridge. A new printer costs $160. Also, the owner's manual states 1,200 pages can be printed per cartridge. I was able to print nowhere near the 1,200 pages. Someone who blindly believes everything that a corporation throws in front of his or her face would change the cartridge with no questions asked. When a new cartridge is purchased, the company conveniently provides a prepaid label to ship the old cartridge back for environmental reasons, to be 'recycled.' In reality, the company probably adds ink to the partially-full cartridge and sells it to a new customer. What a racket. Millions of customers may have been cheated like this in the US alone. This is another easy-to-prove class-action lawsuit.

"*Tinder/Facebook (class action)* – As mentioned before, I signed up for a Tinder dating application using my Facebook profile. On Facebook, my birthday is set to private (only visible to me), however, Tinder displays my age to everyone who views the profile. I am unable to adjust the settings and hide my age on Tinder without paying a subscription fee. I am effectively being 'held hostage' by Tinder. This is a class-action lawsuit against Facebook for privacy violations, for forwarding private data to a third party without the owner's consent, and against Tinder for using this 'private' data to request money.

"*Facebook* – It has been several months since I updated my profile. Why do I continue to receive messages with a link from FB stating: 'You last updated your profile 2 weeks ago'? When I click the link, a field to update a blank portion of my profile becomes available. Also, in my case, a 'We are experiencing technical difficulties' message is displayed when someone tries to post on the timeline of a friend who recently blocked the person. Why would the company make up a story and waste people's time? Why not just display the message, 'Sorry, this friend blocked you'?

"*Google* – During Gmail sign in, I continue to receive requests to provide my phone number. 'Tell Google how to reach you in case you forget your password, lose access, or there's unusual activity on your account.' It appears the main reason is to acquire additional information about a user. Scare tactic warning messages may be used so a user would willingly give out the information.

"Nissan Motor (brake fluid – personal, class action) – The 2015 Leaf Service and Maintenance Guide states that brake fluid on a Nissan Leaf should be changed every 15,000 miles. Per my knowledge, there isn't any other car on the market with such short brake fluid change intervals. I asked the question at the local Nissan dealership and was told it is due to regenerative braking and because the brake fluid is a special hydroscopic fluid that easily accumulates moisture. The person also stated the interval is 15,000 miles or every six months. :-o This is total BS because regenerative braking uses less brakes. The electric motor is used in conjunction with friction-based braking to charge the car's battery. I called Nissan corporate and was told the same reason: regenerative braking. The person stated, however, that the Leaf is using super duty DOT3 brake fluid, and that the fluid is used on all Nissan vehicles. So why such a short brake fluid change interval? The Leaf doesn't require oil changes. It looks like a bogus reason to change the brake fluid was made up to replace lost oil change revenue.

"Car maintenance is the number one revenue source for dealerships. People are questioning the logic of the accelerated brake fluid change intervals on many online discussion forums.

"Here is a typical car dealership business model:
1. New car sales generate work for the service department – no profit is made.
2. Service department's revenue pays everybody's salaries, all bills and taxes – no profit is made.
3. Used car sales generate profits for owner(s).

"Nissan Motor (Ecopia 422 tires – personal and class action) – I went to the local Nissan dealership to rotate the Leaf's tires at 22,500 miles. The dealership refused to rotate the tires and tried to sell me new ones. I questioned why all four tires would not last longer than 22,500 miles and was told to go to Firestone to file a complaint. Per Leaf's Warranty Information Booklet, the OME tires have zero mileage warranty. Why? Per Firestone corporate: the tires are made exactly according to Nissan's specification, and they are made to wear out faster because different rubber compound is used to manufacture the tires so fuel economy is improved. On an electric car? :-) I purchased two Ecopia 422 tires from Firestone, visually no different from the OME tires. The tires were automatically warrantied for 60,000 miles. Apparently, the OME tires are designed to wear out before a two-year lease is up in order to generate additional revenue for dealerships. There are many online complaints regarding these tires. Per conversation with my mom's neighbor, the narrow Ecopia tires on his electric BMW i3 wore out faster than

expected. The rear tires had to be replaced at around 10,000 miles, the front tires were replaced in less than 18,000 miles.

"Nissan Motors (Leaf's electromagnetic field – personal and potential class action) – I drove more than 20,000 miles in eighteen months using the Leaf and experienced many symptoms linked to EMF radiation exposure: fatigue, tiredness, heart palpitation, concentration difficulties, dizziness, nausea. I went to countless doctors but no one was able to figure out the cause. I significantly reduced time spent driving the Leaf and my health improved. Many scientists consider the limit for EMF radiation exposure to be 2mG (milligauss) or less. The official recognition of the health risk comes in a leaked United States National Council on Radiation Protection (NCRP) report funded by the Environmental Protection Agency and written by eleven leading American experts in EMFs. Rob Edwards, in the October 7, 1995 issue of *New Scientist*, writes that the report recommends an EMF safety limit of 2mG. He writes: 'EPA officials say the report is the most comprehensive study ever on the health effects of low-frequency EMFs. Its findings represent a fundamental challenge to the electricity industry. The authors say that their recommendations, if accepted, could force "complex and costly" changes in society's use of electricity.' Unfortunately, on October 11, 1995 the NCRP issued a press release and stated, 'Draft material formulated by NCRP Scientific Committee 89-3 on ELF (extremely low frequency) EMF has been improperly disseminated and does not reflect NCRP recommendation.' The final report was supposed to be approved and to be publicly available in early 1996, but final approval of the draft has never been acted upon.

"According to the World Health Organization, epidemiological studies have consistently shown a two-fold increase in childhood leukemia in children exposed to residential power frequency magnetic fields above 3 to 4 mG.

"Here are the Leaf's measurements:
"Driver's floor – up to 9.2 mG, top of the seat – up to 5.3 mG
"Passenger floor – up to 13.1 mG, top of the seat – up to 4.9 mG
"Back row floor – up to 31.3 mG, top of the seat – up to 4.5 mG
"Back row, top of the elevated floor panel at the center of the vehicle – up to 12.6 mG
"The measurements are way above the 2mG limit and increase the closer a person sits towards the center of the car. Many children sit on the back seat daily. There is no question that long-term exposure of up to 31.3 mG could make many children sick. Why wasn't the car properly shielded? This will become a serious public health concern as more electric cars

will be manufactured in the future. I am curious to see what the measurements are in Teslas and hope that company did not cut corners.

"This lawsuit is challenging but very rewarding at the same time. The settlement could be in the hundreds of millions of dollars. The final cost of VW's Dieselgate will be anywhere between $15 to $87 billion and no one was hurt.

"Again, we will not settle until the company agrees to recall/fix all the vehicles and modifies the manufacturing process. After the settlement, we will test electric cars from other manufacturers and file similar lawsuits, if necessary.

"*Manufacturers of Nissan Leaf superchargers* – Per my observation, the thirty-minute, 440V quick chargers at Nissan dealerships are air cooled and frequently don't work on hot days after a person completes a charge. This happened to me twice in a row; the charger cooled for about forty-five minutes before it worked again. A dealership employee even said to me the chargers don't work if a car is parked at close distance to the charger. What if a person has an important doctor's appointment or another emergency? This is a hazard. Evidently, many chargers are cheaply made and not designed for consecutive charges. Various manufacturers are used to produce the same chargers for different Nissan dealerships. For example, chargers at Nalley Nissan of Atlanta don't have this problem.

"Is the company serious about Leafs? I am not sure but here is one example: Nissan at South Morrow is less than a mile from I-75, doesn't have a quick charger and, in my case, their one and only 7kw 3-hour charger was broken. The closest dealership was Nissan Union City, about fifteen miles away from the interstate. What if someone doesn't have enough battery reserve?

"*Georgia Lottery (online plays – class action)* – The player deposit limit is set at $2,500 per month. All the instant games are way too simple and stupid. It appears the games are designed for a person of lower IQ who is a gambler. The $2,500 monthly spending limit is way too high for a person of lesser IQ, who is usually a low-income earner. Evidently, the state takes advantage of the less intelligent, less educated people in total disregard for the people and their families. How are their kids going to live after mom or dad gambles away most of their earnings? In reality, the state maintains the gambling monopoly and fuels gambling addiction. We will not settle until a player's limit is set to no more than $500 per month. The government should provide services to citizens and not try to become another Las Vegas.

"Procter & Gamble (Old Spice men's deodorants – class action) – The 3oz family package purchased at Sam's Club has a defect; in my case, the tip always fell off with about 10% of the product attached. I experienced the problem for years. The more expensive 3.25oz stick doesn't have this issue. Why has the company never fixed it? Selling the family package is not as profitable as selling individual sticks. It is a well-known fact that Walmart/Sam's Club dictates product prices to manufacturers who would like to supply the stores. The company has to make money somewhere. This is similar to Nissan Leaf; the higher-end model doesn't have Ecopia tires but has Michelins that last past the two- or three-year leases. There are plenty of customers who might have been cheated over the years.

"Atlanta Gas Light (maintenance fees – personal and class action) – Atlanta Gas Light was the sole supplier of gas to the Atlanta market until the early 2000s when deregulation was implemented. I live in East Cobb and my current provider is Constellation. My typical summer bill consists of these charges: gas purchase with tax – around $10 and AGL maintenance fee to maintain the gas related infrastructure, between $25 to $35 per month. I lived in Smyrna until 2015, Austell Natural Gas did not have any maintenance charges and the typical summer bill was around $13 per month. Does it cost more to maintain gas pipes in white-collar neighborhoods than in blue-collar neighborhoods? Richer people don't question a $30 surcharge. Apparently, AGL knows it can get away with it.

"AGL Personal lawsuit – My original 1983 gas meter was replaced on August 7 2017. What are they doing with all this "maintenance" money collected from me? – about $360 per year.

"Bank of America (credit cards – personal and class action) – When I was opening a credit card account, the exact interest rate was not disclosed, even when I asked several times. Only a 13.74 to 23.74% range was stated. I was told the exact interest rate is based on the credit score and will be disclosed to me via mail after the account is opened. This is deceptive practice because the bank can charge you any rate within the range. The only option is to close the account but everyone knows that opening and closing accounts hurts your credit score. It looks like the bank gambles on this fact and knows a person will keep the high interest credit card account open for some time. I did not check with other banks but suspect this practice is now the industry standard. This wasn't the case in the 2000s; I was always told the exact interest rate before the credit card account was opened.

"*American Home Shield Insurance and related contractors (personal and class action)* – I had an insurance policy with this company for almost three years and most of the time it was the same story; the damage is not covered because it is not normal wear and tear. This appears to be an elaborate scheme between the insurance company and its contractors, such as plumbers and electricians. . . within a few minutes the contractor states a bogus reason such as 'electrolysis' of copper pipes (in my case), and the repair is not covered. I was immediately quoted $8,000 to replace the pipes in the whole house. Per my knowledge, copper pipes corrode because of water acidity (normal wear and tear) not because of 'electrolysis.' In 2016, I was told by a plumber sent by American Home Shield that the whole bathroom, including the bath tub, had to be replaced otherwise the splash wall would soon collapse. This reason was totally fabricated. There are hundreds of thousands of people in the US who may have been cheated. Evidently, in my case, this company can always find reasons not to cover repairs, such as lack of maintenance. Mortgage brokers and real estate agents push the insurance as well. In 2015, my future lender stated I was not able to purchase points with the leftover $1,500 of funds intended for repairs or use the $1,500 to lower the principal. The $1,500 was going to be returned to the seller if not used to purchase two years' worth of insurance.

"*Mr. Sparky and the others (class action)* – Evidently, here is the company's business model: to pay an electrician a small flat fee to drive to a house for an estimate. If the electrician doesn't make a sale, the company will not pay him anything above the small flat fee. Why should they? The money is needed for countless advertisements. Much of the work is commission-based and many electricians may flat-out lie to people to sell unneeded services. In the worst-case scenario, electricians can pull permits without telling customers the associated risks; the City or County will then force homeowners to upgrade the electric grid in the whole house if it's not up to the latest codes.

"We will set up multiple locations and call technicians from different companies for estimates. Once pattern of fraud is established, class-action lawsuit against the corporation(s) will be filed.

"*Goodyear, Firestone, Pep Boys and the others (class action)* – Have you ever taken your car for an oil change and been quoted $1,000 worth of must-do repairs? Millions of people may have been cheated by these and similar companies. All we have to do is bring the same car to these places and compare the repair estimates for discrepancies. Our mechanic would tell if that's what is really wrong with the car. We would than ask for the unnecessary repairs to be performed and re-inspect the car to see if the repairs were actually performed.

"*Long-term plasma donation (class action)* – The US maintains the Western world's least restrictive plasma regulations and donation centers are controlled by five corporations. The centers have policies assured to lure those with ongoing need for small sums of cash: around $50 for the first five donations, then about $60 per week if you are willing to go under the needle twice a week. Plasma donation is a multi-billion-dollar business. The US has 5% of the world's population but its donors account for 70% of worldwide collections. Apparently, the companies are taking advantage of low income and homeless people. There is no central database and no caps on plasma donations. Long-term plasma donation negatively affects mental state. A person is more susceptible to social anxiety, panic attacks, depression, and mental illnesses, such as schizophrenia. In addition, the immune system is weakened, making a person more susceptible to all kinds of diseases and infections that normally the body is able to fight off.

"*Rizatriptan migraine medicine (class action)* – Canadian manufacturer recommends 20mg per 24 hours at most for people living in Canada. The US manufacturer recommends a maximum dose of 30mg per 24 hours for people living in the USA. Is the US population genetically different from the Canadian population for manufacturers to implement double standards? It looks like the government/FDA goes hand in hand with US drug manufacturers to maximize profits. This is most likely the reason why antidepressants and antibiotics are prescribed to children and adults like candy. Countless new medications with terrible side effects are introduced to the US population each year. Why does a flu shot contain mercury and aluminum?

"*WD, producer of portable hard drive (class action)* – 2TB is advertised, however only 1.81TB is available.

"*Manufacturer of Roundup (class action)* – In 2017, the European Parliament voted to ban glyphosate by 2022. Effective 2017, California lists Roundup's active ingredient, glyphosate, as a known carcinogen. TruGreen and other large and small landscape companies may pollute soil, rivers and underground waters with thousands of gallons of these chemicals every day.

"*Naked Juice and other products (class action)* – Per the manufacturer, the 64oz 'Strawberry Banana' juice contains 94 strawberries, 6 bananas,

7.25 apples and a hint of orange. It retails in Publix for $6.50. It contains no added sugar but from a taste perspective has the same sweet taste as 'Green Machine' juice, which contains different types of veggies and fruit. In Publix, 25 fresh strawberries (1lb) retail for about $3. I find it hard to believe the Strawberry Banana juice contains all the listed ingredients and only sells for $6.50. This appears to be false advertisement. We would first send the juices to a lab for testing. There are many other products that use questionable advertising methods: PH+ water, non-GMO, cage-free eggs where chickens are raised by individual family farms. Many high-end food products have so many beautiful stories written all over them. Are the stories real or fake? Has anybody ever tried to verify the stories? Were the ingredients ever verified by independent third parties? Are all the organic ingredients really organic?

"Publix Guacamole (class action, easy to prove) – Here is the ingredient list of Publix Deli mild guacamole, made in Mexico: avocado, tomatillo, onion, jalapeno pepper, salt, cilantro, garlic. In my case, the only problem is the green paste stayed green for days after being opened. Everybody should know that the top of guacamole turns brown the next day once opened, just as Whole Food's guacamole does. It appears Publix 'forgot' to mention the countless preservatives contained in its green paste.

"Walmart (class action) – In my case, the 80/20% ground beef contained way more water than normal ground beef. The patties shrank beyond recognition while on a grill. The fat didn't even solidify at the bottom of the grill like it does when you buy the same type of beef at Publix. We can buy meat packages from different stores and send them to a lab for analysis. The less educated people, who are least likely to question product quality, shop at Walmart. The company knows it and may prey on these customers.

"Even restaurants like Papouli's Mediterranean Café and Christos use a 'beef and lamb mix' processed meat cone that is shaved into thin rectangular patties. Gyros consisting of this meat makes my stomach bloated. Ingredients of the 'beef and lamb mix' are nowhere to be found on their menus. On the other hand, Christos' real lamb gyros are delicious.

"The quality of home-prepared food differs by area. Publix subs, for example: I love these sandwiches and noticed in Stockbridge the buns are harder, and the veggies and meat are drier than in East Cobb. Same goes for Kroger – the cafes aren't as nice, with worse selection in poorer areas. People should question why cashiers are not allowed to sit on a chair, as it is customary in many different countries, but have to stand in one spot for eight-plus hours. Per my knowledge, why is LA Fitness in Alpharetta the only club in Metro Atlanta that has a filtered water fountain?

"Leslie's Pool Supplies (employee class actions) – As soon as I walked into the small store located in the Publix shopping center on Delk Road in Marietta, I smelled a strong chlorine odor and in less than a minute became light-headed. Next to the cash registers, there was a pyramid of large chlorine buckets. I said/asked the cashiers the odor is ridiculous, how come it doesn't bother them and why aren't most of the buckets moved to a storage room in the back of the shop. 'We are not allowed to move the buckets. The odor bothers us but we get used to anything,' one of the women employees said, and opened the front door to vent out the odor. Chlorine is toxic with adverse short- and long-term health effects. What if a female employee is pregnant? Is this how the self-proclaimed 'World leader in residential and commercial pool supplies' treats its employees? Hardware and grocery stores display countless amounts of products that may be releasing toxic odors. How is the health of those employees going to be affected in the long run, especially if the enclosed area has insufficient ventilation?

"WebMD (class action) – The purpose of the lawsuit is to stop the spread of medical and nutritional fake news that endanger public health. Sodas are really not that bad for you. Processed food is hard to identify. What is processed food? Carrot is a rabbit food. Sitting too close to the TV will not damage your eyes. Really, what about the blue light LED screens emit? 'Keeping a nightlight on in your baby's room may actually help them learn to focus and develop important eye coordination skills when they are awake.' This comment about nightlight directly contradicts WebMD's other article named 'Light Exposure May Cut Production of Melatonin.' Who in their right mind would promote the use of nightlights? Apparently, WebMD is a for-profit organization mainly serving as advertisement tool for various industries. It's sickening how much common sense/evidently misleading information this company spreads. You can always find and pay some doctor who then writes whatever you want. This is similar to the so-called 'reputable scientists' that claim global warming is not real. Here are the articles.
"http://www.webmd.com/eye-health/fact-fiction-myths-about-eyes#1-2
"http://blogs.webmd.com/food-and-nutrition/2014/03/what-is-processed-food-exactly.html
"http://www.webmd.com/diet/features/sodas-and-your-health-risks-debated#1

"https://www.webmd.com/sleepdisorders/news/20110119/light-exposure-may-cut-production-of-melatonin

"T-Mobile (class action) – Phone purchase. Every time you go to a store and upgrade or purchase a new phone, you have to pay a $20 service charge even when you want to switch an existing SIM card yourself. This even applies to a $75 Alcatel flip phone, mainly used by elderly people like my mom. The only way to avoid this charge is to go to the T-Mobile website and purchase the phone online. The only catch is that you might not be able to purchase the Alcatel phone online as in my case, for some reason, the 'Add to cart' button was always gray.

"Alpine Dental and others (class action) – I went to this dentist for years and always received a free Oral-B toothbrush. The toothbrush was so hard my gums were hurting after the first use. I hope most people are aware of the fact that gums recede faster when a hard toothbrush is used, thus artificially creating more work for dentists. Why are so many dentists pushing people to buy electric toothbrushes at their offices? Are they concerned about your health or making a sale? Maybe the dentists are mostly concerned about creating more work for themselves since excessive usage of electric toothbrushes contributes to receding gums and loss of protective tooth enamel. Let's not even go into mandatory X-rays 'required' during every single visit.

"False advertisement for newly established businesses (class action) – In spring of 2017, I formed a company to venture into residential construction. The newly created legal entity received several threatening advertisement letters resembling governmental warning letters from Labor Poster Services telling the entity to post an OSHA informational employment poster otherwise a stiff fine may follow. Of course, Labor Poster Services provided a convenient way to order the poster directly from the company. Apparently, the company didn't bother to find out I have no employees and no office.

"Nonprofit activities

"Public awareness campaign to limit the use of plastics – Plastics are used everywhere these days. There are seven categories rated by numbers listed at the bottom of each product. Some are more dangerous than others. For example, plastic #1 PET is widely used as a drink container. It may release a harmful chemical (antimony trioxide) in warm temperatures reached in places such as enclosed storage areas, garages, and cars. How is the Fiji water stored before the customer buys it? When

should you throw away your child's plastic sippy cup? Dishwasher detergents can contribute to chemical release from plastics. When should you throw away your plastic coffee maker? When should you replace polyethylene (HDPE) drinking water pipes in your house to avoid chemical leaking? Why are to-go cups in places like Quick Trip and Chick-fil-A made out of plastic #6 – polystyrene? Hot coffee warms the cup and human carcinogen styrene can be released. When inspecting my plastic 'Mr. Coffee', made in China, I lifted the metal filter with cover and saw partially melted glue leaking from all sides. The glue was hanging right over the coffee pot. . . yummy. How do you know the Chinese will really use high-quality plastics to make these products?

"Manufacturers frequently use #1 PET plastic to bottle products such as honey. The expiration date for honey is at minimum three years from the production date. What if the container is exposed to heat or sunlight for a prolonged period of time?

"Various producers of plastic containers exposed to food (class action) – The truth is, none of your plastic products such as water filter pitchers have warnings of when to dispose of or how to properly use the plastics to prevent chemical leakage.

"According to *Science* journal, between 5 and 14 million tons of plastics are thrown into oceans each year. The Mediterranean Sea has 1.5 million micro plastic particles per 0.6 mile and fish frequently eat these particles. There are several larger microscopic plastic garbage patches in the world's oceans. The ultimate goal of the campaign is to change consumers' habits, persuade or sue companies to find alternative materials, and lobby or sue governments to change legislatures. There is absolutely no reason to use plastics as food containers. There are better alternatives, such as paper, glass, and metal.
"https://www.ecowatch.com/7-types-of-plastic-wreaking-havoc-on-our-health-1882198584.html

"Public awareness of questionable products such as petroleum-based food dyes, rBST growth hormone and dishwasher detergents. The three most common petroleum-based food dyes, red #40, yellow #5 and #6, may contain cancer-causing chemical benzidine and can cause allergic reactions. The FDA has stated that ingestion is typically under the 'concern threshold.' In Britain, manufacturers were requested to replace artificial food colors with natural alternatives, such as turmeric and beet juice. There are no warnings on the packages in the US, as there are in the EU, that alert parents that the dyes contained in the foods have been shown to cause behavioral changes and attention issues in children.

Another disturbing fact is that it's permissible to use the rBST growth hormone in livestock to increase milk production, right here in the USA. This substance has been banned in Canada, Australia, the European Union, New Zealand, Japan, Israel and Argentina due to severe negative health effects on the animals and hard-to-prove adverse health effects on human consumers. When the FDA legalized the growth hormone, it basically stated: 'It's OK to drink milk from cows that may get sick after the growth hormone is administered.' Apparently, as long as adverse health effects on a population are hard to prove and you have deep enough pockets, you can always find friends in any governmental agency who will rubber stamp anything you want.

"My wife keeps buying family size dishwasher detergent from Sam's Club. This detergent doesn't completely wash off and leaves an invisible film. I have to rinse a glass before use otherwise the refreshing water would include a foam. Maybe the dishwasher is old and dishes should be rinsed after the dishwashing cycle is over, who knows. More testing is needed. One time, Mom gave me natural dishwasher detergent purchased at Whole Foods and this problem went away. I have a feeling there are many products on the market with hard-to-spot negative health effects. We'll just have to keep our eyes open.

"Public awareness campaign to limit EMF exposure – the International Learning Academy in Jonesboro is a standalone building with no other buildings in sight. Do you know why? It was built close to a power station and right next to an 'interstate highway' of high-voltage powerlines. The EMF radiation the children are exposed to is way over the 2mG limit. The human body is electric and children especially are sensitive to this type of radiation. My wife Romana registered our daughter Julia at St. Catherine's Pre-K. I later found out the church/school is next to high-voltage powerlines. At least the school is next to only one and not multiple lines like the school in Jonesboro. It is not uncommon to see cell phone towers in parks and on school properties. There is a reason why most people would not live next to high-voltage power lines or cell phone towers. The public should question why, in the mid-1990s, the FCC approved human exposure guidelines for microwave radiation that may have been written by the cell phone industry itself. The FCC basically stated 'It's OK to hold and use a device that emits electromagnetic radiation in the microwave range directly against a brain.' Microwave ovens is another example. I have yet to see an owner's manual where a manufacturer would recommend a minimum safety distance for a person to stay away while a microwave oven is in use. In my case, an electromagnetic field at three feet was 14mG when a microwave was in use. As I was slowly approaching the

microwave oven, EMF radiation was rapidly increasing and at a distance of about a foot from the oven, my 100mG EMF meter ran out of range. The government's EMF standards for human exposure are way below Europe's. The Austrian Medical Association developed a set of EMF diagnosis/treatment guidelines. The public should be aware of the risks and associated health consequences. There are ways to make electronic products safer, such as the use of material to shield the interior case of a product. Legislative changes will be required to force manufacturers to produce safer products. Why are Americans the richest and at the same time unhealthiest people on the planet?
"http://electromagnetichealth.org/electromagnetic-health-blog/oak-emf-guidelines/

"Reduce government waste – Have you ever wondered why trees along interstates are cut further away from a road as time goes by? I-75 in Bartow County is a sad example; tree branches closest to the road are completely cut from the side facing the road and the trees look like toothpicks. Besides the esthetics, the trees are weakened and prone to fall during a major storm. Apparently, it makes perfect sense to weaken trees in order to create more work for buddies in the private sector, the buddies who may give the elected officials nice kickbacks. Why was the contract to fix the collapsed I-85 bridge awarded to one company without any bidding whatsoever? It would have taken a day at most for companies to submit their offers. In many cases, why are paid express lanes being built alongside interstate highways, instead of additional 'free of charge' lanes? Historically, federal dollars have been used to build, maintain, and expand the interstates.

"FTC, GA Consumer Protection unit and other governmental agencies – I reported several charitable online scams to FTC and always received the same response: a generic email on how to spot online scams. Apparently, the agency didn't launch a formal investigation. Evidently, the GA Consumer protection unit didn't investigate non-transparent fundraising activities performed by a Chick-fil-A restaurant but referred the response back to the company to answer the complaint. 'Contact the consumer directly with any response,' was stated in the letter. CFA's legal department referred me to the store where the incident happened. The letter stated: 'We are not responsible for actions of individual franchisees.' The store owner of course never answered. It appears people at these and similar governmental agencies are there to collect paychecks and shuffle work somewhere else. The Georgia Secretary of State did launch a formal investigation regarding a scam Christian

charity called Destiny Institute International. I was impressed with the agency's updates.

"*Mall revitalization* – Many malls across the country are on the verge of going bankrupt because of online shopping. Our nonprofit group would partner up with owners to help them design a sustainable business plan with competitive advantages over online shopping. Malls are small islands surrounded by a sea of asphalt. Why not build multilevel parking decks and convert most of the current parking area to greenery, with nature trails, a small theme park, miniature zoo, playgrounds and/or community gardens where people could plant fruits and vegetables? Restaurants and cafes would be strategically placed within the green zone for parents to socialize while their children were playing. A certain percentage of retail space should be rented free of charge to qualified nonprofit or governmental organizations, such as a county library, to create the perfect mix of shopping/learning/entertainment experience for the whole family.

"*UnitedHealth Group and other health care insurers (class action)* – Apparently, this insurance company, and most likely all the others as well, constantly screen and evaluate people for liability after a substantial claim is filed. I kept receiving numerous calls from the company's investigators. 'Talk to my doctors,' I thought, and never called back. Optum mailed a letter to find out why I needed chiropractic care; is it because of a car- or work-related accident? Optum determined my injuries were not caused by someone else and paid for the treatment. This is just the tip of the iceberg. What type of approval process/screening is required for someone requiring long-term care? During 2015 to 2017, the company's net annual income almost doubled from $5.81 billion to $10.56 billion. In general, how convenient it is to use Obamacare as a constant excuse to decrease medical services and raise premiums. We will need strong public support to win this lawsuit because the government goes hand in hand with the health insurance industry. We will not settle until the insurance companies agree to significantly change their practices. Legislative change will be required as well. The public will have to continue to donate funds for us to fight this seemingly endless court battle. Pharmaceutical companies are not too far behind; who can afford to pay $475,000 for CAR T-cell cancer treatment therapy? Why is the price so high when R&D might have been paid for using taxpayers' dollars? Are the health insurance companies going to write a $475,000 check with no questions asked for every patient who needs the therapy?

"'In God We Don't Trust' campaign – Georgia is one of a few states that allow an 'In God We Trust' sticker, available at DMV for free, to be placed on a car tag over the area where a county name is listed. The government, together with religious people, effectively advertise their religious beliefs and at the same time silence the religiously unaffiliated: a quarter of the American population, by not providing an alternative 'In God We Don't Trust' sticker. The stickers could be easily modified to include the word 'Don't.' I will be the first to go ahead with this plan and advertise it on social media sites. A police officer will pull me over and issue a ticket. We will continue to appeal based on First Amendment violation and separation of Church and State. This case may very well end up in the U.S. Supreme Court. In the 1950s, the government mandated the phrase 'In God We Trust' be printed on all legal tender notes and changed the Pledge of Allegiance to include 'one Nation under God' instead of 'one nation'. It is no coincidence this happened in the 1950s.

"This indirectly relates to the recent NFL kneeling protests. Did you know you can even publicly burn the American flag? This form of protest falls under the category of protected speech. In 2000, Marilyn Manson chose this form of protest while performing at Tabernacle concert hall in downtown Atlanta. Coincidently, this happened about a month before the U.S. Supreme Court decided the presidential election by a five to four vote. So far, the freedom of speech is protected under the First Amendment of the U.S. Constitution. The public should be educated to not force their views on other individuals. The so-called 'patriots' who were appalled by the kneeling protests should realize that everybody has the right to a peaceful protest. To tell someone what to do, try to make someone feel ashamed, to organize people to hate others because of different beliefs, are exactly the same methods the communists used when an individual or group of people were disliked."

"I don't know much about law," Christine said.

"Where are we going to get the funding? Ronnee, how good are the lawsuits?" Jessica added.

Ronnee was looking into an empty space and didn't reply. There was about a thirty-second silence as we all looked at Ronnee.

"Some are easier than others, but we definitely have a chance to make this happen," she said, and smiled at the three of us.

"Initially, we will help Ronnee with anything she needs, sort of like paralegals," I said. "She will give us a crash course and tell us where to look for information, how the court system works and how to properly fill and file court documents. As we get better, Ronnee will shift more complex tasks to us. We are intelligent people with college degrees and can self-study and manage ourselves. I can put $100,000 towards the business."

Jessica and Christine answered almost simultaneously, "I don't have that much cash lying around."

I then continued: "Even if each of us put in $50,000, that's $200,000 total. It is enough money to get started and pay ourselves the same salaries we make at our current jobs, until we generate a steady cash flow. Don't worry about the initial investment, take your time and think about the amount at home. Be fair, but don't overstretch yourselves. I will loan you the difference if needed and you can pay me back once the firm has excess money. We will be equal partners with 25% ownership stakes. So, what do you guys think?"

"It sounds great but I have to think about it," Ronnee said.

Jessica and Christine agreed with her.

"Yes, think about it and let me know," I said, paused, and continued: "Here is where I would like the company to be in the near future. I truly believe the business will take off quicker than you might think. Money is not the primary motive for me doing this and we should agree on our salary caps ahead of time. I think $200,000 per year in today's dollars is more than enough for us to do whatever we like. It is, however, not enough to become rich. We should stay motivated and continue to work, use most of the earnings to grow the business and for the greater cause. The big picture is to positively impact the world around us so all children will have a brighter future. Any of you can, of course, leave the organization at any time but I hope you see this as a long-term commitment. The more lawsuits we win, the more law firms will follow the green pastures. This is great because we don't want to be the only good law firm on the block. It is necessary from a security perspective as we will attract attention of both good and bad people. Somebody is profiting from all the injustices. The more complex lawsuits we win, the more powerful people will be pissed off; the people at the top of the pyramid who are connected to the politicians. We will in fact teach average people to think logically for themselves, to question things, and not to swallow everything that corporations throw in front of their faces.

"I would like us to partner up with nonprofit organizations like Quality Care for Children for joint projects. We will sponsor (60% of average annual pay) selected moms of different backgrounds to be at home with their children for four years. The parents will be separated into three different groups and the children will be monitored from birth until the age of fifteen. The homes will be monitored 24/7 with web cameras and all communication will be recorded.

1. The moms will not be paid to be home with children. This group will represent the 'business as usual' American family. Both parents will work, use babysitters, and do as they please. We will compensate the families for monitoring and testing only.
2. The moms will stay home with babies and toddlers for four years and dads will work. Occasional use of relatives and friends as babysitters will be permitted upon approval. The families will be able to live whatever lifestyle they choose.
3. The moms will stay home with babies and toddlers for four years and dads will work up to forty hours per week. Both parents will adhere to strict sets of rules. Occasional use of relatives and friends as babysitters will be permitted upon approval. Grandparents will be involved in children's lives at least once a week and will have the children every other weekend. Fast/processed/restaurant food, including sodas, will be allowed two times per month. The parents (mostly moms since dads will work) will cook all meals from scratch using fresh unprocessed ingredients only. The family will eat specific portions only. The parents will read, sing, and hug their little children throughout the day and before bedtime. The children will play with other kids of different backgrounds inside and outside of the house, will spend a certain amount of time in nature, learn to play musical instruments, read a certain number of books, play sports, and will be taught how to be independent from age six. The use of TVs, computers, and cell phones will be limited per the following: 0 to 3 years old – not allowed, 4 to 9 – limited to 1 hour per day, 10 to 15 – limited to 2.5 hours per day, with exemptions on an individual basis to grow talent. For example, a child who expresses interest in IT. The families will vacation four times per year, one week each time: summer – beach, fall – domestic and world cities (New York, Paris, Moscow, Tokyo. . .), winter – skiing, spring – outdoors (camping, hiking, exploring. . .).

"The children will be tested on overall health, well-being, and development from a psychological perspective such as: ability to learn and cope with stress, social interaction, levels of empathy. . . and many more. The parents will be tested on everything except for child-related issues. We will be releasing the test results to the public as soon as they become available.

"I have an idea what the outcome will be, but we need solid data that no one will question. We will show the public a far superior family lifestyle that is different from what the food, entertainment, and pharmaceutical industries would like people to live.

"As mentioned before, the business will become a cash cow fairly quickly. To win one large lawsuit is all it takes. At that point, I would like us to start another nonprofit organization, a totally separate entity from the law firm. The nonprofit will indirectly pick fights with selected corporations by placing carefully designed public awareness ads all over the internet, social media, newspapers, and TV (Jessica, you are the communication expert) of this type:

"'Do you think real chicken nuggets should contain the below listed ingredients? McDonald's definitely think so. The Sodium Aluminum Phosphate sounds delicious. . . yummy. Don't forget to watch the movie *Super Size Me* (2004). :-)

"'Ingredients in McDonald's chicken nuggets (per the company's website):
"'White Boneless Chicken, Water, Vegetable Oil (Canola Oil, Corn Oil, Soybean Oil, Hydrogenated Soybean Oil), Enriched Flour (Bleached Wheat Flour, Niacin, Reduced Iron, Thiamine Mononitrate, Riboflavin, Folic Acid), Bleached Wheat Flour, Yellow Corn Flour, Vegetable Starch (Modified Corn, Wheat, Rice, Pea, Corn), Salt, Leavening (Baking Soda, Sodium Aluminum Phosphate, Sodium Acid Pyrophosphate, Calcium Lactate, Monocalcium Phosphate), Spices, Yeast Extract, Lemon Juice Solids, Dextrose, Natural Flavors.'

"McDonald's will not initially sue the nonprofit entity because there is no basis. There is nothing in the advertisement that would fall under legal definition of defamation/slander. 'The Sodium Aluminum Phosphate sounds delicious. . . yummy. Don't forget to watch the movie *Super Size Me* (2004).' These sentences are pure opinions protected under various anti-SLAPP statutes. By the way, the USA is the land of free speech. The company will have to sue us eventually because of declined sales. By that time, our name will be out there and the nonprofit entity will ask the public for donations to fight the lawsuit. Our law firm will offer legal assistance to the nonprofit entity. ;-) We will stop the advertisement only after the company agrees to make ALL food healthier by removing the unnecessary/unhealthy ingredients and discloses the percentage of chicken meat vs other ingredients, such as water. It is possible. Trader Joe's Tuscan Pane whole wheat bread only contains stone-ground whole wheat flower, water, salt, and yeast. The advertisement can apply to any processed food product. For example, CFA's fried chicken sandwich contains monosodium glutamate (MSG), yellow-5 and blue-1 artificial food dyes. Do you know what happens to the law firm in the 1998 movie, *A Civil Action*? The firm runs out of money and goes bankrupt before settlement is reached. This will not be an issue since the public will fund most of the advertisements and the defense.

"Many other law firms will copy our strategy and the law suits will become harder to win. At that point I would like to start a church."

The girls simultaneously exploded into laughter like there was no tomorrow. "Ha, ha, ha. . . Start a church? Joseph, you are really fucked up in the head," Jessica said.

"Yes, that's a great idea. I'll be the Virgin Mary," added Ronnee, continuing to laugh and asking Christine, "What is your role going to be?"

Christine looked at her, paused for a few seconds and answered, "I will be the main nun; the bitch who will tell all the girls to abstain from sex until they marry, ha, ha, ha."

At that point even I laughed like crazy and said, "Ronnee, if you want to be a virgin again that can be arranged. I read about a medical procedure called hymen repair, whereby virgin membrane is restored to its original condition. The procedure is popular among older women. This would be a great present for your husband's fifty-sixth birthday. Don't you think?"

Ronnee smiled to herself and kept silent, apparently giving it some serious thought.

"OK, girls, my stomach hurts and I can't laugh anymore." I chuckled and continued to speak. "Seriously, I would like us to open a church. It will be the church for everybody: Christians, Jews, Muslims, Hindus, Buddhists. . . you name it. We will study the Bible, Koran, or whatever the religious documents may be to look for subjects that unite us, not the subjects that separate us. The members will eventually realize that deep down all people are the same, regardless of background. We will teach the members to think for themselves, to question things and not to believe and swallow everything the mainstream churches throw at them – such as the mainstream clergy that preaches water but drinks wine.

"Many churches are nothing more than glorified corporations hiding behind nonprofit status. Here are a few examples. . .

"St. Catherine's preschool has a cafeteria with a full-size kitchen but, to my knowledge, it is not used to provide freshly cooked nutritious lunches for the children. On one afternoon the kitchen was in use, meals were about to be served on tables full of china plates accompanied by crystal wine glasses. There was a speaker stand, normally not present, overlooking the cafeteria. At the 2017 Fall Festival organized by the preschool, the kitchen was in use again and my four-year-old, Julia, was charged $5 for a small hot dog. The china plates and crystal glasses were gone and meals consisting of chips, chili, hot dogs, CFA's chicken nuggets, water, and lemonade were served on paper or plastic. In front of the school/church, there was a 'youth center' where a man who appeared to be the dad, with two boys no older than fifteen, assembled a porch. Multiple donation boxes were strategically placed at different locations within the perimeter of the Fall Festival event. There was a man in his early fifties walking around the area with a beer in his hand, talking to different people. He occasionally approached women from behind to rub backs and massage their shoulders. Anyway, at least the schoolteachers were always friendly, used creative teaching methods and didn't preach religion to small children.

"I volunteered as a greeter at Buckhead Church. The offices are beautifully decorated with stylish furniture and the latest available teleconference equipment. The common areas are modern as well and include moving stairs. I wish all MARTA stations had these stairs as it is customary in subway stations throughout Europe. This reminds me of PulteGroup, located across the street, where millions of dollars were spent to remodel the offices in a similar style. It appears the church spared no expense on remodeling the premises and why would they? Apparently, their corporate office, 'North Point Ministries,' correctly calculated the luxurious environment would continuously bring back people living in and around the Buckhead area. To tell people exactly what they want to hear, to steer their way of thinking away from reality into false dreams, lies, and delusions, appears to be the purpose of the Sunday services. It looks like, from a psychological standpoint, the stories are told in such a way that the human spirit is thrown into bondage and consequently has no problem opening up a wallet and giving away hard-earned money. Volunteers and people attending the church were always friendly but a few things stood out. The welcome package consisting of one T-shirt was mailed to me via regular mail. The postage was $6.65. Why not save money and give out T-shirts in person?

"North Point Ministries organized a 2017 Christmas Event for singles at the Atlanta College Football Hall of Fame. Hundreds of people were charged a $30 entrance fee to attend the party, where water, coffee, and cakes were served. 'It would be nice to offer you a glass of wine or beer,' I said to a few single women. 'We drank before we came here,' was the usual response.

"Apparently, North Point Ministries, Inc., relies on armies of volunteers to coordinate much of the operation of their three churches; North Point Community Church, Buckhead Church and Browns Bridge Community Church. According to the organization's 2011 Operating

Budget Summary document, $18.7 million out of $41.2 million worth of charitable contributions was spent on salaries and benefits. How many homeless shelters does the group operate? Does it cost $5.7 million annually in salaries and benefits to maintain the North Point Ministries Fund? The fund itself had contributions of $222,300. It looks like the accountants are making a killing. :-) In my opinion, if you need someone to tell you what to do, to influence your life and to consistently speak with friendly staff, this is the place for you.

"In 2017, I visited MUST Ministries. Detailed financial information going back several years is available on the organization's website. According to the 2016 990 income tax return, the group has an annual operation budget of only $10 million and runs a homeless shelter located close to Kennesaw Mountain. Besides the warm bed, employment services and job training are also available on the premises. Free meals are provided to everyone who shows up at the cafeteria.

"Darkness and sadness overcame my body as I walked into the main building's interior. Memories of hardships and sufferings endured by every single tenant who ever entered the building to rest his or her body, to close both eyes, to forget about everything for just a few hours, were suddenly released from the walls and felt by my body at once. The shelter itself has military-style bunkbeds lined up next to and above each other. Light hardly penetrates the ground level since the windows are mostly covered up. On second thought, everyone has to be out of the shelter throughout the day so daylight is not that important. Single men sleep on the ground floor, women with children in the basement and there is one family room. A small playground adjacent to the building has a few basic toys and bicycles for the kids to play with. The place is very basic but serves its purpose. I wish more churches would act like MUST Ministries.

"As I was walking through the area, my thoughts switched to memories of the homeless shelter for single moms where I lived in 1994. A stranger walking by the building wouldn't have had any idea it was a homeless shelter. The building was surrounded by a grass area and there was a playground. The government-operated shelter was recently remodeled, was immaculately clean and had basic amenities, such as a front desk person/security guard dressed in plain clothes who made sure unwanted people weren't entering the building. Common areas included several bathrooms and a large room with TV, board games, and toys for children. Each mom with kid(s) had a separate room with beds, nightstands, a couple closets, and a sink. The walls were white with a few pictures to cheer up the residents. The best feature of each room was a large panoramic window. Bright sunlight penetrated the window of our room on many mornings and what a difference this had on my spirit, mind, and mood. Life difficulties became miniscule and it appeared I was able to solve any problem with ease.

"Organized religion is nothing more than another form of government designed to control the mind. Organized religion causes irreparable damage to the human thought process. A person is not a freethinker anymore but becomes an obedient puppet. That's why we have directions on shampoo bottles. The people will eventually realize that organized religion is a fraud. Once this happens, we will advise them to read *Goblet of the Truth*. A few selected individuals will open franchises across the US first, later around the world. The four of us will have to educate ourselves on philosophy, all religions, and different cultures. We may have to travel the world to gain the knowledge. It will be necessary for us to have the knowledge because people will ask us for guidance and advice. At that point, the four of us will only direct the operations of the law firm and the nonprofit entities from a high level, as selected individuals will manage the teams and oversee details of the day-to-day operations.

"At this moment, don't think and worry about it. First things first, we need to establish the law firm and the three of us have to catch up with Ronnee regarding law. The Nissan lawsuit will put our company over the edge. I estimate the settlement from the personal lawsuit will be around $150 million. Why not? If a woman can get almost $3 million for burning her pussy with hot coffee, why can't I win $150 million since I have all these unexplained medical issues? The firm will get 40% – $60 million, which leaves $90 million for myself. This is what I would like to do with the personal money:

"Fifty million dollars – donate this sum to Mikhail Khodorkovsky for him to fight and overthrow Vladimir Putin. The US is a nation of laws where up to a certain point you can fight battles in the courtroom. The legal system doesn't work in Russia. Muscles and weapons are needed to fight battles. We will have a powerful ally once Mikhail is elected as the President of Russia. He will be a great help once we begin to establish our worldwide church franchise.

"Twenty million dollars – donate the funds to Quality Care for Children and to other domestic/foreign nonprofit organizations similar to Quality Care.

"Fifteen million dollars – hide part of the funds in safety deposit boxes and other places worldwide. Deposit some of the money in Swiss banks. Only the four of us will know where the money is located. The funds are to be used by us only in case of an emergency. Do you remember what I told you about the bad people who will eventually notice our actions?

"Three million dollars – carefully help (over a longer period of time) my family members. If an individual is given too much money too quickly, he/she will not appreciate it and will blow it like there is no end in sight. In the long run, the person will not be happy and may eventually blame you for all the bad. I would advise you to do the same when the law firm pays each of you a one-time $5 million bonus.

"Two million dollars – keep part as a safety net and spend the rest. I'll buy a car that gets more than eighty-five miles per charge, probably a Tesla or maybe a Dodge Challenger Demon – that car would definitely make me the 'Bad Mother Fucker.' :-) All of you should treat yourselves as well, up to a certain point. It is good for the psyche; subconsciously your mind will know the money is real and not just some numbers sitting somewhere in a bank.

"This is what I would like our firm to do with the $60 million:

"Fifteen million dollars – divide this among Christine, Jessica, and Ronnee.

"Twenty-five million dollars – grow the business, hire employees and establish teams, start the nonprofit entity and one church to test/solidify processes before franchising the operation. Partner up with Quality Care for Children and start the 'New Moms at Home' project.

"Twenty million dollars – purchase a few acres in the North Carolina mountains and build an energy independent, sustainable work/recreational/garden center to be used by us, our families, all our employees and their families. I don't know how high the tide will be once the judgment day arrives. We need to ensure the operation will continue as normal once this happens. My high-school chemistry teacher, Mr. Puckett, once said, 'One day we will live on Marietta beach.' For some reason, this sentence stuck in my mind. In the early part of 2017, many things that were stuck in my mind became reality. I am confident the Friends will provide us with some sort of warning before the incident.

"Here are some thoughts about our corporate culture: all employees are to be treated as human beings and with respect, not like some numbers that could be exploited and replaced at any time. Establish processes/standards so everybody works as efficiently as possible. Create communication channels so everyone, regardless of position, can express new ideas or concerns. No one will work more than forty hours per week unless there is a drop-dead deadline or other emergency. Everyone will enjoy the following benefits:
1. Employer-sponsored medical insurance with $0 deductible and $0 copay – provided for free.

2. $100k life insurance – provided for free.
3. Four weeks of paid vacation after 2 years of employment. Two paid weeks between 0–2 years.
4. After 3 years of employment – new moms will stay home for 6 months with full pay and after the 6 months will have the option to work part-time (20 hours) mostly from home with all benefits for up to 3.5 years. This benefit ensures the new moms will devote most of their time to their babies/toddlers for 4 years.
5. Establish a reservation system to ensure fair use of the NC center.

"I have one more person in mind that I would like to bring in as an equal partner. Her name is Leah."

Before I had a chance to say anything else. . .

"Leah, the woman you fell in love with a few years ago?" Ronnee said, in a surprised tone of voice, giving me the look of a sad girl who was just unexpectedly dumped by her boyfriend.

I felt horrible, this was not what I had in mind.

"Ronnee, please don't hold it against me," I thought, then quickly pulled myself together and continued to speak. "Leah has certain qualities that would supercharge the whole operation.

"*Leah* – a natural-born leader, is patient and great with details but at the same time sees the big picture. This quality is extremely rare. She has charm and people's personality but at the same time is down-to-earth. She is fair and treats everyone with respect. According to my observation, at age fifty, she is not too happy she has been treated as a second-class citizen her whole life by the Southern Baptist Convention.

"The companies that will be sued are publicly traded. Leah (and later her team) will perform forensic tax accounting and the firm will be able to nail some of the corporations for tax fraud. Also, she knows how a church operates and would be the perfect person to help start and direct the initial location.

"There are a few more lawsuits I would eventually like us to start:

"*IRS (same reporting standards for individuals, businesses, and nonprofits)* – In summer of 2017, I was a member of Meadowgrove Swim and Tennis club. I have been a member for three years and nothing appeared to ever be maintained or upgraded; the pool was leaking water, there were holes in the surrounding concrete, many tables and chairs were broken. A board member named Zack stated the club received a $20,000 donation a couple years ago to upgrade the facilities. The 2017 fees were raised from $350 to $495 with a promise to perform the much-needed repairs. I requested three years' worth of tax returns from the IRS and received 990 forms with no supporting schedules. I wrote back to the IRS and specifically requested the supporting schedules. I received a phone call from the IRS stating the agency doesn't have any additional documents for this entity. As a result, the 990 forms became useless sheets of paper. Does the IRS have different reporting standards for nonprofit, businesses, and individuals?

"IRS (level the playing field for churches and regular nonprofits; very difficult and expensive class action) – The goal is to mandate all churches to open their accounting books to the public and for the churches to stop accepting cash donations. (Cash donations were not accepted during the February 28 2017 Chick-fil-A's Spirit Night fundraiser for the little girl Taylor.) End income tax exemptions not available to other nonprofit organizations and individuals, including Medicare/Social Security, self-employment tax and housing allowance. Repeal IRC Section 7611 – Restrictions on church tax inquiries and examinations. Unfortunately, Section 7611 also applies to church employment tax inquiries and examinations. File form 990 tax returns and be subject to the same audit standards as other entities and individuals. We may have to partner up with organizations like Freedom From Religion Foundation in order to succeed. In 2014, the IRS had the nerve to tell FFRF to become an 'atheist' church so its 'ministers' could qualify for the housing allowance!?! We will win the lawsuit once we have enough public support.

"IRS (to establish progressive Flat Tax system; very difficult and expensive class action) – Is it fair that a person who earns more than $127,200 doesn't have to pay any Social Security taxes on a portion of the income greater than $127,200? There are many loopholes similar to the above that mostly benefit wealthy individuals and powerful corporations. The goal is to have a 'Flat Tax' system without any deductions or exemptions. This is the only way to assure fairness to everybody regardless of stature or income. We will win this lawsuit once we have enough public support.

"IRS (establish online disclosure requirements for all charities; very difficult and expensive class action) – I recently came across an organization called Destiny Institute International on LinkedIn. The contact person, Tiffany Sonnier, MBA, only asked for money in every single post generated multiple times per day. When I asked her for the tax ID number to verify the Christian charitable nonprofit organization with the IRS, I was basically told to leave her alone and was

disconnected as a friend. To prevent scam charities from operating and reputable charities from embezzling funds, the IRS should require all charities to post the following information on their websites: FEIN number, three years of federal tax returns and percentage of funds collected vs funds donated for every single project. We should form a partnership with someone like FFRF and ask the public for support.

"The four of us should first establish the law firm: lease/furnish a nice office and brainstorm the details on where to begin. Once this is finished, we will post an employment ad: 'Law/CPA firm is seeking equal partner with corporate tax background, minimum fifteen years' experience. Pay and benefits are negotiable.'

"The three of you will reach out to Leah and invite her to lunch. At the lunch, don't ask her any technical questions. Don't even bother to learn any basics since in about two minutes she would know that you don't know anything. Tax accounting is very difficult and is designed in such a way that it wouldn't make sense to most people. Tax laws have been written by the wealthy, for the wealthy, to hire armies of skilled tax accountants to help them avoid paying taxes, shift resources, and hide wealth. Tell her it is all about the 'fit' and get to know her, joke with her, tell her stories, ask her to tell you her stories. In other words, see if you like her as a person. If any of you don't like her, we will not bring her in. I am sure the three of you will like Leah once you get to know her. The five of us would be the perfect team.

"This is it, girls. It will not get any better than this. The goal is for us to have lives with purpose; to perform work that we like and to have fun at the same time. I am excited about the thought of what we can accomplish. As a team, we can accomplish something that none of us would ever be able to do as individuals. Not all will go according to plan and we may not accomplish everything. But let me tell you, we have about thirty years of productive lives left and that's plenty of time to cause a lot of damage. No matter the difficulty of our task, we will always come back stronger than ever and ready to fight. That's what winners do. We have to in order to become next season's winners, not last season's losers. The world will be a much better place if we accomplish just half of what is planned. Think about it and let me know.

"Why don't we have a toast anyway? Even if you don't want to do this, I am hell of a glad to see you all today! I really miss the lunches at Argos," I said, and poured the last of the red wine into four glasses and we toasted.

"Argos was never the same after you left. I thought about you many times and remembered when you used to come to my cubicle to talk. The lunches were a lot of fun and we miss them as well," said Ronnee in a soft tone of voice, and her eyes penetrated mine.

Unconsciously, her body stripped her of the filters most people put on to protect their image. She was just there, totally exposed and fully naked. Ronnee's face was radiating her true feelings she was forced to bury deep down in her soul after I left Argos. She looked so vulnerable, sweet, and innocent. In her mind, at this moment, she was ready to fully give herself to me. This was only possible because she truly loved me. Naturally, Ronnee would never admit it because she has been living her life in a certain way for twenty-plus years.

"I wouldn't feel right pulling her away from the life she has been working so hard to build and maintain for such a long time," I thought to myself, then ended the eye contact, pulling out my phone to send a few text messages.

The ladies were having a good time and started to talk about female-related issues. I kept quiet, was looking at everyone as my thought process was accelerating, not out of control like during the game but slowly, so I could manage. I was replaying the plan in my head and realized one important piece of information was missing from the puzzle. . . "If they agree to form the venture, it changes everything. I can never sleep with any of them, including Ronnee. I can show my love and affection, but equally to the four of them. I can hug and kiss them on the cheeks, but that's where it stops. If I preferred one over another what would the other girls think? Truly, I love them all in different ways, so why fuck up a perfectly good thing? It has to be this way for the operation to survive in the long run. In order to succeed, the five of us will have to learn to trust each other with our lives. All for one and one for all. There will always be an excuse why I can't make it to a date, if asked. By the way, the girls are happily married and I don't want to break up anyone's marriage. This is why the Friends wanted me to experience the swingers' lifestyle, so I wouldn't have any funny ideas about certain group activities with my future partners." I smiled to myself and was happy the meeting turned out better than expected.

I watched the girls as they were laughing and chatting like in the good old days. To me, that was the most pleasant aspect of the day.

"The best way to mitigate the risk of an affair is for the ladies to spend as much time with their families as possible, away from the office," I thought, then abruptly joined their conversation and said the following: "I just came up with a great idea to retain talent in our future firm. We are the partners and can do whatever we want to. Why don't we normally work Monday to Thursday, forty hours per week? We will work on Friday only if there is a hearing, deadline, or an emergency. It's

313

a great idea and our future employees will surely appreciate it. What do you guys think?"

"Anything you say, Joseph. At this point I'm having a nice buzz going on from the wine," Christine said.

"Sounds wonderful but we still haven't even decided what to do in the first place," Jessica added.

"OK, so here's how I see it," I replied. "We will get some attention once the book is published and our name will be out there after we win a couple major lawsuits. After the judgment day, people will really start to listen to what we have to say. At that point, I would like you to run for public offices and lobby the public to put pressure on the lawmakers to redefine the term 'Natural Born Citizen' so it applies to anyone who has been a naturalized US citizen for at least twenty years. Once that is accomplished, I will run for the presidency," I said, with a slight smirk on my face.

Jessica immediately reacted. "You know what Joseph? You should be a professional bullshitter, or sort of fairy tale storyteller for young children. Just to let you know, we agreed not to sleep with you no matter what you say or how drunk you get us. . ."

Christine yelled at the waiter standing at the other end of the restaurant. "Waiter, please bring us another couple bottles of wine! We're not going anywhere anytime soon." She briefly paused, then spoke in a normal tone of voice. "I don't know about you all but I am being pleasantly entertained. Girls, what are we going to do with him? So Joseph, please continue and don't mind our occasional interruptions."

Ronnee was not saying anything as she was smiling, looking down at her phone and texting her husband not to expect her home anytime soon.

"OK Jessica. . . ;-) fair enough. I give up. So don't sleep with me, but hear me out. I know this sounds crazy but let me tell you the reasons why I would like us to accomplish this task." I finished the sentence as the waiter brought another two bottles of the delicious California Pinot Noir.

Chapter 13
The Meeting/Government

The waiter opened one bottle and offered us a taste.

"We trust the wine will taste great since we've already had several bottles, please just fill our glasses to the top!" I said.

The waiter poured the contents of one bottle into our glasses, opened the other bottle and left the table. I continued to speak.

"For you to understand why I would like us to accomplish this task, we need to look first into our nation's history. We live in interesting times where, to some people, greed and power mean more than freedom, love, and character. This wasn't the case just a few decades ago because adults of that time were raised differently – with love, virtues, and empathy, by their parents who lived through the Great Depression and fought in WWII. Today, more people than ever try to live off other people and cheat anything and anyone more than ever before. As a result, society itself is spiraling out of control and it is more important than ever before to make a difference; fight for freedoms, be involved in politics and community. The freedoms listed in the U.S. Constitution are not guaranteed for everyone because special interest groups and people at the top of the pyramid have a different interpretation of those freedoms than the people at the bottom.

"As Trump has stated many times, the current state of politics is a disaster. I read almost daily how the federal, state, and local governments openly ignore the separation of Church and State, placing corporations and the military ahead of the common people. Here are a few examples:

"Violation of the separation of Church and State
1. SB-436; on June 9 2017, Florida legislative chambers passed the SB-436 bill encouraging students to perform religious rituals in public schools regardless of religious beliefs. Apparently, Satanist and Gothic students are encouraged to freely express themselves as well. This bill will invite avoidable lawsuits, create confusion, and distract students from learning.
2. Between 2014 and 2017, the City of Pensacola spent almost $100,000 of taxpayers' money to fight and appeal a lawsuit that everybody with common sense knew the City was going to lose. In 1969, the City installed a thirty-four-foot concrete Christian cross in Bayview Park, a public property. What happened to other religions, such as Judaism and Hinduism? I don't see their symbols being displayed in the park. In June 2017, a Florida judge declared the cross unconstitutional. Consequently,

Christian fundamentalists have harassed Monica Miller, the attorney who won the lawsuit against the city.

3. On June 30 2017, four different Planned Parenthood clinics were forced to shut down because religious fundamentalists in the Iowa government turned down free money, $3 million dollars of federal funding designated for a family planning program.

4. In May 2017, the state of Nevada outlawed anti-gay conversion therapy for children under eighteen. This dangerous and inhumane practice leads to depressions and suicides. Everybody, such as psychiatrists, social workers, nurses, have to abide by this rule. Everybody except for members of the clergy. Are members of the clergy above the law? It appears in the state of Nevada members of the clergy are free to abuse children as they please. This is no surprise since so many child molestation cases committed in the name of God went, and are going, unpunished.

5. Maine Criminal Justice Academy performs prayers before meals.

6. Louisiana judge Charles Schrumpf is telling first-time drug offenders to attend Christian programs called 'Life Choices' offered by local churches. Did Mr. Schrumpf ever read the U.S. Constitution? Does he understand the separation of Church and State? What happened to common sense?

7. Johnson Amendment – In May 2017, Trump communicated to churches that his administration will not enforce the Johnson Amendment. This presidential executive order stops the IRS from revoking a church's or nonprofit's tax-exempt status if it chooses to support a political cause. I don't want to live to see the day when the United States becomes a nation openly ruled by religious fundamentalists, like in the movie *Demolition Man* (1993). FFRF's 'You're Sued!' campaign was the only logical outcome. This was not a surprise since White House staffers and cabinet officials hold weekly Bible study sessions. What a great use of taxpayers' dollars. :-) Yes, please increase my taxes and organize more of these sessions. What if someone refuses to participate? Will that person be excommunicated from the White House clique, or in the near future be publicly crucified? On August 5 2017, an episode of *Fox and Friends* clearly showed how the mainstream media are controlled by special interest groups behind the scenes. A host of a show is supposed to be unbiased, but not Brian Kilmeade, who misled the public by stating atheists represent 7% of the population. The official number of the religiously unaffiliated is at least 23%.

8. In March 2017, leaders representing American Atheists, the American Humanist Association, the Center for Inquiry, and the

Secular Coalition for America sent a joint letter to the White House welcoming Donald Trump as the 45th President of the United States. The letter urges President Trump to continue the Obama Administration's policy of regularly engaging with the nonreligious community. To this day the White House hasn't had the decency to respond to the letter or offer any formal recognition to the 23% of Americans who identify themselves as religiously unaffiliated. I have no further comment, just use your imagination.

9. In May 2017, Russian ultraconservative parliament member Vitaly Milonov urged the Russian government to ban all sex toys and sell them only after approved and prescribed by a doctor to cure perverted sexual behaviors. This is the reason why all Americans with common sense should get together and rise up to protect their freedoms, freedoms like the Johnson Amendment, to prevent this nightmare from becoming reality.

"Corporate power protected
1. Volcker rule – Section 619 of the Dodd-Frank Wall Street Reform and Consumer Protection Act was enacted in 2015 to stop the use of customer deposits by banks for risky and speculative purposes. The Trump Administration is all about deregulation and would like to repeal the Volcker rule. Consequently, financial institutions would again be able to freely gamble with other people's money. But who cares, since taxpayers will fund bailouts when the next financial crisis arrives. There was previously a similar rule in place; the Glass-Steagall Act was passed after the 1929 crash to separate commercial banking from the securities and investment business. Unfortunately, the act was repealed in 1999 by the Clinton administration and in less than ten years the great recession happened.

2. The Paris Climate Agreement was signed by 196 countries, 159 of which have ratified it. Most scientists agree man-made global warming is real. The only scientists disagreeing with this fact are the ones receiving monetary compensation from special interest groups such as oil, gas, and automotive industries. There is no point in going into any more details. In June 2017, the US withdrew from the agreement. The withdrawal was performed swiftly and without any sort of public referendum. It is a national disgrace to borrow from future generations to appease short-term interests and the insatiable greed of a few entities at the top of the pyramid.

3. Student loans – If the student loan overhaul proposed by the current administration is passed, it will cost more for low-income students to borrow for college, graduate students will spend a longer time repaying their debts and public/nonprofit employees will lose loan forgiveness.

4. In May 2017, Trump called the Germans 'bad,' wanted to impose a 35% tax on imported German cars and negotiate a separate trading treaty with Germany. He asked Angela Merkel eleven times before realizing that trade deals could only be negotiated with the EU as a whole and not with individual member states. This raises the question why, so far, Dieselgate has cost VW almost $30 billion. It would be interesting to see if a domestic car manufacturer would receive similar fines and penalties in the case of emissions fraud.

5. In 2006, despite objections from both parties and intelligence/security officials, President Bush endorsed the takeover of shipping operations at six US seaports – New York, New Jersey, Baltimore, New Orleans, Miami, and Philadelphia – by Dubai Ports World, a state-owned business in the United Arab Emirates. Bush said that protesting lawmakers should understand his approval of the deal was final. In May 2017, the current administration announced plans to sell half of the nation's emergency oil stockpile and allow drilling in the Arctic National Wildlife Refuge, ending the practice of sharing oil royalties with the states along the Gulf of Mexico and selling off government-owned electricity transmission lines in the West. I hope the assets will not be sold to Middle Eastern or Chinese investors.

6. Affordable Care Act – The number one priority of this administration was not to fix but to completely repeal Obamacare to again allow the insurance companies to do whatever they want, such as cherry-picking healthy individuals and dropping or pricing out the sick ones. This led to the outrage of millions of people and to desperate actions by one particular individual. Violence will never solve any problems. I tried to figure out why sixty-six-year-old James Hodgkinson resorted to this appalling act: trying to kill high-profile government officials by shooting close to fifty bullets. Maybe he was tired of politics and his family member or friend was about to lose health care coverage again. Shortly after the incident, I saw many members of Congress from both parties crying and in total shock. I was able to see the fear in their eyes, the fear of being next in line for the wrongdoings that are happening to Americans and people

around the world on a daily basis. The members of Congress weren't this worried when they wanted to deny health care coverage to twenty-four million individuals. Mr. Ryan stated, 'An attack on one of us is an attack on all of us.' Maybe the American people should finally come together and say: 'An attack on twenty-four million of us is an attack on all 330 million of us." And what was the Tyson food lobbyist doing at that charity baseball game anyway? Does it really take an eighty-year-old with a brain tumor to realize that quality affordable health care for everyone is a basic human right and not a privilege?

". . . and the military is above us all
1. In June 2017, the US complained that China was building artificial military base islands in the South China Sea. The White House stated the international community was outraged by their actions. Aren't the Chinese allowed to build military bases close to their shores? If not, why not? U.S. Navy ships routinely pass by the man-made islands, creating tensions and protests from China. Has the international community ever been outraged when the US built an overseas military base?
2. On June 30 2017, the US announced it would sell $1.4 billion worth of weapons to Taiwan. This act violated the one China policy the current administration agreed to honor.
3. In early June 2017, Saudi Arabia, Yemen, Egypt, and Bahrain cut all diplomatic ties with Qatar because the state supported and financed terrorism. Trump also stated Qatar is financing terrorism and asked the country to stop financing and marketing its extremist ideologies. A week later, the US announced Qatar had made significant improvements regarding terrorism and approved the sale of thirty-six fighter jet planes worth $12 billion dollars. Is it possible for a nation to change from terrorist supporter to trusted ally in just seven days? Seven days is plenty of time and it actually is possible when Jesus and Allah get together for a beer to make a dollar. I have no further comments.

"This leads to the next subject: US global military presence via a vast network of 800-plus military bases and installations. A few months ago, I read an article called 'The United States Probably Has More Foreign Military Bases Than Any Other People, Nation, or Empire in History And it's Doing us More Harm Than Good.' It was written by David Vine, published on *TomDispath.com* news website and in *The Nation* magazine in September 2015. There is no point in me telling you

319

my opinion or giving a shorter version of this article. This matter is so disturbing and complex, I feel you should know all the details without any abbreviations or sugar coating. Here is the article:

"'With the US military having withdrawn many of its forces from Iraq and Afghanistan, most Americans would be forgiven for being unaware that hundreds of US bases and hundreds of thousands of US troops still encircle the globe. Although few know it, the United States garrisons the planet unlike any country in history, and the evidence is on view from Honduras to Oman, Japan to Germany, Singapore to Djibouti.

"'Like most Americans, for most of my life, I rarely thought about military bases. Scholar and former CIA consultant Chalmers Johnson described me well when he wrote in 2004, "As distinct from other peoples, most Americans do not recognize—or do not want to recognize—that the United States dominates the world through its military power. Due to government secrecy, our citizens are often ignorant of the fact that our garrisons encircle the planet."

"'To the extent that Americans think about these bases at all, we generally assume they're essential to national security and global peace. Our leaders have claimed as much since most of them were established during World War II and the early days of the Cold War. As a result, we consider the situation normal and accept that US military installations exist in staggering numbers in other countries, on other peoples' land. On the other hand, the idea that there would be foreign bases on US soil is unthinkable.

"'While there are no freestanding foreign bases permanently located in the United States, there are now around 800 US bases in foreign countries. Seventy years after World War II and 62 years after the Korean War, there are still 174 US "base sites" in Germany, 113 in Japan, and 83 in South Korea, according to the Pentagon. Hundreds more dot the planet in around 80 countries, including Aruba and Australia, Bahrain and Bulgaria, Colombia, Kenya, and Qatar, among many other places. Although few Americans realize it, the United States likely has more bases in foreign lands than any other people, nation, or empire in history.

"'Oddly enough, however, the mainstream media rarely report or comment on the issue. For years, during debates over the closure of the prison at the base in Guantánamo Bay, Cuba, nary a pundit or politician wondered why the United States has a base on Cuban territory in the first place or questioned whether we should have one there at all. Rarely does anyone ask if we need hundreds of bases overseas or if, at an estimated annual cost of perhaps $156 billion or more, the United States can afford them. Rarely does anyone wonder how we would feel if China,

Russia, or Iran built even a single base anywhere near our borders, let alone in the United States.

"'Without grasping the dimensions of this globe-girdling Baseworld," Chalmers Johnson insisted, "one can't begin to understand the size and nature of our imperial aspirations or the degree to which a new kind of militarism is undermining our constitutional order." Alarmed and inspired by his work and aware that relatively few have heeded his warnings, I've spent years trying to track and understand what he called our "empire of bases." While logic might seem to suggest that these bases make us safer, I've come to the opposite conclusion: in a range of ways our overseas bases have made us all less secure, harming everyone from US military personnel and their families to locals living near the bases to those of us whose taxes pay for the way our government garrisons the globe.

"'We are now, as we've been for the last seven decades, a Base Nation that extends around the world, and it's long past time that we faced that fact.

"'The Base Nation's Scale
"'Our 800 bases outside the 50 states and Washington, D.C., come in all sizes and shapes. Some are city-sized "Little Americas"—places like Ramstein Air Base in Germany, Kadena Air Base in Okinawa, and the little known Navy and Air Force base on Diego Garcia in the Indian Ocean. These support a remarkable infrastructure, including schools, hospitals, power plants, housing complexes, and an array of amenities often referred to as "Burger Kings and bowling alleys." Among the smallest US installations globally are "lily pad" bases (also known as "cooperative security locations"), which tend to house drones, surveillance aircraft, or pre-positioned weaponry and supplies. These are increasingly found in parts of Africa and Eastern Europe that had previously lacked much of a US military presence.

"'Other facilities scattered across the planet include ports and airfields, repair complexes, training areas, nuclear weapons installations, missile testing sites, arsenals, warehouses, barracks, military schools, listening and communications posts, and a growing array of drone bases. Military hospitals and prisons, rehab facilities, CIA paramilitary bases, and intelligence facilities (including former CIA "black site" prisons) must also be considered part of our Base Nation because of their military functions. Even US military resorts and recreation areas in places like the Bavarian Alps and Seoul, South Korea, are bases of a kind. Worldwide, the military runs more than 170 golf courses.

"'The Pentagon's overseas presence is actually even larger. There are US troops or other military personnel in about 160 foreign countries and territories, including small numbers of marines guarding embassies and larger deployments of trainers and advisors like the roughly 3,500 now working with the Iraqi Army. And don't forget the Navy's 11 aircraft carriers. Each should be considered a kind of floating base, or as the Navy tellingly refers to them, "four and a half acres of sovereign US territory." Finally, above the seas, one finds a growing military presence in space.

"'The United States isn't, however, the only country to control military bases outside its territory. Great Britain still has about seven bases and France five in former colonies. Russia has around eight in former Soviet republics. For the first time since World War II, Japan's "Self-Defense Forces" have a foreign base in Djibouti in the Horn of Africa, alongside US and French bases there. South Korea, India, Chile, Turkey, and Israel each reportedly have at least one foreign base. There are also reports that China may be seeking its first base overseas. In total, these countries probably have about 30 installations abroad, meaning that the United States has approximately 95% of the world's foreign bases.

"'"Forward" Forever?

"'Although the United States has had bases in foreign lands since shortly after it gained its independence, nothing like today's massive global deployment of military force was imaginable until World War II. In 1940, with the flash of a pen, President Franklin D. Roosevelt signed a "destroyers-for-bases" deal with Great Britain that instantly gave the United States 99-year leases to installations in British colonies worldwide. Base acquisition and construction accelerated rapidly once the country entered the war. By 1945, the US military was building base facilities at a rate of 112 a month. By war's end, the global total topped 2,000 sites. In only five years, the United States had developed history's first truly global network of bases, vastly overshadowing that of the British Empire upon which "the Sun never set."

"'After the war, the military returned about half the installations but maintained what historian George Stambuk termed a "permanent institution" of bases abroad. Their number spiked during the wars in Korea and Vietnam, declining after each of them. By the time the Soviet Union imploded in 1991, there were about 1,600 US bases abroad, with some 300,000 US troops stationed on those in Europe alone.

"'Although the military vacated about 60% of its foreign garrisons in the 1990s, the overall base infrastructure stayed relatively intact. Despite additional base closures in Europe and to a lesser extent in East

Asia over the last decade and despite the absence of a superpower adversary, nearly 250,000 troops are still deployed on installations worldwide. Although there are about half as many bases as there were in 1989, the number of countries with US bases has roughly doubled from 40 to 80. In recent years, President Obama's "Pacific pivot" has meant billions of dollars in profligate spending in Asia, where the military already had hundreds of bases and tens of thousands of troops. Billions more have been sunk into building an unparalleled permanent base infrastructure in every Persian Gulf country save Iran. In Europe, the Pentagon has been spending billions more erecting expensive new bases at the same time that it has been closing others.

"'Since the start of the Cold War, the idea that our country should have a large collection of bases and hundreds of thousands of troops permanently stationed overseas has remained a quasi-religious dictum of foreign and national security policy. The nearly 70-year-old idea underlying this deeply held belief is known as the "forward strategy." Originally, the strategy held that the United States should maintain large concentrations of military forces and bases as close as possible to the Soviet Union to hem in and "contain" its supposed urge to expand.

"'But the disappearance of another superpower to contain made remarkably little difference to the forward strategy. Chalmers Johnson first grew concerned about our empire of bases when he recognized that the structure of the "American Raj" remained largely unchanged despite the collapse of the supposed enemy.

"'Two decades after the Soviet Union's demise, people across the political spectrum still unquestioningly assume that overseas bases and forward-deployed forces are essential to protect the country. George W. Bush's administration was typical in insisting that bases abroad "maintained the peace" and were "symbols of... US commitments to allies and friends." The Obama administration has similarly declared that protecting the American people and international security "requires a global security posture."

"'Support for the forward strategy has remained the consensus among politicians of both parties, national security experts, military officials, journalists, and almost everyone else in Washington's power structure. Opposition of any sort to maintaining large numbers of overseas bases and troops has long been pilloried as peacenik idealism or the sort of isolationism that allowed Hitler to conquer Europe.

"'The Costs of Garrisoning the World

"'As Johnson showed us, there are many reasons to question the overseas base status quo. The most obvious one is economic. Garrisons overseas are very expensive. According to the RAND Corporation, even *when host countries like Japan and Germany cover some of the costs, US taxpayers still pay an annual average of $10,000 to $40,000 more per year to station a member of the military abroad than in the United States. The expense of transportation, the higher cost of living in some host countries, and the need to provide schools, hospitals, housing, and other support to family members of military personnel mean that the dollars add up quickly—especially with more than half a million troops, family members, and civilian employees on bases overseas at any time.*

"'By my very conservative calculations, maintaining installations and troops overseas cost at least $85 billion in 2014—more than the discretionary budget of every government agency except the Defense Department itself. If the US presence in Afghanistan and Iraq is included, that bill reaches $156 billion or more.

"'While bases may be costly for taxpayers, they are extremely profitable for the country's privateers of 21st-century war like DynCorp International and former Halliburton subsidiary KBR. As Chalmers Johnson noted, "Our installations abroad bring profits to civilian industries," which win billions in contracts annually to "build and maintain our far-flung outposts."

"'Meanwhile, many of the communities hosting bases overseas never see the economic windfalls that US and local leaders regularly promise. Some areas, especially in poor rural communities, have seen short-term economic booms touched off by base construction. In the long-term, however, most bases rarely create sustainable, healthy local economies. Compared with other forms of economic activity, they represent unproductive uses of land, employ relatively few people for the expanses occupied, and contribute little to local economic growth. Research has consistently shown that when bases finally close, the economic impact is generally limited and in some cases actually positive—that is, local communities can end up better off when they trade bases for housing, schools, shopping complexes, and other forms of economic development.

"'Meanwhile for the United States, investing taxpayer dollars in the construction and maintenance of overseas bases means forgoing investments in areas like education, transportation, housing, and health care, despite the fact that these industries are more of a boon to overall economic productivity and create more jobs compared to equivalent military spending. Think about what $85 billion per year would mean in terms of rebuilding the country's crumbling civilian infrastructure.

*"'**The Human Toll**
"'Beyond the financial costs are the human ones. The families of military personnel are among those who suffer from the spread of overseas bases*

given the strain of distant deployments, family separations, and frequent moves. Overseas bases also contribute to the shocking rates of sexual assault in the military: an estimated 30% of servicewomen are victimized during their time in the military and a disproportionate number of these crimes happen at bases abroad. Outside the base gates, in places like South Korea, one often finds exploitative prostitution industries geared to US military personnel.

"'Worldwide, bases have caused widespread environmental damage because of toxic leaks, accidents, and in some cases the deliberate dumping of hazardous materials. GI crime has long angered locals. In Okinawa and elsewhere, US troops have repeatedly committed horrific acts of rape against local women. From Greenland to the tropical island of Diego Garcia, the military has displaced local peoples from their lands to build its bases.

"'In contrast to frequently invoked rhetoric about spreading democracy, the military has shown a preference for establishing bases in undemocratic and often despotic states like Qatar and Bahrain. In Iraq, Afghanistan, and Saudi Arabia, US bases have created fertile breeding grounds for radicalism and anti-Americanism. The presence of bases near Muslim holy sites in Saudi Arabia was a major recruiting tool for al-Qaeda and part of Osama bin Laden's professed motivation for the September 11, 2001, attacks.

"'Although this kind of perpetual turmoil is little noticed at home, bases abroad have all too often generate grievances, protest, and antagonistic relationships. Although few here recognize it, our bases are a major part of the image the United States presents to the world—and they often show us in an extremely unflattering light.

"'Creating a New Cold War, Base by Base
"'It is also not at all clear that bases enhance national security and global peace in any way. In the absence of a superpower enemy, the argument that bases many thousands of miles from US shores are necessary to defend the United States—or even its allies—is a hard argument to make. On the contrary, the global collection of bases has generally enabled the launching of military interventions, drone strikes, and wars of choice that have resulted in repeated disasters, costing millions of lives and untold destruction from Vietnam to Iraq.

"'By making it easier to wage foreign wars, bases overseas have ensured that military action is an ever more attractive option—often the only imaginable option—for US policymakers. As the anthropologist Catherine Lutz has said, when all you have in your foreign policy toolbox is a hammer, everything starts to look like a nail. Ultimately, bases abroad have frequently made war more likely rather than less.

"'Proponents of the long-outdated forward strategy will reply that overseas bases "deter" enemies and help keep the global peace. As supporters of the status quo, they have been proclaiming such security benefits as self-evident truths for decades. Few have provided anything of substance to support their claims. While there is some evidence that military forces can indeed deter imminent threats, little if any research suggests that overseas bases are an effective form of long-term deterrence. Studies by both the Bush administration and the RAND Corporation—not exactly left-wing peaceniks—indicate that advances in transportation technology have largely erased the advantage of stationing troops abroad. In the case of a legitimate defensive war or peacekeeping operation, the military could generally deploy troops just as quickly from domestic bases as from most bases abroad. Rapid sealift and airlift capabilities coupled with agreements allowing the use of bases in allied nations and, potentially, pre-positioned supplies are a dramatically less expensive and less inflammatory alternative to maintaining permanent bases overseas.

"'It is also questionable whether such bases actually increase the security of host nations. The presence of US bases can turn a country into an explicit target for foreign powers or militants—just as US installations have endangered Americans overseas.

"'Similarly, rather than stabilizing dangerous regions, foreign bases frequently heighten military tensions and discourage diplomatic solutions to conflicts. Placing US bases near the borders of countries like China, Russia, and Iran, for example, increases threats to their security and encourages them to respond by boosting their own military spending and activity. Imagine how US leaders would respond if China were to build even a single small base in Mexico, Canada, or the Caribbean. Notably, the most dangerous moment during the Cold War—the 1962 Cuban missile crisis—revolved around the construction of Soviet nuclear missile facilities in Cuba, roughly 90 miles from the US border.

"'The creation and maintenance of so many US bases overseas likewise encourages other nations to build their own foreign bases in what could rapidly become an escalating "base race." Bases near the borders of China and Russia, in particular, threaten to fuel new cold wars. US officials may insist that building yet more bases in East Asia is a defensive act meant to ensure peace in the Pacific, but tell that to the Chinese. That country's leaders are undoubtedly not "reassured" by the creation of yet more bases encircling their borders. Contrary to the claim that such installations increase global security, they tend to ratchet up regional tensions, increasing the risk of future military confrontation.

"'In this way, just as the war on terror has become a global conflict that only seems to spread terror, the creation of new US bases to protect against imagined future Chinese or Russian threats runs the risk of becoming a self-fulfilling prophecy. These bases may ultimately help create the very threat they are supposedly designed to protect against. In other words, far from making the world a safer place, US bases can actually make war more likely and the country less secure.

"'Behind the Wire

"'In his farewell address to the nation upon leaving the White House in 1961, President Dwight D. Eisenhower famously warned the nation about the insidious economic, political, and even spiritual effects of what he dubbed "the military-industrial-congressional complex," the vast interlocking national security state born out of World War II. As Chalmers Johnson's work reminded us in this new century, our seventy-year-old collection of bases is evidence of how, despite Ike's warning, the United States has entered a permanent state of war with an economy, a government, and a global system of power enmeshed in preparations for future conflicts.

"'America's overseas bases offer a window onto our military's impact in the world and in our own daily lives. The history of these hulking "Little Americas" of concrete, fast food, and weaponry provides a living chronicle of the United States in the post-World War II era. In a certain sense, in these last seven decades, whether we realize it or not, we've all come to live "behind the wire," as military personnel like to say.

"'We may think such bases have made us safer. In reality, they've helped lock us inside a permanently militarized society that has made all of us—everyone on this planet—less secure, damaging lives at home and abroad.'

"Written by David Vine

"*http://www.tomdispatch.com/blog/176043/tomgram%3A_david_vine,_o ur_base_nation/*

September 2015

"In 2016, I watched Oliver Stone's Untold History of the United States (2012), a documentary series on Showtime. This is one of the most provocative historical documentaries I have seen in my life. It shows a more two-sided story of our nation's history, the history not taught in schools, the history our government doesn't advertise. The film series implanted a virus into my brain that made me question why the mainstream media, government and its institutions don't talk about our nation's history from different perspectives. The bottom line is you always hear the same one-sided story everywhere you go: 'We are the greatest people and the greatest nation on Earth with the greatest and most powerful military. God gave us the mission to protect and police the world. Our opinion matters the most because we spread freedom, democracy, and are always right.'

"Why would we, the American people, be so eager to police the world since the global network of 800-plus overseas military bases and installations cost the US taxpayers over $160 billion per year? Our country is almost $20 trillion dollars in deficit and counting. The government debt-to-GDP almost doubled from 2006 to 2016 (62.5% to 104.8%). As of 2017, US debt to China is $1.102 trillion, 28% of all foreign debt. I think these factors qualify us as an indebted nation. As a nation, we need to save every dollar we can to provide quality education, affordable health care, and other social services to all of our citizens. We have almost 7,000 nuclear warheads, so who in their right mind would attack us anyway? Do we really need 800-plus foreign military bases to maintain world peace? Russia has twelve and China has one overseas military base, in Djibouti, Africa. On July 11 2017, China opened the base and shipped eleven troops to be stationed in Africa. All we, the United States, have to do is sit down at a table, show our muscles and negotiate. Sooner or later every nation on Earth will give in to our demands. The real reason why our country has so many overseas bases is to carefully and smartly vacuum/reallocate taxpayer's dollars to be 'tunneled' – to enrich the people at the top of the pyramid. The people consisting of shadowy/invisible government and military contractors who in return provide hefty kickbacks to our elected officials."

Chapter 14
The Meeting/True Rulers of Planet Earth

"Here is the perspective of how the invisible/shadowy government views its history, present, and the future," I said, drank some more wine and continued to speak.

"Until WWII, the US economy was a peaceful, self-dependent domestic economy. Yes, we were a global empire, but most Americans at the time strongly opposed us being involved in military conflicts. This changed when WWII began and our peaceful economy transitioned to a wartime economy. In 1945 our friends, the military contractors, realized there was too much money at stake if we returned to the pre-WWII peaceful economy. With a promise of hefty kickbacks, we agreed to continuously search for real and imaginary enemies, fight any kind of war to create demand for new weapons and expand global military presence at all costs. The idea was not too difficult to sell to the public because the spread of communism had become a real threat.

"In the 1950s, we started to search for internal enemies of the state by accusing anybody we didn't like of being a communist. We accused anybody who was opposed to our idea of maintaining a permanent wartime economy and US global dominance. We had people such as Ronald Reagan who helped our other friends in health insurance and pharmaceutical companies to sell the following idea to the general public: 'A single-payer health-care system is an un-American socialist idea that will never work. Don't you want to be able to choose your own doctor?' Ads similar to these were all over TV and radio. In order to climb up the pyramid, Ronald Reagan had no problem accusing his fellow actors of being communists as well. Not everything went smoothly and according to plan; when John F. Kennedy was elected as president, his virtues and beliefs were too strong and unsuitable for re-education to be administered by our military and corporate friends. No big deal, shit happened, so we disposed of him and blamed it on the 'lone wolf.' After the 'incident' we had a party since nobody else had the balls to oppose our military intervention in Vietnam anymore. It was a fucking gold mine, people were dying left and right but we didn't care because there was so much money coming in. The only problems were the hippies and people like Martin Luther King, who dreamed too much. Thank God that drugs, alcohol, people like Charles Manson and 'lone wolves' took care of this 'annoyance' for us, otherwise we and our special interest friends would have been in deep trouble sooner or later.

"Another hiccup happened when religious Islamic fundamentalists overthrew our buddy Mohammad Reza Pahlavi, who was the Shah of

Iran. We searched and found our man, our longtime ally Ronald Reagan, to fix this mess. He was a great actor and the perfect front man; we were able to count on him 100% to help us with our agenda. He encouraged the average person to only think about him- or herself, to pursue the American Dream of overconsumption and not to worry about foreign affairs or the government too much. The big dogs were going to take care of the average person and the wealth was always somehow going to trickle down from the top of the pyramid to the average Joe Blow. Why would the average people want to stick their noses into politics? Greed was good and that's all that mattered to most people anyway. Our man Ronald really knew how to take care of his military and corporate buddies. 'Deregulate as much as possible and the market will take care of itself,' was his idea of the market economy. Reagan was the founding father of the 'Star Wars' program. His administration eagerly supported our Middle Eastern friends such as Saddam Hussein and Osama bin Laden. Money and weapons were given to Osama for him to fight against the Soviets in Afghanistan. We also made a killing from the sale of weapons to Iran and from the bogus war on drugs. The opium trade provides a significant source of income to finance independent operations. Why do you think we never secured our borders? Because we needed, and need, armies of cheap slaves to babysit our kids, work on farms, build and clean our houses, cut our grass. The select few at the top knew very well the American Dream was unsustainable unless the nation had a steady flow of undocumented sub-humans: the silent, expendable, and exploitable 'numbers' with little or no human rights. In order to make it to the top of the pyramid and achieve the American Dream, you have to be able to live off and use other people, regardless of emotions.

"The Soviet Union was not able to keep up with our military spending and the Communist Party realized that socialism cannot work because of human nature. We became the winners of the Cold War and didn't need people like Saddam or Osama any longer because we were practically free to do anything we wanted. The world was ours, just like in the movie *Scarface* (1983). We had a slight problem, there were not enough real enemies and our new president was not as supportive to our cause as Reagan and Bush. Nevertheless, because of the internet, there was the requirement to modernize every office, every piece of civilian and military equipment, therefore, our revenue stream did not dry up and we and our friends were making as much money as ever. The public was appeased as well since the new internet economy would provide limitless growth forever. There even were a few years of budget surpluses. Given how everything was mismanaged, as the special interest groups were sucking money from everywhere they could, the surplus years were true miracles given to our great nation by God Almighty Himself. Why not let a small number of selected friends make a few extra dollars in a little insurance scam?

"Everything changed on September 11 2001, when the twin towers fell. We realized the intelligence agencies were sloppy and underestimated the threat because everyone was so confident something like this could never happen on the US mainland. Osama bin Laden was underestimated as well because he was rich and surely only cared about money, like we all did. In 1991, Osama stopped caring about money once he realized the Christian soldiers would never leave the holy lands once their boots touched the shores. This fact went against his religion and it was an insult to everything he ever believed. You don't have to be a genius to realize that Christian military has no business in the Middle East. Again, like in the prior years, our top man saved the day. George W. Bush had no problem facing and lying to the American public on live TV when he announced that weapons of mass destruction were found in Iraq. The president also announced that any country that supports terrorism will face military action. This was great news and exactly what we wanted because we could invade any country on Earth based on false intelligence. Since that point, we have been able to easily make up imaginary enemies and our guy in the Oval Office will sell it to the American public with no questions asked. 'You are either with us or against us,' was Bush's message to the world. The message contained hidden meaning intended for the American people: from this point on, you are going to be with us and support all our military actions with no questions asked otherwise we will accuse you of terrorism. Reasons for arrest, including physical evidence, can be easily fabricated. You are either with us or against us, because there is no middle ground.

"The USA Patriot Act, allowing the government to brutally invade anyone's privacy without a court order, was swiftly passed. The culture of terror began to spread through our buddies in mainstream media. Does anybody remember the bogus terror threats displayed on TV? They fluctuated almost daily without any apparent reason or support. All this played into our hands and gave us the reason to raise military spending to new heights. The Great Recession came but we took care of our corporate allies more than ever. We rewarded the top wolves – the smart people who were willing to take unnecessary risks and gambled with other people's money via exotic financial instruments, such as derivatives. Just like in the movie *Casino* (1995), these people were/are the only real winners on the Street, who deserved the bailouts more than anybody else. The USA Freedom Act was passed to further harass and restrict the freedoms of US citizens and everybody else living on Earth.

"Another 'inconvenience' was Obama and his communist idea of socialist health care. What a waste of perfectly good money! How daring he was to persuade Congress and the Senate to pass this work of the Devil. Unfortunately, times have changed, and it became more difficult to dispose of enemies of the State as easily as in the 1950s and 1960s. In 2017, Donald Trump became the new president and what a disaster. He's like an octopus and is fucking everything up! Everything that we worked so hard to achieve in the past seventy years. Donald is too obvious and is inadvertently exposing many of the skeletons hidden in Washington's closets. At least he continues to take care of our corporate friends. He also caters to our third most powerful ally more than any other president in modern history. This third ally consists of religious fundamentalists who help us to keep the average people impoverished, brainwashed, confused, obedient, and away from politics. He better continue to do at least these two things otherwise we would have no choice but to take care of him, like we took care of Kennedy. His arrogance makes him unsuitable for re-education.

"But at this point who cares about Trump? The future for us looks brighter than ever because our fourth strongest ally, the artificial intelligence, just arrived. This ally will help us monitor and analyze the actions of every single American citizen and eventually every person living on this planet to the smallest possible detail. It will help us to identify and eliminate potential enemies of the State and the world before that fact is even known to them. For example, we will be able to hack into a self-driving car and cause an 'accident.' But don't worry, car manufacturers; as always, we will take care of you and blame the incident on Russian hackers or the weather so you won't be liable. The laws are made to work for Corporate America more than for anybody else and we will make sure this will get even better as time passes. You don't believe this is coming? Please turn on the CuriosityStream channel and watch *Next World – Part 1, Predicting the Future.* As of 2017, we already have the capability to predict crime and the power to harass seemingly innocent people because an AI system has predicted there may be a crime in the area. Internet search engines and social media sites already eagerly participate; all activity can be recorded indefinitely and given to us knowingly and unknowingly. We don't have to ask anybody for permission because we can hack into everything, like the iPhone in 2016.

"Sensors will be everywhere and in everything; in the office, on the street, in cars, in all public places, in fields and forests, at your home, in furniture and fixtures, toothbrushes, and under human skin. . . you name it, we will have sensors that predict when problems will arise. AI will predict when you get sick, where your next vacation will be, what the next hit song will be, when and where crime will occur, and your political views. In addition, AI will predict the best possible career for you and even your future boyfriend or girlfriend. 'AI Spy drones' will fly, crawl, and sit next to you at all times. 'AI Spy drones' in the form of birds, plants, butterflies, ladybugs, spiders, ants, rats, and cockroaches. . . You will be monitored at home, at work, at churches, on the street, in all public places, and known/unknown private places twenty-four hours a day, seven days a week. You will be able to run but not hide. Your facial expressions will be analyzed all the time and compared to various situations to identify potentially dangerous thought activity suitable for either re-education or disposal. By 2047, AI will reach singularity, the average person will unconsciously live in a luxury prison but our thoughts and prayers will always be with you. The quest for world dominance will be accomplished and the world will be ours for a thousand years.

"The average person will have no choice but to become a fully silent, obedient puppet and listener to everything that we have to say. You see, we have to restrict your freedoms to new levels in order to maintain the American way of life. As overpopulation and global warming increases, competition for food and natural resources will increase as well and it will become harder and harder for us to maintain our way of life. Since 1971, on an annual basis, the world has been consuming more resources than it can replenish. In 2017, the world's sustainability breakeven point was August 2nd. The US population consists of 5% of the world's population but we consume about 30% of the world's resources. If everyone enjoyed the same living standard as the Americans, the world would need five planets. Well, there is only one planet Earth. To maintain the culture of overconsumption and waste at home, we will have to continue to spread the American Nightmare around the world more than ever before. Friendly regimes, including dictators, the worst human rights violators, will continue to be supported by us to impoverish their people and to establish/maintain friendly corporate culture so natural resources, cheap products and labor can be easily reallocated to the USA. Those who oppose will be crushed, as reasons for military intervention can easily be fabricated. As of 2017, we are catering to the wolves – to the top 10% of the population, more than ever before, just like in the movie *Training Day* (2001). The bottom 90% of the sheep are expendable numbers ready to be slaughtered at any moment. It will only get better as time passes. We are the government for the government.

"Well ladies, what else shall I tell you? The US is under the control of an invisible government that nobody elected, that has no allegiance to the people whatsoever. This invisible government is the true ruling power of this country and the world. This shadowy government behaves exactly the same way the communists did in Eastern Europe; they practically control both parties, seize executive offices, legislative bodies, schools, courts, media, and every agency created for the public protection. As a result, the US government (state and local governments to a certain level) have become one of the worst ruled, one of the most completely controlled and dominated governments in the civilized world – no longer the government by free opinion, no longer the government by conviction and the vote of the majority, but the government by the opinion and the duress of small groups of religious fundamentalists, intelligence agencies, military contractors, and selected corporations.

"The public has been warned about its existence for centuries by many individuals such as George Washington, Thomas Jefferson, John C. Calhoun, Theodore Roosevelt, Woodrow Wilson, John F. Hylan, Edward Bernays, Louis T. McFadden, Franklin D. Roosevelt, William Jenner, J. Edgar Hoover, Dwight D. Eisenhower, Larry P. McDonald, and the most outspoken critic of them all, John F. Kennedy. Here is an excerpt of his famous speech that got him killed: 'It is a system which has conscripted vast human and material resources into the building of a tightly knit, highly efficient machine that combines military, diplomatic, intelligence, economic, scientific and political operations.'

"In 1986, Daniel K. Inouye, US Senator from Hawaii stated, 'There exists a shadowy government with its own Air Force, its own Navy, its own fundraising mechanism and the ability to pursue its own ideas of national interest, free from all checks and balances, and free from the law itself.' The following text is displayed on a poster located in the Holocaust Museum, Washington D.C.:

"Early Signs of Fascism
1. *Powerful and continuing nationalism*
2. *Disdain for human rights*
3. *Identification of enemies as unifying cause*
4. *Supremacy of the military*
5. *Rampant sexism*
6. *Controlled mass media*
7. *Obsession with national security*
8. *Religion and government intertwined*
9. *Corporate power protected*
10. *Labor power suppressed*
11. *Disdain for intellectuals & art*
12. *Obsession with crime & punishment*
13. *Rampant cronyism & corruption*
14. *Fraudulent elections"*

"It has been a long-time speculation of mine," said Christine, "that the government is controlled by special interest groups and not by the voters. This is one reason why I didn't swallow everything I was told about the American Dream."

"Rhetoric about the American Dream is a great way to motivate people, don't get me wrong, but many things about the idea just don't fit," added Jessica, finishing her wine. "First of all, it is pursued by so many people but only achieved by a few. It is almost like winning the lottery. Many people play it regardless of the odds because someone always has to win it."

Ronnee was looking at the table with a sad face. Then she raised her head and joined the conversation. "As young girl, I studied philosophy. My dream was to make the world a better place but I didn't know where to begin. The reality of how people live – mostly pursuing material things, not deeper spiritual values on which you cannot put monetary value – made everything difficult for me. I gave up and went to law school, to align myself more with the mainstream society. Corporate law is a jungle and it never felt right because it was unable to fill my inner desires."

"It is never too late for anything," I said. "Ronnee, you will have your chance to pursue your life dream," and our eyes met for a few seconds. I then continued to speak, "All of you will have a chance to pursue what you like. It is never too late for anything and don't let anyone tell you it cannot be done. Anything can be accomplished as long as you put your mind to it, just follow your dreams."

The conversation paused as we kept to ourselves for a few moments.

"It's about dinnertime and I am starving! Why don't we order some delicious sushi samplers for us to share?" I suggested, trying to cheer everyone up.

"You are reading my mind!" Christine said, and the two girls agreed with her.

We ordered a great variety of food, anything from octopus to tuna nigiri, seaweed salad, miso soup and, of course, a warm sake to toast. As the ladies became happier and were enjoying the dinner, I resumed the political conversation.

Chapter 15
The Meeting/The People's President

"Donald Trump is the one person that just a few years ago nobody even dreamed would be the President of the United States one day, not even himself. He was born with a silver spoon in his mouth, therefore had a head start in life that most Americans could only dream of. Donald was/is highly intelligent and a talented businessman ready to make tough decisions at any moment. Thanks to his father's backing and easy access to credit, he built The Trump Organization and achieved the American Dream.

"As a late teenager and adult, he never had a carefree lifestyle and real friends whom he could trust with his life because he was always in the process of improving himself to grow the wealth. Many people only see the results and not the hard work and responsibility it takes to manage a business of this magnitude. All it takes is one slip, one major wrong decision, to be out of business. Everyone always discusses the success stories. Does anyone discuss the countless business failures, such as destroyed lives and families' wealth gone forever? It takes a special individual to make it this high in the pyramid. A person should be able to question the actions of superiors and to a certain extent make fun of people above them in the pyramid. You can even call them assholes, but there has to be respect, as stated in the movie *Robocop* (1987). Desires for change should always be presented to the people above with logic, love for what you do, and most importantly with clarity and common sense. If all this fails, support from the bottom is needed to push through the change.

"In the late 1970s, the Friends arranged a meeting between Donald and his first wife, Ivana. It was love at first sight but, most importantly, it gave him the reason to visit the paradise island for children surrounded by barbed wire, that 95% of people living in the Western world were not allowed to visit. He experienced something he never dreamed was possible – not much material wealth is needed to live a happy and meaningful life. People can actually love other people regardless of money. People like the little old grandma who always genuinely welcomed him with open arms, with a home-cooked meal, and was never after his wealth. He saw children of all ages running around cities and villages unsupervised, having endless fun. As a result, something happened in his mind that pushed him to think twice about the life back home. In 1987, Trump published a $100,000 newspaper advertisement in *The Boston Globe*, *The Washington Post* and *The New York Times*, stating: 'America should stop defending countries that can afford to defend themselves. . .' What a dangerous idea. This would mean to close most of the 800-plus military bases and installations located worldwide (as of 2017), therefore, revenue streams for the military contractors would dry up. Donald Trump entered politics and later joined the Reform Party of the USA. Here is some information about the party. . .

"In 1995, Ross Perot founded the Reform Party of the United States of America (RPUSA), with headquarters in Bohemia, New York. The party was founded as an alternative to mainstream political parties. The party's ideology is: populism, protectionism, fiscal conservatism, anti-corruption, and electoral reforms. The party wanted real change/reforms and it was no accident the city of Bohemia was chosen as the headquarters. The city was founded in 1855 by migrants who came from the Kingdom of Bohemia (present day Czech Republic). 'Bohemianism' is the practice of unconventional lifestyle with few permanent ties, involving musical, artistic, literary, or spiritual pursuits. Bohemians are associated with unorthodox or anti-establishment political or social viewpoints, which often are expressed through free love, frugality, and in some cases voluntary poverty. The 'medieval hippies' as you can safely call them have been around for centuries because they haven't been abusing drugs to such an extent as people in the 1960s. Their minds and thought processes are free from organized religion, consequently, every Bohemian has to find his or her inner spirit in order to decide what lifestyle to live. The impish American writer and Bohemian Club member Gelett Burgess wrote about the amorphous place called Bohemia:

"*'What, then, is it that makes this mystical empire of Bohemia unique, and what is the charm of its mental fairyland? It is this: there are no roads in all Bohemia! One must choose and find one's own path, be one's own self, live one's own life.'*

"Between 1992 and 1996, the Commission on Presidential Debates, controlled by Democrats and Republicans, conveniently changed its rules regarding how candidates could qualify to participate in the presidential debates. This was the nail in the coffin for Ross Perot, a skilled debater who had previously done very well in the debates. Despite legal actions by the Perot team and a 62% majority of Americans supporting his participation in the debates, the Commission refused to allow Perot to participate. In 1998, Jesse Ventura, who calls himself a Slovak, was elected as the governor of Minnesota and became the party's most successful candidate. In 2000, Donald Trump briefly entered the primary presidential race and was progressive on social issues. When asked about allowing openly gay soldiers in the military, he stated: 'It would not disturb me.' Donald withdrew from the race stating: 'So the Reform Party now includes a Klansman, Mr. Duke, a neo-Nazi, Mr. Buchanan, and a communist, Ms. Fulani. This is not company I wish to keep,' and left the party. As always, Trump was a quick learner and realized that politics is all about power, money, and appeasing special interest groups, and not about the common people or reforms. Joining the Republican Party was the only way to safely and consistently move up in the world of US politics.

"For the first time in modern history, the voters elected a true president for all the people. Trump is not a career politician and is not politically correct. In fact, he is so new to high-level politics that he behaves like a monkey in a glassware store, stumbling over and breaking everything while inadvertently exposing Washington's dirty laundry in the process. He truly is the people's president, unable to keep his mouth shut and his fingers off Twitter. In the Matrix, Trump is the abnormality, the virus that has been planted at the top of the pyramid to teach the average people to think twice about the elected officials and the way our government operates. There is only so much Trump can do, therefore he has to appease religious fundamentalists, military contractors, and corporations in the 'business as usual' way. The 2017 inauguration is a perfect example; the six figures dressed in black and red had almost as much combined speech time as the newly elected president. This is a chilly reminder to the public; no matter who you elect as the president, the religious fundamentalists will always be there. Donald hit the nail on the head many times when he stated, 'One people under one God,' and that our values are threatened. He is a quick learner and in 2020 may upgrade the phrase to the following: 'We have one set of values, are one people in one nation, under one God, and under one leader.'"

The three ladies finished their meals and were just sitting there trying to process the information given to them since early afternoon.

"I hope you liked the food. I know it's a lot of information and something you didn't expect to hear from an average person like myself. The people in power will never publicly admit this so who else than a common person would tell the story?" I said.

Jessica took her glasses off and our eyes locked in full stare for a few seconds. This only happened once as she always wears her glasses. My body was suddenly electrified and I became ecstatic upon the realization of how rare this event was. I became puzzled and couldn't figure out why this happened at this particular moment.

Then Jessica interrupted my thought process by stating, "It will definitely take some time to figure out the connection between Fascists and our government."

"Do you remember the unfortunate event that happened in August at the white supremacy rally in Charlottesville, Virginia?" I asked, and everyone kept quiet as their eyes silently agreed. "It took Trump two days to condemn the neo-Nazis," I said strongly, and continued, "Do you know why it took him so long? Because many people in the government feel sympathetic to racism. Deep down, anger has been building in Trump for decades because the elite people in New York would never accept him as an equal, no matter how much wealth he acquired. That anger buried in him surfaced during the presidential campaign and connected with the angry voters, including white supremacists, who were and are upset by the current state of affairs. This is the main reason why he won the presidency. Anger, hate, and violence will never solve any long-term problems. [*Coincidently, I reached this point in writing the book on August 14 2017, at the Extended Stay hotel, Alpharetta, GA.*] Nobody was able to figure out why events developed the way they did at the infrastructure press conference on August 15th. Well, the Friends are the true masters of puppets. This reminds me of the 1986 Metallica album.

"The shadowy/invisible government has learned from the mistakes the Nazis made. Why invade a foreign country and exterminate certain groups of people? It is a logistical nightmare. It is much easier to build a base to 'legalize' military presence in order to intimidate the local population. The next step is to establish and support a friendly regime that would be more than happy to do our dirty work for us; write laws so our corporate friends would be able to freely exploit the country at will. According to rumors, as we speak, the Air Force flies airplanes full of cash around the world to support friendly regimes and other operations. Thirdly, the regimes, especially in a third-world country, would welcome our religious missionaries with open arms. This is great since it is so much easier to embezzle charitable donations in a third-world country than back home. Will someone from the American public fly to Africa to verify that a water well or a starving child in a photograph is real? I don't think so. I wouldn't give a charity a single dollar unless their financial statements going back five years are available online and include the following: annual report, 990 report (if applicable), audit report, plus a legible and easy to understand summary of the percentage of funds raised and spent on each project. Look at the World Wildlife Fund's website for a picture-perfect example. I do like that in 2017, 'Finance and Administration' accounted for a modest 4% of total expenses.

"Why exterminate people based on race or religion? It doesn't make sense because the greenback is color-blind and doesn't care if a person is white, black, yellow, Christian, Jew, Muslim, or atheist. Nevertheless, the shadowy/invisible government was never able to completely hide their sympathy towards racism.

"The intelligence community knew about the Nazi concentration camps and later, death camps, from the late 1930s, but the camps or the surrounding infrastructure were never bombed. It is understandable; for political reasons this could not have been accomplished until December 7 1941. What happened between December 8 1941 and May 7 1945? Why weren't the camps bombed during this time period? The same question comes up regarding North Korea. As of this moment, it is estimated that at least 200,000 people permanently occupy North Korea's concentration camps. Whole families are held in lifelong detention. Children born in these camps witness their parents being beaten, mutilated, starved, and raped on a daily basis. About 30% of prisoners have deformities such as torn ears, smashed eyes, crooked noses, and faces covered with scars resulting from beatings and other mistreatment. The people receive 13oz of food per day and have to catch rats, snakes, and insects. There are reports of human medical experiments, such as gassing of entire families and practice of surgery by inexperienced medical officers. The internet is flooded by reports of these camps published by reputable world media. The intelligence agencies knew for decades about the camps and the horrific conditions experienced by the prisoners. Why were the camps never bombed, especially before North Korea developed nuclear weapons? I guess it's more profitable to chase imaginary weapons of mass destruction.

"Why didn't each new commander-in-chief try to bomb the North Korean camps in the past? Because they couldn't. It doesn't matter if the administration is Republican or Democrat. It has to act exactly according to the wishes of the shadowy/invisible government, especially when it comes to the military. The last president who acted freely was John F. Kennedy.

"For example, Barack Obama understood and played the political game better than anybody else. As Illinois senator, he quickly and predictably ran away from the State Capitol building every time a vote on a controversial issue was about to begin. He knew that voting on something controversial would hurt him later, diminish his chances of becoming the president. Here is a valuable lesson; if you expose all your cards too early, your enemies will be able to predict your next steps. Obama, Bill Clinton, and other politicians are the same; many beautiful and inspiring speeches accompanied by little action. All of us should give Barack Obama credit – given the cutthroat work culture of Washington and the constant dictatorship of the invisible/shadowy government, he was the first person able to influence enough politicians to pass the Affordable Care Act. It is far from being perfect; however, it is one step closer to the ultimate and only viable long-term solution: universal health care. After Obamacare was passed, for security reasons he had to play both sides and for the rest of his presidency didn't do much except for appeasing special interest groups. I don't blame him, since he has a wife and kids."

"I don't know, Joseph, maybe we should keep this to ourselves," Christine said, and had the same look on her face as I remembered from Argos.

Our eyes met and I was admiring the beauty of her large brown eyes, thick eyelashes, curly dark hair and then her whole face. I remembered one instance when something similar happened between us. The event was preceded by lunch the day before. The other girls had not shown up and Christine and I had lunch alone. We spoke about our families and personal lives. At the end of the lunch, I asked where her cubicle was located. The next day, I grabbed some papers that needed to be notarized to have an excuse to speak with Christine at her desk. The notary person was positioned right across the aisle from her cubicle. As I approached the notary, Christine had just finished notarizing her documents and was getting up from the chair. We were standing about a foot from each other in a room surrounded by at least thirty people. We didn't care, it felt like we were the only two people left in the entire Universe as our eyes locked in full stare. We did not blink and must have been looking into each other's eyes for at least ten seconds. Christine wore make-up, which she rarely did, and I was admiring her beauty the whole time. I didn't want to end the eye contact, so I kept looking through her eyes into her soul. She then genuinely smiled, but at the same time almost completely closed her eyes and it was all over.

I went back on the clock as soon as the event finished replaying in my head and said, "No, we don't have to keep this information to ourselves. That is exactly what makes this country one of the greatest nations on Earth. You can bitch about the government twenty-four hours a day, seven days a week, without fear of being prosecuted, tortured, or killed. It would be highly un-American not to criticize the government. This right is explicitly given to every US citizen, even the naturalized ones like myself, by the U.S. Constitution. If anyone is ever prosecuted for criticizing the US government, then the government would lower itself and would be at the same level as the garbage regimes of Saudi Arabia, North Korea and Russia. In 2016, my wife became a US citizen but didn't bother to register to vote when asked right after the ceremony. Maybe she was tired and wanted to go home but I was so disappointed.

"Unfortunately, the government is trying very hard to limit this freedom without dragging itself into legal trouble. On August 4 2017, the Justice Department announced it will prosecute reporters and media for

341

publishing leaked classified information. This is a dangerous precedent because the department can call any information they don't like or don't agree with 'classified.' If anybody from the government ever comes and asks you about what we do or about the book, just give them an evasive answer. Better yet, be quiet and refer them to me. I will then give them the evasive answer. No, I will remain silent, because I don't have to give them any details pertaining to these subjects.

"This brings up the next subject, how and who will handle the media. If we decide to form the venture, we should have a designated person who will talk with the press. I know it's early to make this decision but I will gladly volunteer for this task. Jessica, you would be great at this, but I know how much you value your privacy. Maybe the two of us could collaborate on this."

"Yes, it is too early for this, but if we decide to form the venture, I will be glad to help you," Jessica said, and gave me the wink.

"I don't think Russia is as bad as Saudi Arabia and North Korea, right?" Ronnee asked.

"Russia is not so bad but it's not too far behind," I said, paused for a few moments and continued to speak. "It's no secret that Putin hires hit men to get rid of political opposition. He even had the balls to poison Alexander Litvinenko with radioactive polonium-210 while he was in Britain. Look what he did to Mikhail Khodorkovsky; as a result of a bogus tax trial, most of his wealth was confiscated and he was thrown in prison for nine years. The media is strictly censored and anybody who doesn't report according to the regime's wishes is shut down sooner or later. The reporters who continue to freely report are disposed of. Unofficially, Mr. Putin is the richest man in the world. According to official asset declaration, he owns two apartments, thirteen bank accounts with a combined balance of 13.8 million rubles ($241,000), 230 shares in Bank Saint Petersburg, two Soviet-made 1960s Volgas and a 2009 Lada 4x4. Putin should be in show business. On an annual basis, he lets himself be photographed half naked while he's running around woods hunting for bears. I think the three of you would find Vladimir kind of cute. ;-)

"I would like to tell you about a few more subjects. One topic is the suppression of labor power in the USA and around the world. It's no secret how badly third-world country workers are treated by multinational corporations. Many companies anonymously own subsidiaries in third-world countries where workers and the environment are exploited to the fullest possible extent. Men, women and children living in near proximity of the manufacturing plants are dying of cancer and other illnesses. They have no one to ask for help as the local governments, for hefty monetary compensation, collaborate with the corporations to fully suppress the people's human rights. It is basically one step above slavery, just do your research. The surprising fact is how badly some employees are treated here in the USA by some of the richest corporations. Facebook, for example; the company made $188,498 profit per employee in the second quarter of 2017. Yet their contract cafeteria employees are treated way differently than the permanent employees. In July 2017, I read a story about a couple and their three children who for years have been living in a two-car garage in Menlo Park and have sometimes struggled to pay for food and medical expenses. They both are working at Facebook's headquarters making about $20 per hour. In Silicon Valley, this wage is not a living wage. The couple said they aren't allowed to take excess food home with them at night and have to watch it thrown into compost. As contractors, they are not allowed to use the company's onsite medical services and gyms, or bring their children to work on Bring Your Child to Work Day. I hope this will change soon since, from July 2017, the cafeteria workers are part of a union. Maybe this could change automatically once the company makes $250,000 profit per employee, per quarter. Or maybe not, why don't we just say fuck these exploitable numbers and once they complain too much hire the next person waiting in line, right? Even someone like Elon Musk, who I think is a visionary and an inspiration to many entrepreneurs, was not too thrilled about unions in the past and said they would only stand in the way of the company's plans. Workers should unite and refuse to work in unhealthy environments, such as enclosed areas with little or no natural light and/or in areas where a high concentration of unshielded electronic equipment emits high levels of EMF radiation.

"Another sad example is Uber. The company claims its commission is 25% of a fare but fails to mention that in many instances, after service and booking fees, it is almost 50%. Each driver has to supply his or her car, pay for gas, maintenance, depreciation and taxes. Per my estimate, after everything is factored in, a driver only receives about 25% of a fare. Does it really take 50% of a fare to make ethical profit, provide support, maintain a website and a mobile application? Maybe such a high percentage is needed to develop self-driving cars to get rid of the numbers once and for all. The situation is even better for drivers who choose to rent a car via Uber. In Atlanta, the rental price for a basic economy car starts at the very affordable weekly price of $214 plus tax. It is a well-known fact that in the Czech Republic, many Uber drivers are illegal aliens recruited by a Mafia. The point is, many corporations will do anything in their power to increase profits, no matter what, as long as they can get away with it.

"People should not be afraid to talk about or express disagreements with corporations in person or through works of art. Here is a great example. In 2013, a company called Mattoni, the number one producer of mineral water in the Czech Republic and the main sponsor of the music competition, 'Golden Nightingale' (similar to the Grammy Awards), refused to pay the $5,000 top prize to controversial rapper Řezník because his songs are too vulgar and don't meet their corporate standards. Oddly enough, in 2016 Mattoni did not have a problem giving the prize to ex-neo-Nazi group Ortel. During the ceremony the singer Radek Banga got up from his seat and said to everyone, 'All of you just clapped to Nazis.' Sadly, he was the only one who left the theater. In 2015, Řezník released the song 'Pořád jenom hate 2,' where he points out Mattoni's strange relationship with public TV network 'ČT' to produce a show called *I, Mattoni*. Millions of taxpayers' dollars may have been used to produce the show that is more like a glorified advertisement. Secondly, the video clip displays the company and its Italian owner acting like the Mafia. In the USA, artists don't have this freedom. Coca-Cola could mail a letter to a writer listing a trademark violation because the word 'Coke' is not capitalized. Google's legal department has been notifying writers because the phrase 'google up' was used instead of 'internet search.' Just to be on the safe side, maybe a writer should call the search engine 'information superhighway' to avoid potential lawsuits. :-) Girls, I can continue to preach like this for eternity, but we only have a few hours left as the restaurant closes at 11 p.m.

"What will happen to us after the judgment day when we enter politics? As always, I have a plan that I would like to share with you at this time."

Chapter 16
The Meeting/Sometime Later

"Here is the plan of the real change, the blueprint of the new world order, the vision of my American Dream…

"Within a few months of becoming the president, I will realize my hands are tied and I am unable to make any real changes. The judgment day will not do much except help me to get elected. The same old government structure will still be present: congressmen, senators, and justices, more than ever, still catering to churches, military contractors, corporations, and other special interest groups, while ignoring the silenced voices of the hundreds of millions of average people. Even when able to influence a piece of legislation or issue an executive order that would have made a difference, corrupt judges will rip it apart.

"'No More Lies' is wishful thinking," I said to myself, and thought of the Iron Maiden song.

"Even during my early years when I was the unknown, jobless Joe Blow writing this book, I knew this was going to be a problem once sitting in the Oval Office. I came up with the ultimate permanent solution – the plan to change everything – to eventually return the power to the people by breaking the spine of the invisible/shadowy government that encircled Washington and the entire globe. The system is designed to confuse and to push people against each other. That's why we only have two mainstream parties with two major fake news media networks. Opinion news is designed to waste people's time, to steer their thought process in order to think in a predetermined way. About two years into my presidency, during an emergency address to the nation, the following scenario will happen:

"Good evening, my fellow Americans. Thank you for taking the time out of your busy lives to hear what I have say to each and every one of you tonight. You have elected me based on the promise that I will bring real change to Washington and ultimately to the entire world. After two years of being your president, I am unable to keep this promise because of how Washington operates and has operated for the past ninety years; catering to churches, defense contractors, corporations and special interest groups while ignoring the average person – the person working twelve hours a day trying to make ends meet to provide for the family. But don't worry, I came up with the backup plan a long time ago when I was the unknown, unemployed, and heartbroken Joe Blow going through a divorce. I always keep my promises and one of them was not to let you down, no matter what. Here is the solution to most of our problems…

"As of this moment, all members of Congress, Senate, and Supreme Court Justices are being arrested. All the generals invited to the White House this evening are also being placed under house arrest. For the past two years, undercover Russian Special Forces have been crossing the borders legally via airports and illegally from Canada and Mexico, bringing with them the necessary supplies. As we speak, there are countless Russian ships and airplanes heading towards the US shores. The Russian military will assist our military forces and local law enforcement until everybody calms down and the dust settles. I am the commander-in-chief who helped the Russians to hack into our defense systems, therefore at this point our military is on standby and waiting for everyone's arrival, eager to shake hands with their new comrades.

"Look, everyone! (*A gentleman joins me at my desk.*) The first Russian person has just arrived and his name is Mikhail Khodorkovsky, the President of Russia. 'Hello, Mikhail, how are you? Smile, you are on live TV,' I say, as we shake hands in front of the stunned and speechless nation.

"'Hi, I couldn't be better. Hanging in there, Mr. President?' Mikhail replies.

"We both sit down, look into each other's eyes and start to laugh.

"'I have a present for you,' says Mikhail, 'in fact, two presents; one is this briefcase and the second is a bottle of the best Russian samohonka, distilled at home by my family just for this occasion.'

"'I hope that I will not lose my vision after drinking this,' I say, and continue to laugh.

"'Don't worry, I "tested" another bottle while flying over here and I am just fine,' Mikhail replies, with a smirk on his face, pouring the vodka into two 1-deciliter shot glasses. 'Make sure you take a deep breath while pouring all this vodka down your throat,' he continues, and we each raise a glass.

"'Salut, Comrade. We did it, like back in the old days, friends forever! To the free world!' I exclaim, remembering the TV broadcast of Václav Havel holding a shot glass, ready to toast while saying; 'to free Czechoslovakia.' This happened shortly after the Communist Party's demise and with the announcement to allow free elections.

"'To the free world!' Mikhail replies.

"I pour the entire contents of the glass down my throat; my mouth, throat, and stomach feel like they're about to catch fire.

"'That's pretty good, strong!' I say, after exhaling the alcohol fumes, barely able see and breathe any longer.

"'Don't worry, I will not make you drink your half of the bottle,' he answers, while continuing to smile at me and the TV camera.

"Mikhail then opens the silver briefcase.

"'Oh, what's this briefcase? No, you did not!' I say, becoming ecstatic. 'A remote control! At this point, the only way to control all the US nuclear arsenal. How sweet of you! I am not sure how to return the favor,' I say, giving him a wink.

"'Well, Mr. President, and the American people, I've had a long flight and need to get some rest,' says Mikhail. 'Good luck and have a great rest of your evening.' And he walks away.

"I say goodbye to him and think of myself as the 'journeyman' whose life will soon bring him peace of mind. The loneliness of the long distance runner is finally paying off. I look back towards the camera and continue my speech.

"At this point, all of you are questioning if this is a dream or reality and are eager to find out the next steps. I can assure you it will not get any more real, any better than this. The world is a few steps away from certain self-destruction. Many of you have awakened after the judgment day but not the invisible/shadowy government, churches, defense contractors, and multinational corporations that are continuing to divide people and spread misery around the world. Believe me, I have thought about this extreme measure multiple times before deciding to realize it. With the current technological advancement and state of affairs, this is the only way to safely move our civilization to the next level. The US government has been exploiting vast areas of our planet for the past ninety years while taking the power away from the people little by little. The American people are no longer able to control the government. The government does whatever it wants without any checks and balances, thinking it's better than the average person, better than anybody else on Earth. Many people's minds are eclipsed by blind belief that the higher authority always looks after their best interests and as a result they don't question anything. According to the *Washington Post* newspaper, democracy ends in darkness. How ironic is this twisted marriage of the beauty and the beast? The people are unable to control the government and the government is using the U.S. Constitution as a smokescreen to do whatever it wants behind the scenes.

"Well, all this has just ended and become part of history. Effective immediately, I therefore indefinitely suspend the U.S. Constitution and I am replacing it with a set of directives. The Constitution will be reinstated once the government is firmly back in the hands of the American people and the people will become the true stewards of planet Earth. In the interim, I have no choice but to rule with an iron fist. Here are the directives:

"*Directive 1* – Effective immediately, the two-party political monopoly, the Commission on Presidential Debates and the Electoral College, are no longer. You can either be involved in business or politics, but you cannot be involved in both. Lobbying is prohibited except to write a letter to a representative via a public method of communication and anyone is able to access the letter at any moment. Campaign finance for legal entities is not allowed and is limited to $10,000 per year for an individual, linked to a Social Security number. Gerrymandering and adding 'pork' to a bill in order to confuse everyone is no longer allowed. At state level, any individual that has at least 1,000 eligible voters' signatures will be able to run for Congress and Senate. Anybody running for president, with at least 3% of eligible voters' signatures, will be able to participate in the initial rounds of presidential debates. The federal and state governments will eventually become direct democracies based mostly on referendums and popular votes at national or state levels. At federal level, the people will be able to introduce new legislature and request a referendum on existing legislature with a petition that has at least 10% of eligible voters' signatures tied to Social Security numbers. The same applies to states; a minimum of 10% of eligible voters' signatures tied to Social Security numbers is required to introduce new legislature or request a referendum on existing legislature. The USA is a nation of one people who live in the same country; consequently, nothing on a federal level should be based on individual states. Direct elections for Congress, Senate, and the presidency, as well as state and local representatives, will be held every four years, with a maximum number of years in office allowed for each individual representative. Supreme Court Justices are to be elected directly by the people; they are no longer appointed by the president. All justices are to be elected directly by the people in federal, state, or local elections.

"Federal and State level – maximum number of years allowed in office:
"President (governor) – 8 years
"Member of Congress (state lower house) – 12 years
"Member of Senate (state upper house) – 12 years
"Supreme Court and Federal justices (state supreme court, down to magistrate court justices) – two 12 year terms
"Local Level – maximum number of years allowed in office:
"Mayor – 8 years and everyone else 12 years

"*Directive 2* – Close most of the 800-plus military bases worldwide and most of the hundreds of domestic bases, except for fifty, strategically located within the USA. This will save hundreds of billions of dollars annually. While departing, destroy military and governmental infrastructure in all countries whose governments oppress and torture its citizens, so the citizens can rise up and form new governments. Finally, restructure all branches of the military into special elite forces and create a separate New Defense Force – an army of highly skilled IT experts/hackers ready to assist the military and the governments with anything at any moment. Increase Air Force capabilities to be able to swiftly deploy troops and equipment anywhere in the world in case ground invasion is the only available option. Overhaul of NASA; the agency needs to focus more on partnerships with private companies to explore the Universe for scientific and commercial purposes. Ban the development and production of all nuclear and chemical weapons. Empower the UN Security Council for its inspectors to enter any country unannounced to inspect for possible development and/or production of nuclear and chemical weapons. Automatically destroy military and governmental infrastructure of any country that refuses to comply. Reduce the US nuclear arsenal to a maximum of 500 missiles and, when the time is right, decommission the remaining missiles.

"*Directive 3* – Consolidate and/or close the following intelligence agencies under the newly created New Defense Force: Defense Intelligence Agency, National Geospatial-Intelligence Agency, National Reconnaissance Office, Military Intelligence Corps, Office of Naval Intelligence, Twenty-Fifth Air Force, Intelligence and Security Command, Marine Corps Intelligence, Coast Guard Intelligence, Office of Intelligence and Analysis. The National Security Agency (NSA) is closed permanently to honor Edward Joseph Snowden, Reality Leigh Winner, and as a personal favor to me. The second gestapo-like agency, the Central Intelligence Agency (CIA), is closed permanently as well, to honor all the known and unknown victims that have been tortured and silenced. Consolidate and/or close the following intelligence agencies under the FBI: Bureau of Intelligence and Research, Office of Terrorism and Financial Intelligence, Drug Enforcement Administration, Office of National Security Intelligence, Intelligence Branch, Office of Intelligence and Counterintelligence. The two remaining intelligence agencies will report everything to the executive and legislative branches and to the people on a yearly basis; they are no longer able to classify a document unless part of an ongoing operation. Repeal of the USA Patriot and the USA Freedom acts.

"*Directive 4* – Cut diplomatic, economic, and military ties with all oppressive regimes around the world, the many human rights violators like Saudi Arabia and North Korea. Place real sanctions with real effects; freeze all foreign assets and place global arrest warrants on the members of these governments. I have ordered a ground invasion of North Korea to liberate the concentration camps.

"Cut diplomatic and military ties with the totalitarian European Parliament in Brussels. The European Union is not about cooperation. It is about creating the United States of Europe, where each state becomes a province of this new empire. This nomenclature does whatever it wants without voters' support. People of Europe, you don't need someone to micromanage your lives. Each state is capable of managing its own affairs based on the Swiss direct democracy model. The two positive items are free trade and open borders within the Schengen Area. Much else is a smokescreen to hide theft and lies.

"Cut diplomatic, economic, and military ties with countries that do not agree to collaborate to enforce effective birth control in order to reduce the global population, to a pre-Industrial Revolution number of 529 million. At that level, all humans will be able to live decently, using 100% recyclable resources, and will no longer be a burden to Earth's ecosystem.

"Collaborate with all countries on Earth to establish real Peace Combat Force under the direction of true international law. This army of soldiers will be deployed into any country to put down terrorism, insurrections, wars, criminality and aggression. It will be mandatory for every nation on Earth to equally participate in financing this new global army. This is the only way to achieve long-term peace on this planet. Dismantle the ineffective and powerless UN Security forces.

"Fully secure the borders with Mexico and finally build the wall. Legalize illegal immigrants currently in the country who have not committed serious crimes. Suspend further immigration indefinitely. Ban all drugs except marijuana. Punish the dealers, not the users. All drug cartel smugglers are to receive a minimum twenty years of excommunication without any chance of being paroled or deported. All foreign visitors are to wear two items received at airports and border crossings with no questions asked: a GPS bracelet and AR glasses, visually no different than ordinary glasses, using direct patterned 2k X 2k OLED displays, serving as tour guides, and to record all activity while visiting the USA.

"*Directive 5* – Permanently ban organized religious activities. This applies to religious organizations that behave like businesses. In August 2017, I went to Cumberland Mall in Atlanta, GA, and close to the entrance there were three advertisement posters right next to each other luring people to churches. A church can either be a spiritual place or a business, but it cannot be both. It is perfectly fine to find inner spirit, to pray by yourself, with family/friends or in small-scale churches as long as there is no money involved. This excludes the necessary funds to purchase, build, or maintain properties. This meditation is necessary to find yourself and eventually reconnect and become part of nature. All cash donations are strictly forbidden. Small-scale churches are only able to conduct noncash charitable events and are to be 'remodeled' with the latest surveillance equipment. Clergy will have GPS microchips implanted under the skin and wear AR glasses to record their activity while away from home. Clergy are forbidden to host events larger than six (excluding family) at their homes. Cancel all special tax exemptions except for the ones available to regular nonprofit organizations. Tax returns including all supporting schedules/information are to be made publicly available. People 'employed' by churches that are involved in spiritual teachings are to become volunteers receiving $0 pay. Repeal all religious freedom bills: the smokescreens for legalized discrimination. Prayer caucuses no longer have any business in the American political system. The phrase 'In God We Trust' is no longer the national motto and will be removed from all legal tender notes. The phrase 'under God' is no longer part of the Pledge of Allegiance. The phrase 'In God is our trust' is no longer part of 'The Star-Spangled Banner.' Cut diplomatic, economic, and military ties with countries that do not agree to ban large-scale religious activities and implement similar measures. Foreign visitors from those countries are banned from entering the USA.

"*Directive 6 – Individual Income Taxes*; revise tax codes to progressive flat tax. All deductions, including charitable, are eliminated. There is no longer an income cap on Social Security contributions. State income tax will cap at 7%, local taxes remain unchanged. Financial institutions are prohibited to do any business on behalf of an individual with countries known as 'tax shelters.'

"Individual – Annual Income Tax
"$0 – $20,999:   0%
"$21,000 – $40,999:   15%
"$41,000 – $120,999:   20%
"$121,000 and above: 30%
"All capital gains and dividends are to be taxed at 30%.

"*Directive 7 – Corporate Taxes and Accounting*; close the accounting loopholes and revise/simplify the whole accounting system to be more legible and understandable to the average college-educated person. The era of a CPA firm advising governments on tax reforms and at the same time advising clients on how to avoid taxes is over. Break up the Big Four CPA firms – the masterminds of multinational tax avoidance schemes costing governments and their taxpayers around the world an estimated $1 trillion per year. The Big Four CPA firms will be split into at least twenty separate and independent firms. Privately owned CPA firms are no longer allowed to advise federal and state governments on anything related to taxation. Tax codes are revised to progressive flat tax, necessary business expenses are deductible. All other deductions and subsidies are eliminated except for the following scenario requiring legislative and executive approval on a case by case basis and vote of the people: a product or service that would benefit the advancement of mankind and/or protect the planet. There is no longer an income cap on Social Security contributions. State income tax will cap at 7%, local taxes will remain unchanged. For corporations with an annual net income greater than $10 billion; the primary objective is to help mankind and protect the planet, using the portion of income over $10 billion. Financial institutions are prohibited from doing any business on behalf of a corporation with countries known as 'tax shelters.' Corporations are no longer 'people,' no longer having personal rights under the law as people do, because they do not have the same feelings as people – feelings of love, caring, and compassion. Up to this point, the only feeling a corporation has ever had was to make money, disregarding everything else in the process.

"Corporate – Annual Corporate Tax
"$0 – $20,999:   0%
"$21,000 – $40,999:   15%
"$41,000 – $120,999:   20%
"$121,000 and above: 30%
"All capital gains and dividends are to be taxed at 30%.

"A good example of a corporate tax deduction that most people would surely approve is to create 'The Company,' a truly global corporation specializing in space exploration for scientific, commercial, and industrial purposes similar to Weyland-Yutani (*Aliens*, 1986 movie). Sadly enough, Weyland-Yutani is known as the greediest corporation in the galaxy. Maybe someone like Elon Musk and Richard Branson will get together with other global business leaders to create 'The Company' that will help to push mankind into the 22nd century. If that ever happens, as a personal favor to me, please use 'Building Better Worlds' as the company's slogan. Since I was a kid, I've always liked the sound of that sentence.

"*Directive 8* – The legal system is to be revised so it makes more sense to the average college-educated person, with clearer precedence on what to expect. Legal documents are to be written in plain English and the legal definition 'Act of God' is to be renamed 'Natural Disaster.'

Establish mandatory caps on all attorney fees for each task to eliminate corrupt lawyers that only wealthy, powerful individuals and entities can afford. Some 'good' lawyers use interesting methods to get clients off the hook. A 'good' lawyer usually starts as a prosecuting attorney and naturally develops a friendly, buddy-type relationship with judges. A few years later and in the same jurisdiction, the prosecuting attorney opens a private practice and becomes known as very expensive 'good' lawyer – the connected middleman with whom the judges feel comfortable and have no problem accepting bribes from. It's possible to receive $1,000 fine and probation when charged with thirteen drug possession felonies.

"Coincidentally, many lawmakers and politicians use similar methodology to that of the 'good' lawyer. A politician often accepts hefty bribes from a lobbyist – the middleman who performs the dirty work for a corporation. In many cases, retired politicians become lobbyists themselves because they know the system and, in the past, have accepted bribes from the same entities they now work for. This is a very convenient insurance policy to make the corporations, lobbyists and politicians feel comfortable that no one will ever talk. Lobbying is nothing more than a smokescreen for legalized bribery.

"Courts will no longer waste anybody's time and resources. For instance, a calendar call is more efficiently handled via teleconference call or email instead of in person. All courts will strive for similar efficiency and professionalism as The Municipal Court of Atlanta. Based on the Swedish model, divorcing parents will automatically receive 50/50 joint legal and physical custody unless drugs, domestic violence or similar circumstances prevent them from being good parents. To restore balance between pro-business and anti-worker, the labor laws will be more aligned with those in Europe. An open-door policy is just a smokescreen to keep workers silent and divided. No one can be sued for wrongdoings caused purely by accident. For example, a person cannot be sued if a ten-year-old child drowns in his/her pool while swimming, unless something in the water prevented that child from swimming. People and entities are no longer able to share any personal data, for any reason, without the person's consent. The food industry is no longer allowed to pump unnecessary chemicals into foods to make products last way longer than they should, to get consumers addicted to certain tastes, to trick consumers' brains into thinking they're still hungry, therefore indirectly forcing people to buy more products. It doesn't make sense for a person living in the state of Georgia to eat bread made in Canada and to drink water imported from Fiji. Advertisement of processed foods is no longer allowed, including a toy given when certain processed foods are purchased. Corporations are no longer allowed to 'recommend' and punish consumers for something that is unreasonable. For example, a car manufacturer is no longer allowed to recommend changing brake fluid every six months or 15,000 miles. Sale of all products that contain cancer-causing chemicals is no longer allowed. Sale of one-time plastic bottles and containers is no longer allowed. There are plenty of paper, glass and metal containers available. Trash companies must take and recycle all recyclable materials, no longer cherry-picking what to recycle. Laws pertaining to homeowner's associations are to be updated to put more emphasis on transparency. The associations are no longer able to create rules that unreasonably restrict people's freedoms.

"*Directive 9* – Implement an efficient food management system. One third of all food grown worldwide, costing $3 trillion, is wasted every year. Annually in the US, 50% of all produce (60 million tons, worth $160 billion) is thrown away when one in six Americans is hungry. For instance: the only purpose of a chicken's life is to live so it can be killed and eaten by you and your family at dinner. That chicken deserves tremendous respect from the people who will eat it. Thanks to the farm subsidies, food in the US is too cheap and people don't have any respect for it. Waste can be greatly reduced if, to a certain point, food is sold for discounted prices after expiration. I am ending farm subsidies to generate prices that demand respect. Effective today, all food up to 10% of total volume is allowed to be wasted. In five years, the amount will be reduced to 5%. All farms, food manufacturers, distributors, and grocery stores will pay fines that equal 100% of the retail price of food wasted above the 10% allowed limit. Food imports from countries that do not impose similar restrictions on waste are prohibited. Production and import of biofuels is prohibited.

"*Directive 10* – Social Security retirement is to equal 60% of the average national pay, or 60% of average pay achieved during the last ten years prior to retirement, for individuals who have worked thirty-eight years or more. Financial institutions are only allowed to charge their customers one annual flat fee to administer and grow a 401k plan. Create an affordable health care system for every person living in the USA. Affordable health care for every citizen is not a privilege but a basic human right. Nobody is allowed to profit from human misery, therefore health insurance companies are to become nonprofit entities with caps on executive pay. The health plans are to be designed by the federal government and the insurance premiums are to be paid directly to insurance companies. The insurance companies will pay all claims to the states, who will reimburse the medical institutions and doctors. The premiums will be based on a person's lifestyle, not income. Someone who eats unhealthy fast food, smokes a pack of cigarettes and drinks alcohol every day cannot expect to pay the same price as an individual living an active and healthy lifestyle. For children under eighteen, college students, and poor people, the government will pay the premiums. With all the military savings and tax overhaul, there are plenty of available dollars to pay for it. Secondary insurance to pay for additional services, like fine dining while in a hospital and/or a luxurious private hospital room, is an option. Prices of drugs and medical services, except for cosmetic procedures, are to be regulated. Implement stricter requirements for antibiotics and antidepressant prescriptions; they are no longer allowed to be given out like candy to everyone, including children.

"*Directive 11* – Revise the penal system. Abolish the death penalty and any kind of torture, including enhanced interrogation techniques. Inmates are to be excommunicated to secluded areas where they will continue to work, educate themselves, and learn from their mistakes so they do not repeat the mistakes upon their return. The inmates are to be separated by sex and all activity recorded/monitored by GPS bracelets and AR glasses. For example: a Midwestern farm surrounded by electrified barbed wire could be used to house prisoners and to provide work for the prisoners. Family and conjugal visits are to be allowed based on a preset schedule affected by behavior and other factors. All prison communities are to be administered by governments and not by for-profit corporations. Increase the pay by 50% for all emergency response units, nurses, and police officers patrolling the streets. In return, police officers will wear AR glasses while at work to record activity. We want our law enforcement officers to provide safety and not to become Judge Dredds.

"*Directive 12* – To use clean and renewable energy to generate electricity based on regional availability. New residential construction is to be equipped with solar panels and its own water source, if water is available, and have a minimum of one acre of land. Ban clear cutting of every single tree when building a subdivision. All land is to be treated with the same respect as in 'Sandy Springs Conservation Area.' The entrance sign to the neighborhood states: '*This area is protected as a plant and tree reserve to conserve natural and cultural heritage. Please do not disturb the plants and trees.*' They even have crossings for chickens. Northside Drive, that runs through this area, is to be renamed MLK Drive. Immediately start constructing a network of solar power plants in southwest deserts and upgrade the power grid to carry all this energy across the nation. Create a battery power grid backup system, similar to Australia's, to be used at night and in case of a blackout. Decommission nuclear, coal, oil, and gas power plants within a ten-year time frame. Build networks of desalinization plants on the West Coast. Stop farming in desert areas using ground and underground water. Fully recycle all sewage water. Ban the sale of passenger gasoline and diesel vehicles within ten years from today. All electronic equipment is to be shielded to eliminate EMF radiation. Redesign cell phones to direct the signal away from callers. Ban offshore drilling for oil, gas, and using the fracking method within ten years from today. Build an efficient, safe, and reliable public transportation network in every metropolis and individual city of 50,000 or more people.

"*Directive 13* – Break up the Big Five corporations owning 90% of the mainstream 'fake news' media market to at least twenty separate and independent entities, free from external influences. Indefinitely limit social media to a combined two hours per day for all accounts linked to a Social Security number. Go outside to a nature reserve, to a park, to a restaurant, or to dance to form deeper connections and meaningful relationships. Have deeper personal conversations. Touch the other person, look at the other person; look her or him in the eyes to generate feelings of love, caring, compassion, and ultimately form true friendship. You will never achieve this by looking at digital squares of facial pictures and by keying hundreds of words to hundreds of virtual friends. Social media and all internet companies, including search engines, are no longer allowed to collect unnecessary personal data and share the data with anyone, especially the advertisers and governments. 'Mark, why do you have all this desire to collect so much personal information on each friend? Your mom was a psychiatrist, maybe your childhood wasn't as much fun as you wanted it to be, who knows. I kind of like your support of universal basic income. It's a dangerous idea. If you lived in the 1950s, someone like Ronald Reagan would have been more than happy to accuse you of being a communist, to throw you into prison.'

"*Directive 14* – Government schools; pre-k, elementary, middle, and high schools are free of charge to everyone. Private schools are to abide by the same rules as public schools. Teachers are no longer allowed to shift teaching responsibilities to parents and tutors. Teachers' primary focus is to teach and not to worry about watching movies, organizing fundraisers and parties for children. Schools will ask for only one donation at the beginning of a school year. Schools are forbidden to act as churches and beggars by constantly putting unwanted pressure on children and parents to raise funds. Taxpayers do pay more than enough taxes, therefore it is only the government's duty to fully fund all public schools.

"The schools are to have emphasis on long-term learning instead of endless amounts of standardized tests. Good and proven learning methodologies will not change on a yearly basis to confuse students and parents to justify someone's job. All schools are to provide to students nutritious hot meals cooked from scratch. Kids in first to fourth grade elementary school are to have the same primary teacher. Elementary and middle school children are to wear uniforms, attend mandatory swimming and nutrition classes, and take two one-week-long trips with their class per year: skiing and 'School in Nature.' High-school students are to attend mandatory etiquette classes; learn how to think for themselves, how to spot dangerous religious and extremist ideologies, learn the value of direct democracy, learn how to correctly participate in community and politics, learn how to behave when stopped by a police officer so there are no misunderstandings and learn about the importance of safe sex and contraceptives. Condom vending machines are to be installed on the premises of all high schools and universities. All schools are to be safe and provide the same quality learning experience for everyone. Cellular phones and wifi networks are banned in every school. Construction of cell phone towers on school properties is forbidden. Existing cell phone towers are to be removed from school properties immediately. Students who habitually disrupt learning are to be expelled indefinitely. With government supervision, parents of those students are to be held fully accountable for home schooling and be punished if those children fall behind. Revise tuition for public and private universities/colleges. Total dollar amount charged for each program cannot be more than what is expected to be made in the first two years of employment after graduation. This is to prevent a school charging $300,000 for an arts degree after which the graduate only makes $40,000 per year.

"*Directive 15* – In the interim period, until the U.S. Constitution is modified, reinstated, and added to the directives, all citizens and residents are to report to the nearest hospital to have a GPS microchip implanted under an inconspicuous area of the skin. The 'invitations' for the procedure will be sent to each person via registered U.S. mail. To gather at groups of more than twenty without informing the authorities is forbidden. Force will be used to restore order in case of large-scale disobediences.

"*Directive 16* – In the interim period, until the U.S. Constitution is modified, reinstated, and added to the directives, I am freezing all prices except food. Prices of food are allowed to fluctuate by no more than 300% from today's prices during the next eight years. Everything else will cost you the same tomorrow as it costs you today, including real estate, bonds, stocks, precious metals. Anybody caught raising prices will face excommunication. Foreign currency exchange rates will remain intact and frozen because I am asking everyone so nicely. If not, we will cut all political and economic ties with those countries. Stock and commodity markets are open to trade at today's prices only. Prices of everything such as real estate, stocks, and commodities will begin to fluctuate one month from today but are not allowed to fluctuate by more than 50% from today's price during the next eight years. IPO stocks are to be available to large and small investors simultaneously.

"*Directive 17* – All new mothers, regardless of background and income, are to stay home with their babies and toddlers for two to four years. The women are to receive 60% of the average annual pay, paid monthly. If the new moms decide to stay home for less than four years, they would still receive the same amount of money. This is the only way to reverse certain self-destruction and for us to eventually become true stewards of the planet Earth. No one is allowed to have more than two children until the global population stabilizes at 529 million. After-school programs such as sports and summer activities, including camps, are to be provided free of charge to all children aged seventeen and younger regardless of background and income. We just closed over 800 foreign military bases and saved $160 billion per year. We can afford to give something back to our youngest citizens. Ghettos are to be declared protected military zones; no one can get in or out without a thorough search and background check. Ghetto residents are to be provided medical, financial, housing, job training, and employment assistance or will be excommunicated if all this fails. The ghettos themselves are to be eliminated since no human being should live in such conditions.

"*Directive 18* – Washington D.C. is no longer the nation's capital. The US government is to be moved from Washington D.C. to the city in the Southeast that escaped the floods, to the city surrounded by a forest. The new capital is to be named Atlantis, after the mythical ancient Greek city lost in a flood.

"*Directive 19* – The target date for the interim period to end is eight years from today, if everyone behaves according to the directives and everything else goes as planned. We will hold free elections eight years from today. Effective immediately, all current members of Congress, Senate, and Supreme Court Justices are fired and will not be eligible to run for re-election.

"I appoint the following people to implement the new policies, except for military; I will provide assistance with anything if asked and the four of you can help each other as needed:

"*Christine Dias* – Find the right people and oversee anything related to business, except for tax. Instruct state and local governments as well.

"*Jessica Wilganowski* – Find the right people and oversee anything related to social services provided by the federal government. Instruct state and local governments as well.

"*Leah Dryden* – Find the right people and oversee the IRS, instruct state and local governments and help Christine with business.

"*Ronnee Pedersen* – Find the right people and oversee anything related to law at federal level. Instruct state and local governments as well and help Jessica with social services.

"Sorry girls, I know it's a shitty deal, but you don't have a choice. At this point, it is all up to you, so get going. Don't worry, the four of you are very intelligent, extremely resourceful, and will eventually find the answers. In case I get assassinated or 'accidentally' injured and I am no longer able to perform my duties, I appoint Jessica Wilganowski as my successor. She never falls under pressure, is smart as can be and fair to everyone. I am 100% confident she will get the job done.

"Once the country is transitioned back to the people, my services to the United States will end. I will not run as your president again and will retire to exile in Russia, provided by my buddy Mikhail Khodorkovsky. The Russian forces will leave with me. This is the end of the directives.

"My fellow Americans, relax! It's not as bad as it seems. Go out, go shop, go exercise, get laid or do whatever makes you happy. I am certain, and promise you, that your lives will change for the better. I have one more surprise for you so you can't say I am such an asshole. I'll throw you a bone. If everyone behaves nicely, I will cancel part of Directive 15 and you won't have to report to a hospital for GPS chip implantation. There is one other thing I forgot to mention. The USC system of measurements has been replaced with the metric system."

Chapter 17
The Meeting/Tunneling

"Joseph, are you done? Anything else you would like to share with us? This is one crazy American Dream!" said Christine, with Jessica and Ronnee staring at me with open mouths, not moving at all.

"Relax girls, I am just fucking with you," I said, smiled and continued to speak. "Even after the judgment day, no one will elect me because I am a non-believer. Atheists in this country are the most discriminated against minority, more hated than LGBT and Blacks combined. More than 40% of eligible voters will not vote for a non-believer regardless of personality. Maybe Donald Trump will implement the changes for us!" I said, and we were laughing while the girls believed I was just joking. "I had such a hard time remembering the names of all those intelligence agencies," I said.

"I would like to know what the intelligence agencies are doing," said Christine.

"I'll tell you what they are doing," I replied. "Their classified purpose is to 'tunnel' taxpayers' dollars, to reallocate funds under 'white horses,' to enrich the shadowy government and military contractors. Nobody knows what they're doing. That's why everything is classified and top-secret."

"What do you mean by 'tunnel' taxpayers' dollars and what is a 'white horse'? Please speak English," asked Ronnee.

I looked at their faces one by one, starting with Ronnee, then Jessica and Christine, and said, "You don't know what tunneling means? Back in the Czech Republic that is a household term every child is familiar with. Do you remember the 1987 movie, *Wall Street*, when Gordon Gekko wanted to break up Bluestar Airlines? 'Tunneling' takes this one step further; a company's management, together with outside entities such as customers, judges, and law enforcement, dig a 'tunnel' to reallocate the company's assets until there is nothing left except an empty shell and the name of the business. A great example of this is the infamous Star Wars program; the Reagan administration carefully shifted over $200 billion of taxpayers' money to a program everyone knew was not feasible with 1980s technology, and in the process enriched everyone in the pyramid scheme from top to bottom including third parties like the defense contractors. The 'friendly personnel' – top management of the defense contractors, the so-called 'white horses' – returned some of the money to the politicians and executive personnel in such a way that no one, including the IRS, can ever find them. The military-industrial-congressional complex runs like a well-oiled machine.

"The country is so badly mismanaged, there is tunneling going on everywhere you look: fighting non-existent or greatly exaggerated enemies, using imaginary intelligence as an excuse to go to war, passing new legislature that no one reads, adding unrelated 'pork' to new legislature, you name it. No wonder the country is almost $20 trillion in debt and counting, since there is no accountability. There are so many vacuum cleaners to suck in taxpayers' dollars. Did you know that the Pentagon's financial records have never been audited? The first ever so-called audit to appease the critics is scheduled for fall 2017. I am not surprised that the USA's projected 2018 defense budget is $700 billion. On an annual basis, hundreds of billions of dollars' worth of defense contracts are awarded without bidding. Nobody will miss $10, $20 billion reallocated elsewhere. For comparison, Russia's estimated 2018 defense budget is only about $50 to $60 billion."

I was getting looks from the three girls and Christine said, "Come on, Joseph, it can't be that bad."

"Yes, don't be so paranoid," Ronnee said.

Jessica was not saying anything. She was just looking directly into my face, not smiling, not moving at all. "If Jessica and I were sitting alone, what if I unexpectedly kissed her at this moment, how would she react? Would she kiss me back or slap me in the face?" I thought.

"On second thought, the word 'tunneling' is of Czech origin, like the word 'robot', which was first used in Karel Čapek's 1920 hit play *Rossum's Universal Robots*. Čapek was a prophet when he wrote The *White Disease (1937)* play," I said. I paused for a few moments and resumed speaking. "Let me tell you a few stories about 'tunneling' and politics in the Czech Republic."

Jessica became ecstatic and said, "Tell us, Joseph, as always you are doing a great job of entertaining us!"

Christine and Ronnee agreed and all three girls gave me a wink.

"OK, if you get bored just tell me to stop," I said. We looked at each other and smiled. I then started to talk.

"The way I admire Václav Havel, I can't say the same thing about Václav Klaus, another leader of the Velvet Revolution. Havel wanted real change for the people and helped to organize the revolution from his heart, for the love of his country. Klaus, however, did it mainly because of money and power. He became the Minister of Finance in 1989 and was the father of the privatization for the chosen ones. The privatization was done swiftly, without appropriate laws and enforcements. Nobody was asked where the money to buy the assets came from. Technically, every citizen could have participated in the privatization but there was a slight problem; after forty years of the Communist dictatorship, 90% of people lacked the necessary business skills and capital to be successful in the new market economy. Klaus took full advantage of fifteen million Czechoslovak citizens and utilized his business skills, acquired at Cornell University, by making the following statements: 'Regulations are not needed because the invisible hand of the market will solve everything. I cannot tell any difference between clean and dirty money.'

"He of course was unable to steal directly for himself, so apparently hired his first white horse, Victor Koženỳ. This backfired because Koženỳ was way too greedy, stopped paying his duties and eventually ended up in exile in the Bahamas. It looks like Klaus learned from the mistake and probably hired his second white horse, Petr Kellner. This was a good move because Kellner, during Klaus' regime, became the richest person in the country. In 2012, Petr's invisible hand renovated and 'rented' a castle to the 'Václav Klaus' Institute,' a nonprofit public benefits organization. Kellner's PPF financed the renovation and will finance the castle's operations for several decades. Just before Klaus' presidency ended, he issued amnesty for anyone whose court proceedings were in process for more than eight years – effectively freeing many of the economic criminals, the 'tunnelers' of the 1990s. As a result of public petition the senate charged him with treason but he was not convicted due to lack of votes.

"In 2008, Klaus issued a presidential pardon to Zdeněk Kratochvíl, the person charged with significant economic crimes, stating Mr. Kratochvíl is psychologically ill and unable to attend the judicial trial. To this day, however, Mr. Kratochvíl is in charge of his company, ICOM, with over 2,000 employees. In 2014 and 2015, ICOM wired a sponsorship present of one million crowns to the 'Václav Klaus' Institute.' Is the Institute just a smokescreen for Vašek to receive some clean money? The whole country knows what kind of person Klaus is but nobody does anything about it. Consequently, he publicly laughs at people in the business as usual way and negatively influences the country's development.

"In 2007, architect Jan Kaplickỳ won a competition to build the new National library using his unique, futuristic design, called 'Blob.' Klaus didn't like the design and lobbied politicians and courts to block the construction. I wish he had been this involved with the fight against corporate interests to prevent the 2017 demolition of a historical building located at Wenceslas Square. This is one of the reasons I could never move back to the Czech Republic. I have lived in the US for twenty-three years and consider myself too Americanized; I am used to business rules, ethics, and transparency. The prosecution and punishment of individuals involved in Enron, WorldCom, and other accounting scandals of the early 2000s is proof the USA is a nation of laws where strong business ethics are a must to be successful in the long term. I wouldn't have a problem doing business by handshake with someone like Jeff Mathis, knowing he would do what he promised.

"Klaus is not the only one but he is the worst of them all. There were others like the young prime minister, Gross, who in the early 2000s stated: 'The origin (of money to purchase luxury apartments) is so crystal clear that even crystal couldn't be anymore crystal clear than this.' In 2004, his political party, the ruling ČSSD, sold the remainder of the national coal mining company, OKD, to Karbon Invest, at about 50% below market price. In two months, Karbon Invest was sold to Zdeněk Bakala. In addition, Bakala bought over 40,000 apartments belonging to OKD for CZK 40,000 (about $1,800) apiece with a contractual obligation that the apartments would be sold to the miners and their families below market prices. It appears the apartments were not maintained and the workers were charged a monthly rent of several hundred dollars. The sale to the miners never happened, as in 2015, the apartments were sold to Round Hill Capital for an undisclosed amount. Unfortunately, everywhere you look there is a tunnel being dug somewhere.

"Czech politics is not always about fraud and theft. Many times, it is a lot of fun, especially when you have someone like Miloš Zeman as president. Here are a few examples of his presidential actions:

"In November 2014, during the live quarterly presidential radio interview called 'Hovory z Lán,' Miloš Zeman was asked about the imprisonment of Pussy Riot; a feminist punk rock group opposed to Putin's regime. Zeman said, 'Oh yes, Pussy Riot and other Russian political prisoners that are suffering. It's a pornographic group because one member participated in public group orgies while in advanced stage of pregnancy. The members are hooligans. Do you know what pussy means in English?' The interviewer corrected him on how to pronounce 'pussy' and before he had a chance to say anything else, Zeman said, 'Cunt, so I am sorry but in musical texts of this group you hear cunt here and cunt there, really good example of being a political prisoner.'

He was then asked about his opinion regarding amendments to 'Service Law' performed by newly elected government representatives. 'In my opinion, the parliament made one important mistake; it gave in to Mr. Kalousek's demands and fucked up the Service Law from its, let's say, Italian model, where the state confidant remains in place even if the government changes every year,' Zeman said. 'Mr. President, why are you being so vulgar?' the radio host asked. 'I am inspired by Mr. Schwarzenberg (ex-secretary of state and 2013 presidential candidate) who says shit after every other sentence,' answered President Zeman. As a result of this broadcast, the radio station faced fines for violating public broadcast rules about vulgarity and seriously considered canceling the quarterly presidential interviews, going forward.

"In May 2017, Miloš Zeman exited the NATO summit building drunk, barely able to walk consistently, and said to the reporters, 'We need to fight against Islamic State, that's the first thing.' He briefly paused and continued to speak. 'Secondly, we need to raise the army's budget like I did when I was premier, goodbye.' 'Mr. President, are you going to speak with the American president Trump soon?" a reporter quickly asked. 'Maybe all of us are going to speak with him soon,' said Zeman, while his secret service person smiled.

"There were many other instances Zeman was publicly drunk. In May 2013, the original Bohemian Crown Jewels became available for public viewing to celebrate the newly elected president. The newly elected President Miloš Zeman came to the opening ceremony drunk, stumbling, and barely able to stand straight. The government officials standing next to him smelled alcohol fumes and confirmed he was drunk. Later that day, the Presidential Office issued a statement that the president was sick with a virus.

"On April 3 2017, President Zeman announced that a hacker from Alabama installed child porn onto his computer. Miroslav Kalousek immediately tweeted: 'There are many perverted old men watching child porn. The only one that told on himself is the President of the Czech Republic.'

"Has the FBI ever found the hacker from Alabama? The president would surely appreciate it. Is this what really happened? Maybe Mr. Zeman was searching for porn and all of a sudden, the girls appeared way too young so he got scared and made up the story to cover his tracks. He has a great reputation for keeping everyone in suspense. The whole country is eager to know what's going to happen next, how embarrassing the next situation may be and how far he can push the low points of political boundaries."

"This is crazy, what a fucked-up president," Jessica said, in disbelief.

"No kidding, I am so glad we have Trump and not Zeman," Christine added.

"Why did the people elect somebody like him?" asked Ronnee.

"Don't ask me. I haven't lived there since 1994," I answered, and continued with the story.

"Here is why Zeman acted the way he did during the November 2014 'Hovory z Lán' interview. He knew the vulgarities would create media attention and the average person would then actually listen to the whole interview. For his seventieth birthday, he asked the radio station to play 'Demokracie,' a folk song written by Karel Kryl. The song explains the true intentions of churches, refers to 'King Václav' and his friends as 'tunnelers,' and explains what is happening to democracy in general. At this point, Zeman had reached the status of 'The Good Soldier Švejk' (*Schweik* in English), a famous Czech folk figure. A person likened to the character of Švejk is pictured as an unlucky, simple-minded but resourceful little man oppressed by higher authorities. This is because, historically, the small Czech nation was always torn among larger nations of the East and West and the people had to adjust accordingly. The 1938 Munich Conference is the perfect but sad example of this. The US foreign policy of not to negotiate with dictators is actually based on the Munich Conference; a dictator or terrorist will always make additional demands, there is no point in negotiating as he or she cannot be appeased.

"At age eleven, I saw and heard Miloš Zeman speak at Leteňská Plan during the Velvet Revolution protests. He gave a very powerful speech, about how backward Czechoslovakia became during the forty years of communism when compared to Western nations. Nobody knew who he was at that time. I admire Miloš Zeman for several things; he fought hard for decades against returning Church property the Communists had confiscated in the 1940s back to the Church. He knew very well the Church had no right to own the property again since it was gained by enslaving and torturing people in the first place. He tried to form closer ties with China regardless of the EU's or Czech government's opinion. He always said what came to his mind regardless of image and never pretended to be somebody else. Zeman has the image of an old, vulgar, chain-smoking drunk. This is who he really is and he knows it. He doesn't try to hide it or persuade the public to think of him otherwise. Miloš Zeman is the first president directly elected by the people and who kept his promise of being the president for the bottom ten million people. I would rather have Zeman as my president than someone like the two-faced George W. Bush who consistently and politely smiles directly into your eyes, but kisses the faces of dictators – the worst human rights violators, like Saudi king Abdullah – behind your back."

Chapter 18
The Meeting/Later that night

As the night progressed the four of us were in a great mood. I was glad to make the girls relax and laugh after I steered the conversation from US to Czech politics. The lights were dimmed and it was so comfortable to look directly into the two candles placed on the table. The restaurant was emptying out but I didn't want to end the night just yet.

"I can only drink so much red wine and it's time for me to switch to a beer. I can't drink alone so I will order you another bottle of wine," I told the girls, who gave me a surprised look.

Christine looked like she was about to say something so I said, "Don't even say anything, I will not take 'no' for an answer. Don't worry about being a little drunk. The three of you can share Uber and because I am such a gentleman, I will pay for it."

"That is nice of you, Joseph, but we can pay for it. You know, we're not that broke," Ronnee said.

"You are right, it would be sad to see a broke corporate attorney with twenty-five years of experience," I replied.

As we laughed, the waiter came to us and asked if we would like anything else.

"You came at the perfect time. Please bring us another couple bottles of wine for the ladies and I would like a nice large lager beer chilled from the seventh step," I said, and the waiter went to get the drinks.

"Why do you want the beer to be chilled from the seventh step?" Christine asked.

I opened my mouth and almost started to talk but decided to stop. "That's a whole other story. I will explain it to you some other time, otherwise we would sit here till morning," I answered.

"I still don't fully understand why Czech politics is so obviously corrupted and nobody does anything about it," said Ronnee.

"OK, let me try to explain it," I said, then paused, looked down at the candle and thought of how to best explain this in a short and sweet way. "In the mid-1980s, my stepdad Milan, and Mom went to a meeting with Milan's overall boss, named Běťák. This boss was in charge of all restaurants, bars, pubs, and food stands in Prague 8 district. At the meeting, Milan asked him for a promotion – to be the general manager of a large restaurant/bowling bar complex. Běťák answered, 'Yes, I will give you the place and your official pay will be Kčs 4,500 per month, but you will bring me Kčs 10,000 cash every month.' Do you see the paradox? The boss asked Milan to bring him more than twice what he would be officially making, as a bribe, forcing Milan to steal. If my stepdad refused, he would never get the promotion.

"My biological dad was also working in the restaurant industry and told me a story once. Back then, waiters bought their own bottles of liquor at a grocery store and sold them as shots or mixed drinks at their place of employment. There are two famous unwritten Czech folk rules: 'Who doesn't steal from the State, steals from the family,' and 'A real Czech person will always figure out ten ways to legally get around new legislature before the proposed legislature is made into a law.' This is especially true when it comes to proposed tax changes. For example, to get around reporting all sales live, via the internet, to the central tax department and to get around the new anti-smoking law passed in 2017, pub owners have been converting their businesses to private nonprofit clubs where membership is required to enter the premises.

"Anyway, back to my stepdad. Prague 8 is a large district with countless pubs, restaurants, and sports bars. Per conservative estimate, let's say for example that Běťák was taking a Kčs 10,000 bribe from twenty different restaurants. That's Kčs 200,000 per month in a country where the average official pay was Kčs 2,500 per month. Interestingly enough, Miloš Jakeš complained about the singer Zagorová officially earning Kčs 600,000 per year but it didn't bother him that someone like Běťák was unofficially making at least Kčs 2.4 million per year. The whole Communist system operated like this behind the scenes; therefore, over forty years the regime effectively raised a nation of thieves. Many strong-willed people like Václav Havel didn't allow their minds to be corrupted by the regime and acted righteously regardless of the political situation. If a person did not want to live from paycheck to paycheck, he or she had to steal because there was no other legal way to make money. Prior to 1948, people didn't behave like this. It was customary to do business with a handshake. Products and services were of high quality because it was the right way to do business. Even gamblers willingly gave away property lost in card games since the agreement was solidified by a handshake. Back then, most people didn't need lawyers. This is the reason why Czech politics is so corrupt. Everybody is bitching about it but nobody knows what to do about it.

"In September 2017, the Czech Parliament stripped away political immunity from Andrej Babiš, who was the Minister of Finance until May 2017, so he could face corruption charges. Babiš' strongest argument is that everybody steals. As always, there is light at the end of the tunnel. A new generation of politicians and businessmen born in the 1980s and 1990s is gaining respect and popularity. The Pirate political party would like to establish direct democracy based on the Swiss model and its 2017 campaign slogan is 'Not everybody steals.' There are people like the Kasov brothers who have built something from nothing without stealing. In 1999, students Martin and Petr Kasov founded the www.kasa.cz internet shop and grew it into a multimillion-dollar business. Their first sale consisted of CD cases, hand-delivered in a book pack to a customer. I know this is difficult to understand by somebody who hasn't personally experienced it. Living under communism was like living on a different planet," I said.

"Joseph, thanks for the explanation," said Jessica. "Everything now makes more sense but it's getting late and my head hurts from the wine. Let's forget about politics and talk about something else."

"Don't complain to me, you asked the questions and I gave you the answers. I know none of you are broke but I insist on calling Uber," I replied.

"OK, Joseph, go ahead if you insist," Ronnee said, and gave me a wink. Laughing a little, she added, "I kind of like the idea of building the employee work and garden center in the Appalachian Mountains. Maybe, when no one is around, I can finally have some privacy and sunbathe nude while surrounded by nature."

"I don't know about that. I will sunbathe topless but not totally nude. I would like the guys to be fully nude," Christine said, and we laughed.

I replied in a loud but playful tone of voice, "That's great Christine, so the women will be naked from head to waist and the guys from ball sack to their feet. Unexpected visitors will be in such shock that they will not be able to recover from this for some time."

"That's a good point. We should all be naked," said Jessica, and we laughed some more.

As the laughs were increasingly louder and longer, the conversation was increasingly hotter and spicier as well. The ladies were reaching a certain point, the sweet spot – the perfect balance between being too sober, not wanting to have sex just yet, and being drunk to the point of throwing up and falling asleep. This is the dream situation of every man who takes out a woman on a first date with the intention of getting laid. My situation was quite unique. I was surrounded by three smart, beautiful women and didn't know what to do with them. Too much love and respect stood between them and myself, and sexual desires that were steadily increasing in the four of us. I would not want the girls to do something they might regret later on. Anyway, this was not the purpose of this meeting. As I was juggling between the conversation, feelings of love, respect, and thoughts of sexual orgies, the lights above us went from being romantically dimmed to bright and sharp.

"This is it, ladies, the staff is officially kicking us out of here! Let's sit outside for a minute," I said.

We left the restaurant and before we had a chance to sit down on a bench located on the front porch, the UberBLACK car arrived. I approached the car, opened the passenger door and said, "Call me once you make the decision. I already know the answer to this question because 2017 is the year of the gathering to win the prize. Why would you want to break up the winning team?"

"Give us some time and we will let you know," Jessica said, and was the first to approach the car.

Our faces were about a foot from each other; I kissed her on the cheek, we smiled and said goodbye. The same happened when Christine approached me. I kissed her as well, we smiled, said goodbye and she disappeared into the car.

Ronnee approached me and our eyes locked in full stare. My heart was beating very fast and I felt the palm of my right hand slightly shaking. I managed to keep my emotions under control and just stood there still with frozen face. The moonlight was reflecting from her eyes and face, making her skin smooth and soft. We stood there for about a minute as our eyes were speaking their own elegant words made up entirely of love, and heat, and sex and chemistry. "What a perfect night for the first kiss," I thought, then placed my arm around her waist and gently pulled her body towards mine. Ronnee closed her eyes, our lips almost touched, but I finished by kissing her on the cheek. We looked into each other's eyes again. Her sad eyes were telling me she was disappointed but at the same time I was able to tell she understood why I did it. Ronnee didn't say a word and disappeared into the darkness of the night.

I closed the door of the black Lexus and the girls entered their own dimensions, gone out of my life again. I regretted not kissing Ronnee on the lips when I had the chance. "I will somehow have to learn to control the strongest force in the Universe. I am not sure how, but I will manage it. You can accomplish anything if you put your mind to it. I wish Leah had been at the meeting as well, the girls would have liked her. What a bummer," I thought, and went for a short walk. I had to clear my head, sober up, and digest the wonderful experience of seeing the girls after such a long time.

. . . and we accomplished many great things together. Most importantly, the five of us each discovered our life's purpose, lived happier lives, and did our jobs with passion and love. Prophecies were fulfilled and we eventually left this world in much better shape than when we were born.

Chapter 19
Back Home and a Few More Thoughts

"It's this late already?" I thought, looking at the clock. I'd been sitting at home in front of the computer for hours and had completely lost time perception as I was daydreaming about the girls and the meeting. None of it happened but it felt so real! I had let my brain think uncontrollably on purpose. This was required to open the wormhole to a different time and space where I was able to enter Christine's, Jessica's, Leah's, and Ronnee's precious private little orbits and access their thoughts, feelings, and souls. As my way of thinking slowly entered the real world, I realized the girls might like the story but probably were going to blow me off. It didn't matter at this point because I had sunk too deep into *The Abyss* (1989 movie) of writing the book. I always knew this was going to be a one-way ticket for the following two reasons.

Firstly, the intelligence agencies record all internet communication. Their AI systems scan and analyze it based on code words such as "NSA." I have used this word countless times and expect red flags to be raised somewhere. Secondly, even if the book is published and the government somehow leaves me alone, sooner or later some religious fundamentalist will blow my head off. Wouldn't you be upset to see people leaving your church? The people that are your bread and butter; the tickets to a luxurious lifestyle consisting of storytelling, leisure, and countless sexual pleasure.

Enough of this philosophical thinking. OK girls, it is November 7 2017 at 11.20 p.m. and my fingers are on the mouse, "click" and it's showtime! It's done, and the file is in your work emails. Leah, check your private email. Enjoy the reading, I hope you will be pleasantly entertained. Why not one more surprise? Here are a few stories that happened after the game ended.

The first event happened on August 5 2017 at Lake Allatoona's Payne campground. The kids had a great time as we were swimming and playing in the lake for hours. A campfire was started later in the day and I helped my mom and her husband cook goulash. People right next to us on site #40 began to sing and play musical instruments. Mom and the kids went there first and called me over after about ten minutes. I initially didn't want to go but quickly changed my mind. My mom joined the group and played air piano and guitar. Teresa and Julia were both dancing and singing as well. It was a lot of fun. What a nice surprise, there was this very pleasant older woman with a strong Southern accent, dark blonde hair, wearing classic hippie/bohemian clothes, similar to the one I had seen on the internet the day before when I coincidentally researched the two lifestyles. A few minutes into the conversation, I thought about having sex with her. At first, I was under the impression the people were family, but they were not. The man had two late-teenage kids and had met the woman a few weeks ago. I invited the family to have goulash with us.

After about two hours, I saw the woman going to the bathrooms and then return. Within minutes she came to our site alone since everyone else had gone on a boat. She liked the goulash and especially the blueberry pie made out of fresh yeast my mom had smuggled from the Czech Republic. Initially, we had a great group conversation and talked about our families, nature, travel, and food. The lady was everything I had always wanted a woman to be: open-minded, knowledgeable, natural, not materialistic, but most importantly, down-to-earth. Mom took the kids to bed and the woman and I were alone. Consequently, the conversation became more intimate. I found out a few interesting facts about my new friend. The lady (as always, initially I can't remember the person's name :-() was fifty-three but looked no more than forty-five, had three sons aged thirty-three, thirty, and twenty-eight, and a one-year-old granddaughter. One of her sons had done over 6,000 cliff jumps wearing a wingsuit. In 2016, I saw an extreme sport documentary about cliff jumpers, free divers, and long-distance bikers competing in Race Across America. Since that time, cliff jumping has been the number one item on my wish list. She liked the outdoors, dancing, and snorkeling. She had been exploring caves since the age of nine and did it with her kids from their early ages as well. Her cool car, a 1974 Bronco, was also a tent because the man she was with had a drinking problem and she wasn't going to date him.

"I have a house on top of a mountain. The place is very nice, but I have been living there alone since divorcing my husband over ten years ago," she said.

"I can't believe that such a nice lady like yourself wouldn't be able to find a new spouse," I said, and smiled a little. Inside, I genuinely couldn't believe a woman like her would be single for such a long time.

"I live in Rome. I have standards and there is not much there to choose from," she replied.

"Really, you are from Rome? I have been there once in my life. In 2006, my friend Jeff and I went to Rome to visit his mother's grave. His mom had recently passed away; as you can imagine it wasn't the best trip. We stopped to visit one of his relatives who owns a whole mountain. He lives at the base of the mountain and his property must have had at least fifty junk cars lying around. It's a shame because a few were collectibles," I said.

We spoke some more and just before saying goodbye, I gave her my card. She smiled and went back to her campsite. Within a few minutes, I regretted giving her my number and hoped she would never call me. I live in Atlanta and don't want to get emotionally attached to anyone. She is too real, too nice and sweet, too good to be true; the dream of every man able to discover her qualities. She is a hidden treasure that lives in a house on top of a mountain surrounded by forest, unable to find her true love. What a waste. At her age, if she ever fell in love again and the person left her, it would break her heart to the point of no return. (If you read this book someday, travel around the country, I guarantee you will meet your other half fairly quickly.) On a positive note, I gave the lady my only business card left that had "Accounting & Finance" listed in the center. I thought about my ex-manager, Corey, and remembered a conversation I had with him during my short employment at PulteGroup. "Joseph, I don't tell people anymore that I am a tax accountant. It is a conversation killer. I make something up or steer the discussion in a different direction."

"Good, she is an outdoor person and an office rat like myself would surely deter her from making the call," I thought. I normally don't ask girls for their phone numbers to weed out the BS. If they're interested, I let them call me first. I learned a few valuable lessons that day. At first, I have to think with my brain before giving away phone numbers. Secondly, once the divorce is finalized, I need to start dating college girls or women that don't get emotionally attached. On the other hand, I don't want to be on Tinder every day to screw everything that moves either. I would like to be loved and not only fucked. There has to be a middle ground. Most importantly, I want to be there for my kids and get my life back to normal. Sooner or later, a friend will enter my life. It always happens, especially if you are not looking.

Another event happened a few days prior to the solar eclipse. On the morning of August 19 2017, I helped Teresa with a school presentation on the event. Up to this day, I hadn't realized how rare this occurrence was. I did more research about the upcoming eclipse and was horrified by the potential danger of the cheap $1.99 eclipse glasses. In the afternoon, I went to countless stores, but everybody was out or didn't carry the glasses in the first place. I had a few unanswered questions. "If a welding mask is not going to protect eyes unless it is rated fourteen or higher, how can something that retails for $1.99 do the job? Most hardware stores don't even carry professional welding masks rated at this level. The glasses are 'one-type-fits-all.' How good will the protection be for different age groups?" There were countless articles on how so many fake glasses entered the market. Federal and state governments did not issue emergencies or any kind of warnings to the public. The media was not doing enough to warn people.

Naturally, I had to do something, anything in my power, to warn as many people as possible. I called Christine, Jessica, Ronnee, Leah, Debbie, and left messages on their work phones. Debbie was also called since, as HR manager, together with Jessica, she had the power to issue warnings to Argos employees. I wrote a letter. An edited version of the letter was emailed to the State of Georgia and a few federal agencies, including the White House. The next day, I emailed the edited version to all my Facebook, LinkedIn, and phone contacts. Christine, Jessica, Ronnie, and Leah are the only people who received the full version of the letter, shown below.

Hello girls,
A once in a lifetime event is about to happen on August 21 2017; the first coast-to-coast US solar eclipse since 1918. This is a truly magnificent event. During the 2.5 minutes of total eclipse everything, including winds and birds, goes silent, temperature drops by double digits, plants start to shut down and the Sun's corona appears. . . It is just the perfect moment for a new couple to exchange their first kiss. It is safe to look at the Sun with naked eyes only during the 2.5 minutes of 100% total solar eclipse. Unfortunately, Atlanta will only reach 95% of eclipse, therefore, it is extremely dangerous to look directly at the Sun without proper protection even if everything around will appear almost completely dark. Just a few seconds could cause irreparable eye damage. Would you entrust your vision to glasses that sell for $1.99? Would you trust that a corporation will not outsource the production of these glasses to China where someone will use "fake" material and stamp the paper glasses with the ISO 12312-2 approval code? I wouldn't, so I will take a trip to Clayton, GA to view the total eclipse with my naked eyes. Welding masks will not help unless graded fourteen or higher.

Has the FBI tried to ensure all fake glasses are off the market? Has the federal government issued any kind of warning to the public? Have the state governments issued states of emergency? There are many uneducated people, especially in the ghettos, who don't have access to the internet and cable TV. Who will tell them not to look directly into the Sun when the sky is black?

Have the GA libraries, and schools such as KSU, verified the paper glasses are not fake before distributing them to the general public for free?

Is the mainstream "Fake News" media doing enough; urging the public to be careful?

Why didn't our beloved corporations order more of the protective glasses? On August 19 2017, I went to Publix, Kroger, Walmart, Walgreens, CVS, Ace Hardware, Trader Joe's, LA Fitness, DICK'S Sporting Goods, Target, Whole Foods, Pearle Vision, WellStar East Cobb, MedPoint Urgent Care, and Village Health Wellness Spa in the East Cobb area and everybody was out or didn't carry them in the first place.

Are churches going to warn or give the protective glasses to their members? Are church employees going to warn the less fortunate people in their neighborhoods? I really do hope so.

The good vs the bad force of nature is the ultimate power struggle. I hope the mighty dollar will not win this battle otherwise we may wake up in the world known from The Day of the Triffids *(1951) novel.*

Something happened to me after the December 15 2016 lunch at Argos, something opened up within me. I now have the ability to strip away all the endless bullshit filters churches, governments, and corporations throw in front of my face.

As always, your safety is my priority. Please acknowledge you have read the email.

The three of you will always have a place in my heart. . .

August 21 2017 was one of the most exciting and extraordinary days in my life. I woke up at 6.30 a.m. and went to Teresa's school to make sure she and the kids would not be given the paper glasses. I was assured by the school's principal the glasses will be given only to fourth graders and above with parental consent. Romana received several messages warning her about the dangers but never replied. She had custody of the kids that day and refused to let me take them to North Carolina to see the full solar eclipse, what a disappointment.

A dentist appointment, which I almost cancelled because of traffic warnings, was scheduled for early in the morning. My mom, her husband Milan, and I left the house at 10 a.m. The ride was smooth except for a few bad traffic spots after Highway 400 ended. GPS signal was lost a couple miles before the highway 19/129 junction. I made the decision to turn left against the flow of traffic, deeper into the mountains, away from Cleveland. Countless amounts of spider webs appeared along the winding mountainous road and continued to appear until we reached the next city. It was way past noon, we were running out of time, but for some reason I continued to get lost and looked for the nearest lake to park and view the event. A day earlier, my Vietnamese neighbor, grandma Julia, told me to look at the solar eclipse using the following method: "When I was a child, we took a large bucket of water and looked at the Sun's reflection indirectly during partial eclipse."

374

At a gas station, I was able to buy one pair of "real" fake protective glasses made in China, with a missing ISO stamp. The lady cashier was assured none of us would use the glasses. "I want to keep one pair of the fakes for the record in case someone will later claim there weren't any out there."

We continued to drive into Cherokee County and just before the town of Murphy, made a U-turn and looked for the nearest entrance to Hiwassee Lake. A woman walking to her a car at a nearby commercial plaza of about fifteen mom-and-pop shops told us the police had blocked access to the lake because of an expected influx of people to view the eclipse. I gave up and parked the car next to the nearest body of open water, located right next to the Cherokee County recycling station. The entrance to the pond reminded me of the entrance to the flooded granite mine in the Czech Republic; the pond is a hidden treasure with a broken train bridge and remains of the original road positioned just above the waterline.

Birds were flying, singing everywhere, and there was not a soul present. "What a perfect spot to view the full eclipse," I thought. Idiot Milan took the fake glasses from the glove compartment and stared directly into the Sun for a couple seconds before I yelled and took the glasses from his hand. The only way to see the Sun's reflection in the water was to walk to the other side of the pond. The three of us went through mud to reach the other end. Two young guys were fishing at the other side of the pond, underneath a bridge. I called them over to view the eclipse with us. I recorded the whole event by pointing a cell phone to the water during partial eclipse and directly into the Sun during the 2.5 minutes of total eclipse. It was spectacular, an indescribable once in lifetime event. Here is the edited video of the event.

2017 Total Solar Eclipse in Cherokee Lands
https://youtu.be/n3l8XH_JP9c

As soon as the event ended, stop-and-go traffic towards Atlanta formed instantly. "There is no way we are going to drive in this, especially in a car with broken AC. Why don't we go to Chatuge Lake for a swim?" I suggested, and everyone agreed.

The GPS was turned off as we were approaching the lake, strange feelings overtook my mind and I chose to turn into a side road more suitable for one-way traffic. Again, countless spider webs appeared along the way and we shortly reached the shores of the lake. The scenery, consisting of wooded islands and mountains with little development, was priceless.

I met a woman while swimming at the lake. Deborah Hyatt appeared to be in her late fifties, had a pleasant tone of voice and great people's personality. Her marriage had ended in divorce as the couple grew apart and the husband eventually left due to Deborah's medical condition. We were sitting on the grass next to the shore and I described to her the symptoms I had experienced earlier in the year, omitting the inner thoughts.

"You have sensitivity to electromagnetic field radiation, EMF, and your body was poisoned," she said.

The more details I told her, the more answers she gave me. I found out she is writing a book which is roughly 95% complete.

"How is your faith?"

She asked the question out of nowhere. I didn't know what to tell her and bit my cheeks to prevent myself from laughing. "What is my faith? I have to have faith, everybody believes in something," I thought as I searched for the honest answer, then replied.

"Well, I am a spiritual person. I don't go to church because I don't believe in organized religion," I said.

"I don't believe in organized religion either," Deborah said. She touched my temples with the palms of her hands and continued to speak. "You have to have faith in order to heal."

Deborah had a middle management position in corporate sales at a large biotechnology company, Thermo Fisher Scientific. I often worked with this company regarding tax overpayments when employed at Immucor. She had been with the corporation for years and with each merger the working conditions degraded. Besides working longer hours, her work space decreased from an office to a cubicle and finally to a space similar to a phone booth. She was cramped in a room where 120 computers were lined up side by side. Her physical symptoms worsened to a point where she was no longer able to move, losing control of her muscles during unexpected seizures. Many of her physical symptoms, such the ability to hear and speak, panic attacks, seizures, memory loss, resembled mine and towards the end, her toenails were starting to fall off. She went to countless doctors, but nobody was able to find out what was wrong with her until she met an EMF specialist, Dr. William Rea of the Environmental Health Center in Dallas, TX. A nuclear brain scan was conducted and she was diagnosed with EMF poisoning. Deborah sued her employer's insurance and her case went one level below the U.S. Supreme Court, where it was thrown out due to a technicality. Her attorney lost the battle against an army of corporate lawyers with virtually unlimited resources.

Deborah has an extreme case of EMF sensitivity. These prerequisites are necessary for her to live a normal life:

Live at least 1.5 miles from the nearest cell phone tower.

Do not use cell phones or any unshielded electronic devices. The outer casing of her desktop computer is shielded and she can use the computer for a maximum of one to two hours a day.

The circuit breaker in her house must be turned off unless, for example, a dishwasher is in use. She must use candles at night or a hand flashlight for short periods of time.

Drive an older car. The engine compartments of newer cars are equipped with a GPS tracking device. She cannot drive long distances alone and as a passenger has to be wrapped in special fabric to shield herself from outside EMF radiation.

Hire a shopper. She cannot go to public places such as stores and restaurants because all use electricity, have Wi-Fi signal and people use cell phones. One exception is a small vegetable store in her town that turns off electric appliances when she arrives.

If Deborah were to break any of the above rules, in less than ten minutes she would lose the ability to control her muscles and would just lie on the floor. She had to change her lifestyle in order to live. Losing one court battle, however, didn't prevent her from winning another court battle with the Social Security Administration to receive disability. She is dating a man who doesn't live far away, loves camping at the nearby islands, spends most time outdoors or at her "church" – a cozy area on her property surrounded by trees and branches in such a way it resembles a real medieval church. There is a wooden cross in front of four simple handmade wooden benches. Being there felt peaceful and relaxing, as it should in every true spiritual place.

As we were saying good bye, Deborah said, "Your condition isn't as extreme as mine, you are young and with a few changes should be OK. I like to help people, that's the mission of my life. I would like to help you as well. Joseph, it was no coincidence the two us met on the day of the eclipse. I feel you should be part of the EMF movement which is slowly taking off."

We talked more about details of the EMF. I did let her know the day was special for me as well and that we definitely should see each other again. As we started to drive away from the area, I thought, "Deborah, I could tell you about coincidences you wouldn't believe."

The ride back was much better than driving out of Atlanta. There was no traffic and with partially opened windows the temperature felt comfortable. I had a feeling that Mom's silver 1999 Ford Taurus with almost 300,000 original miles would survive the trip. During a bathroom break in the middle of nowhere, I noticed that way more stars were visible in the cloudless sky than if viewed from a city. To download an application that would tell me the constellations was the first thing that crossed my mind.

I downloaded SkyView augmented reality software and the three of us searched the sky. "I have to see the stars of the Plejaren Friends," I thought to myself. After a few minutes of searching, I pointed the phone to a nearby field and the AR software displayed Pleiades: a cluster of seven sister stars located in the constellation of Taurus. For the remaining duration of the ride, I kept replaying the day's events and realized several important things.

In 1918, the stars were aligned to welcome the United States for helping to win the First World War. August 21 1968 is one of the worst dates in Czechoslovak history. On this day the Warsaw Pact army, led by the Soviets, invaded the country and suppressed people's yearning for freedom. The Total Recall game has not ended, as previously thought, but continues. In the game, the 2017 solar eclipse was another episode of the struggle between the good and bad forces of nature. Will the mighty dollar win this battle and millions of people damage their eyesight or go blind? Not everybody will have this problem because solar eclipse glasses were not required in the seventy-mile-wide zone of the total eclipse. The Cherokee lands were protected for all the injustices that have been committed against these people for centuries.

The next day, I came across an article stating people had searched Google in great numbers for the phrase "my eyes hurt." In later days, I was relieved the apocalyptic scenario from *The Day of the Triffids* novel didn't become reality. Nevertheless, many people damaged their eyesight and the government, together with the media, probably covered it up. In many foreign countries, governments issue warnings for people to stay inside and not to look at the Sun during a partial eclipse. What did our governments do?

August 21 2017 was an important milestone in the Total Recall game. Prior to this day, questions like: "What really happened? Why me and no one else?" were frequently entering my mind. After this day, those questions were no longer there, and the only question left was, "What is going to happen next?" It is no coincidence the Friends chose my spirit to continue the mission. I must have done something positive in my prior lives and was dug up by their AI system as the most able to complete the mission. It was calculated with 100% certainty I would not decline the task once asked. The game has not ended but will continue as long as my spirit will move from body to body, to fight different battles. The battles will be fought for another 800 years until the war between the good and bad forces of nature on this planet comes to an end, and the good force will finally prevail.

As of July 2017, I was unable to look at a computer screen for more than a couple hours without taking a break. Headaches, eye pain combined with light sensitivity, facial pressures/tingling, and chest pains would appear when I ignored early warning signs and pushed beyond the two-hour limit. It was impossible to resume the tax accounting career. I applied for Social Security disability.

At first, everything appeared straightforward but I was soon able to see behind-the-scene machinations once I moved past the smokescreen called "online application." My complete medical history was attached to the online application. I soon received a paper functionality questionnaire where questions like "Do you spend time with others?", "How good do you follow spoken instructions?", "How often do you shop and how long does it take?" were listed. According to the cover letter, a person only had ten days from the date of the letter to mail back the paper questionnaire to disability adjudicator K. Smith/67. In addition, I received a fifteen-year work history questionnaire mailed separately from the functionality questionnaire. The cover letter also stated the person has ten days from the date of the letter to mail back the form to K. Smith/67 otherwise the case would be decided on available information. There was a prepaid envelope included in each package.

The woman at the post office stated, "We don't allow to certify prepaid envelopes."

So here is one government agency that gives you a few days to respond and another government agency, the post office, which doesn't allow the envelopes to be mailed certified to ensure the ten-day window isn't met. How convenient for someone trying to say an envelope was never received. :-)

I went around the system by buying and certifying blank envelopes. I wrote all over the prepaid envelope "Why can't I certify this?" and inserted the documents in the blank envelope.

Within a couple weeks, I received a letter from K. Smith/67 stating my work history wasn't descriptive enough and only had ten days to respond. The ten days in reality translated to five days since it takes the post office a few days to deliver an envelope. I called K. Smith/67 and asked her about the work history.

"Well, waiting tables is not enough. You have to give us more details," she said.

I played stupid and asked, "Like, what else should I say?"

"You did carry plates and glasses, right? Just put that in there."

"OK I will. You know I also filled glasses with soda. Should I write that in there?" I said.

"Yes, and you probably also carried clean plates, right? Write it in there as well. Then you were a tax accountant. What did you do?" she asked.

"I filed taxes, you know. I have a bad memory, oh wait, I used software like Outlook and Excel. Do you want me to put it in there? And I also used specialty software for tax reconciliations. I was the computerized tax accountant," I said.

"Write every detail you remember, including computerized tax accountant. It's OK to use your co-workers to help you fill up the questionnaire," she said, and the conversation ended shortly after.

Within a few weeks, an invitation for a visual exam to determine if I can work was received. Again, I only had a ten-day window to walk into the Cobb/Douglas department of health to complete the exam.

On August 23 2017, odd feelings overwhelmed my body as I entered the health department's premises. Something was wrong as the building had no energy and reminded me of the psychiatric section of the Kennestone Hospital, where the doctors tried everything in their power to prove mental illness, to persuade Romana to sign my life to the system. The Disability Adjudication Services "DAS" administration was well aware of the situation that happened in Kennestone Hospital in January 2017. I entered a paradox; if I behave like a healthy person, I risk being arrested for faking my illness. If I behave too crazy, I also risk being arrested and sent to a mental institution. The subsequent stress threw my body off balance; I had a small panic attack, fell asleep in the waiting area, went outside through the glass emergency exit doors to pick flowers to make a flower bouquet and went into the restroom multiple times where I became nauseous and sat on the floor. Strangely enough, there was always one person in the restroom who never asked me if I was OK. He was just observing me.

The same situation happened when I, on purpose, entered the ladies' restroom. As I was leaving the restroom, there was a woman waiting outside who said, "This is not the men's restroom," then pointed to the missing "Ladies Restroom" sign which was removed while I was inside. And then for no reason at all, with the flip of a switch, my condition improved to normal. I called Romana and spoke in a loud tone of voice so everybody in the waiting area was able to hear me: "I am in Cobb/Douglas County health department for a visual exam regarding my disability. I am sitting in front of the Dental Services office and will be home shortly." From that point on, I sat there like a statue and looked at the floor.

A woman called me to come over to a cubicle, to give her my information.

"You haven't been here before, have you?" she asked, in a pleasant and curious tone of voice

"I haven't," I replied; a complete lie.

"Are you married or single?" she asked.

"I am soon to be divorced. My wife abandoned me because of my medical condition," I said, in a low tone of voice.

"We'll put married," she said, and smiled a little.

"Yes, let's put married. That's a good idea," I said, in a barely audible tone of voice, then looked elsewhere.

I went back to the waiting area and sat on a bench. People sitting in the waiting area were looking at me, then were keying into their cell phones, then they paused and looked at me again and then resumed the keying. It appeared they were taking notes. A woman walked past me, stood behind me and made a strange clapping noise for several minutes. "He has ADD and is faking everything," said a man who sat behind me, and laughed. Two gay guys with a baby walked in, sat right next to me and wanted to start a conversation. I just sat there, looked at the floor and ignored everybody and everything. In the waiting area, there were fifteen people at most at any given time waiting to be seen by different departments.

I waited over two hours for the visual exam. The eye doctor personally came over and told me to follow him.

"How are you doing?" the doctor asked, once we reached the examination room.

"Not too good. I am really tired," I said.

"Why don't you sit down? Have you worked a long nightshift?" he asked.

"I don't work. I am really cold. Can you turn down the air?" I said.

"No problem," the doctor said, and turned on a space heater placed on the floor right next to his desk. For some odd reason he forgot to turn off the large turbine-size fan, placed on the hallway floor, that was blowing cold air directly to where I was sitting. The fan must have been at least five feet in diameter.

"I used to work for PulteGroup and it was against the company's policy to use space heaters because they pose a fire hazard," I said, and completely ignored the large fan.

The doctor did not respond to the comment and the exam began shortly after.

After the five-minute exam," the doctor said, "I will make a copy of the document and mail it for you."

"The woman at the DAS office told me to mail it directly to her within ten days," I said.

"Don't worry about it," he said with a smile, then continued, "I'll take the envelope and mail it for you."

I gave him the prepaid envelope and left the office. After passing through the exit doors of the building, I noticed a group of four people standing on the adjacent sidewalk, about twenty feet away. They were staring at me and as soon as I was seen, the people looked at each other and started to talk. I needed to catch my breath and sat on a bench. There was an older Black woman sitting on a bench a few feet in front of me. The woman was extremely skinny, looked sick, and I became horrified. I only saw people like this in photographs and videos taken in Nazi concentration camps. I walked towards the woman and said, "Hello, have some of my water."

"It is not mine but thank you," she said, and looked directly into my eyes, in disbelief, for several seconds.

"Please go to the hospital, you don't look good at all. You look sick," I told her, and then went to my car where I broke down and cried. I really hoped she was a true patient and not an actor hired by the administration.

The next month, I received a generic letter from K. Smith/67 dated August 29 2017, listing she was missing important documents and to ignore the letter if the documents had been mailed. I called and left a message requesting to cancel the process as I had found employment.

On September 19 2017, I drove to the same building to snoop around, to find out more about their dental services. The same family whose dad made the "He has ADD and is faking everything" comment was present in the waiting area. During my prior visit, I approached the family and asked the kids, "Do you know Michael Jackson, woo-hoo, hee hee?" Nobody, including the parents, said anything as their bodies resembled lifeless statues. To cheer them up, I attempted the moonwalk dance. The dental office was closed for lunch. I left the building.

Apparently, the administration hires actors to screen disability applicants. Actors such as low-income men, women, and children of all ages. The babies and toddlers who should be nurtured by parents in happier places such as natural preserves. The children who should be in schools or playing outside with their friends. The administration even hires gays to screen people with liberal views. Someone's Facebook account can tell the story. After I applied for the disability, I began to receive strange Facebook friend requests from young girls. A few days before the exam, I received strange phone calls. I had twenty-three missed calls with no messages made to my cell phone during the two and a half hours I was in the building.

My new friend Deborah went through a similar examination. She had to go to court to win disability even when multiple doctors stated she is disabled. You see, medical history, pain, suffering and distress evidently doesn't matter to the DAS administration. The applicants are evaluated based on looks and the probability of DAS winning in court if a person sues. Similar to my and Deborah's cases, person will be treated like a criminal unless he or she is paralyzed in a wheelchair. Yes, there are people who try to fake illnesses to get disability. Is someone like Deborah, who achieved a middle management position and worked her whole life, a disability fraud? It must have been obvious to the administration that she is going through excruciating pain and is unable to work. Even the judge made smart comments and initially lectured Deborah on jobs she had never even heard of. Dr. William J. Rea, the EMF expert who saved Deborah's life, was sued by the State of Texas for alleged violations of the Medical Practice Act. Why would the Texas Medical Board sue Dr. Rea? I will let the reader figure this out. Per the 2006 "Letter to the Editor: Will We All Become Electrosensitive?" paper written by Dr. Gerd Oberfeld and Örjan Hallberg: in 1998, 3.2% of the California population was diagnosed with electromagnetic sensitivity. The two scientists released research findings that predicted half of humanity will suffer electromagnetic sensitivity by the year 2017. According to Deborah, many people commit suicide due to lack of hope after being diagnosed. There is no telling how many people have been misdiagnosed and are pumped with countless drugs that are not helping. Why haven't the news networks ever covered this subject?

What happens to the abandoned mentally ill or single people that don't have resources or the will to fight DAS in court? Are those people destitute, condemned to become homeless? I have no choice but to make the following assumptions.

In January 2017, for days, the hospital staff tried everything in their power to prove I was mentally ill. In August 2017, DAS tried everything in their power to break me down, to make me to have a nervous breakdown in order to arrest me and send me to a mental hospital. Their methods, to a certain level, resembled the methods used by the hospital. In January 2017, my medical issues resembled the classic EMF symptoms, so the hospital staff could have been instructed to do whatever was necessary to keep me quiet. What would have happened to me if I hadn't started to hear and speak, and Romana signed my life away to the institution? Would I have become a test subject for new medications? There are countless television advertisements to sell new drugs. What happened to the advertisements that search for human volunteers to test all these new drugs? Where do all the human test subjects – men, women, and children – come from? Maybe my body wouldn't have been used for medical experimentation but would instead have been chopped up in pieces and my organs sold to the highest bidders. Blood plasma donation is a multibillion-dollar business where the U.S. produces 70% of the world's plasma. The US has 5% of the world's population; why does it supply 70% of the plasma? Maybe none of the above would have happened and my body would have been sold to a connected person on top of the pyramid whose hobby is to hunt, torture, and kill people. The movies and media provide a whole lot of inspiration.

All the above is a real possibility for single and/or abandoned mentally ill men, women, and children. It is also a possibility for healthy, single, homeless people of all ages. Who is going to miss these numbers, these forgotten ghosts? It is so easy to produce real death certificates with fake reasons for death.

There are many empty handicapped parking spaces in public places everywhere you go. Per my observation, nobody parks in them except for old retirees and a few people in wheelchairs. Almost half of the adult US population is on some type of antidepressant. Where are the more mentally ill people who cannot regularly work but are able to manage some daily tasks most of the time? How come you don't see them in public? Where are all the metro Atlanta homeless people? I see less and less of them as years go by. Why is there so much opposition to chiropractors by the mainstream medical industry? Is it because chiropractic care focuses on inexpensive prevention instead of expensive cure? Why have so many natural healers in the USA mysteriously disappeared in recent years? If these assumptions are the truth, then this is exactly what my relatives fought against.

The Total Recall game always has a double meaning. The producers designed the game to make me believe the Friends are real and at the same time to create a living witness who touched the tip of the iceberg on how our governments and their powerful special interest friends operate behind the scenes.

The dental office serves two counties, Douglass and Cobb. I was unable to make an appointment for my children until February 2018. Only basic services are provided. New patient exam: $65.00, Tooth extraction or filling: $100–$180, Teeth cleaning: $120–$400.

"Do you provide any discounts to children from low-income families?" I asked a woman during a phone call.

"The dental office doesn't have any money, so we don't provide any discounts," she said. I found this interesting because back in the mid-Nineties, I was the low-income child and the same dental office fixed my teeth for free. Prior to that visit, I hadn't been to a dentist for years and was amazed when the doctor found about five small cavities. I consider myself lucky, as I didn't have to come up with at least $500 to fix the teeth.

The prices are comparable to my current private dentist, Great Expressions Dental Centers, except for cleaning. This service costs $120. It costs $65 when a person purchases their dental insurance for $69 per year, receiving a 20% discount on other services. I was always able to schedule an appointment no later than a week in advance.

In May 2014, Cobb County announced plans for the Atlanta Braves to build a new stadium in the county. Two weeks later, the county commissioners voted five–zero to give the Braves almost $400 million of taxpayers' dollars for the new stadium. Only twelve supporters of the stadium were allowed to speak just before the vote took place. Everyone else was silenced or escorted out of the meeting by police officers. Public referendum was never issued even after it was estimated that only 30% of the county's citizens supported the stadium being subsidized with taxpayers' money. How many homeless shelters does the county operate? How affordable is the so-called "Affordable, $250,000 per unit, senior citizen townhouse project" on Atlanta Road? Why wasn't the county's Central Aquatic Center renovated and the pool upgraded to a 50-meter Olympic size? Why do the center's swimming classes only accommodate six children per class (in my case), so most children don't get in and are placed on a waiting list? Why is the Aquatic Center closed on Sundays when people are at home and not on Mondays when most people are at work? I hope the county is not forcing people into churches. I wouldn't be surprised as no one is allowed to buy alcohol on Sundays until 12.30 p.m.

I heard and continue to hear the following arguments from all sides: "The government should stay out of providing social services to people as much as possible. It is not the government's role to take care of the lazy ones, that's communism. This is America and if you don't like it move back to Europe."

To provide a bed and simple meal to homeless people or to help low-income kids so their teeth wouldn't rot away is a communist idea. It is socialism, so we can't help them. To borrow and give hundreds of millions of taxpayer's dollars to a special interest group and enrich the elected officials for generations, that's capitalism. That's what this country is all about. Did our founding fathers envision this kind of future?

I have four more lawsuits for our firm.

Federal government (human rights violations, extremely difficult class action; file when the time is right) – Deborah and I aren't the only two people who experienced the pleasant atmosphere created by the Social Security Administration. There are countless people who have suffered beyond imagination and would be willing to testify. In addition, there could be countless families whose mentally ill members suddenly died while in hospital care. There could also be countless homeless people who have vanished and were missed by relatives and loved ones. I fully expect us to lose the case in the US court system. The case will then be filed with the United Nations. The victory will not be legally binding but will have significant global effect.

It will be many years before the above lawsuit is filed. In the meantime, our nonprofit group will create an underground operation. We will hire an army of trolls to create countless fake social media profiles to network with real people. The trolls will teach unhappy people to spot injustices at work, in public places or places of business, and to organize and rise up against their employers. The trolls will also refer unhappy people to our and other friendly law firms for free consultation on potential employee/employer or consumer lawsuits. This will create a domino effect and corporations will have no choice but to lobby the federal government to limit fake social media profiles. Facebook and the others will probably never willingly agree to this because their revenue is directly tied to the number of active users. Any person can have virtually an unlimited number of social media profiles. Have advertisers ever asked Facebook how many profiles are real and how many are fake? In 2017, Facebook's stock price reached exorbitant levels and would most likely collapse if the advertisers knew the true number of real and fake profiles. At some point, the government will sue the social media sites to limit the number of fake profiles. This is great because we will indirectly use Facebook's resources to distract the government.

I would like to share information about US embassies since it is indirectly tied to the next lawsuit. In the last century, the US embassies around the world were known as oases of freedom. This was especially true in countries with openly oppressive regimes. In the 1960s and 1970s, my dad frequently visited the US embassy in Prague to borrow forbidden books and music records. Of course, there were secret police agents stationed 24/7 in the building across the street who knew the name of every single person that ever went inside that embassy. Those people or their parents (in case of a minor) were frequently harassed by the secret police. A new $1 billion-dollar US embassy in London will open later in 2017. The embassy is no longer an oasis of freedom, its defense mechanisms resemble a medieval fortress. The US State Department has been harshly criticized at home and abroad for its dreary embassies.

During a 2009 U.S. Senate committee hearing, Senator John Kerry said, "We're building fortresses around the world. We're separating ourselves from people in these countries." The government is also separating itself here in the United States from its citizens. Federal buildings, federal and state courthouses, resemble little fortresses. The people behind the shadowy invisible government, the masters of the puppets that pull the strings behind the scenes are well aware of the misery and injustices that were/are being committed against Americans and people around the world. Obsession with defense has clouded the minds of those people who claim to be the masters of the Earth and the Universe. To seclude themselves from the common people is the only alternative left for them because they know, one day, the common people will gather together to rise up against these oppressions.

Manufacturing of almost everything is outsourced to countries with cheap and abundant labor. How is the security at those manufacturing locations? What if some unfriendly regime or terrorist group such as ISIS bribed someone at a plant to produce the solar eclipse glasses with fake material, to create a health crisis in the USA? Do you think it's possible for someone to install biological agents into millions of cell phones produced in Asia annually and program the phones to release the agents after so many hours of operation? What are the next steps to protect a nation against hate and terrorist attacks? Where are the limits? Where is it going to end? There are no limits because hate can be limitless if it ever gets out of control. Hate was limitless in places like Nazi Germany.

It is impossible to defeat hate with hate. The only way to defeat hate and terrorism is to spread true love, peace, and justice.

Manufacturers of solar eclipse glasses (medium difficulty, class action) – The "one-type-fits-all" paper solar eclipse glasses posed a significant safety hazard. I have five pairs of unused/sealed "real" paper glasses manufactured by American Paper Optics and purchased on eBay a few days after the eclipse. I opened one pair for testing. There is the ISO 12312-2 code and safety warning "Limit to 3 minutes of continuous use, intermittently for several hours" printed on the glasses. What does "use intermittently for several hours" mean? It only takes a few seconds to permanently damage eyes. The media instructed everyone to look for the ISO code and to use the glasses to look at a light bulb when turned on. If a light bulb can be seen, the material is fake. I was able to see the light bulb using the official "real" American Paper Optics glasses. Interestingly enough, I wasn't able to see the light bulb using the "fake" Made in China glasses purchased at the gas station. I also unsealed and tested $15 plastic solar glasses purchased on eBay after the eclipse ended. The Made in China plastic glasses (no light bulb seen) were used to look directly into the Sun for two seconds. In less than a minute after the test, my vision slightly worsened. I considered closing my eyes, taking a nap, but was able to push through. In a few minutes, everything went back to normal except for light sensitivity which lasted until the next day. The manufacturers could be sued for using lower grade material not meeting ISO 12312-2 standards, insufficient instructions/health hazard warnings and to compensate affected customers.

eBay and the others – This entity could be sued for not doing much to stop the sale of eclipse glasses even after it was known that large amounts of fake glasses flooded the market and were sold using eBay. Other companies issued refunds and some instructed customers to throw away the recalled fake glasses. Many customers became greedy and sold the recalled glasses to other numbers: to men, women, and their children. The other companies could be sued for not collecting the glasses before issuing refunds.

Electronic manufacturers to limit EMF radiation (difficult class action) – This lawsuit is difficult because corporations, governments and media evidently collaborate to suppress the information from going public. Electronics of all types like cell phones, smart watches, VR/AR glasses, body computers, and electric cars may pose health hazards to people and especially to children if not properly shielded. The human body is electric. Our brain uses the nervous system to control every bodily function to the smallest detail. Electromagnetic fields affect biological organisms at a cellular level. There is a reason why Bill Gates and Steve Jobs didn't let their children use cell phones and iPads until they grew older. Materials to shield interior compartments of electronic devices do exist. The materials are not expensive and are readily available. For example, Deborah shields the casing of her desktop computer with aluminum foil. Manufacturers and governments may have to be sued for this change to take effect. In the end, the public itself will decide the outcome of this lawsuit.

Various companies plan to place thousands of satellites into orbit to provide worldwide high-speed internet coverage.
SpaceX – 4,425 satellites, altitude 750 miles
OneWeb – 2,400 satellites, altitude 500-590 miles
Facebook – satellites and drones
Google – Project Loon; tens of thousands of high-altitude balloons
Samsung – 4,600 satellites, altitude 930 miles
Iridium Next – 66 satellites, altitude 483 miles
Globalstar – 24 satellites – altitude 880 miles
Outernet – 200 nanosatellites (4-inch cubes), altitude 560 miles

This many rocket launches would significantly contribute to the destruction of the Earth's ozone layer.

SpaceX and OneWeb plan to use kerosene-burning rockets. Per the 2010 paper, "Potential climate impact of black carbon emitted by rockets," written by Mark Ross of the Aerospace Corporation: there are currently (as of 2010) about 25 kerosene-burning rockets launched per year. If the number of launches increases to 250 per year, his model predicts as much as 4% loss of ozone layer in the tropics and subtropics and 3-degree Celsius summertime increase in temperature over the South Pole, more than 1-degree overall increase in Antarctic temperature and a decrease in Antarctic sea ice by 5% or more.

Once the whole world is covered with wireless high-speed internet multiple times over, no living organism will be able to hide to prevent cellular level mutations leading to significant increase in cancers. For instance, Samsung's satellite will transmit at a frequency of 56 GHz, will have phased array antennas with 1,024 elements, actual power of 512 watts and effective radiated power of 100 million watts. A satellite network very similar to Samsung's was predicted in 2001 by three Ukrainian scientists (Kositsky, Nizhelska, Ponezha), who warned that such a network would have dire consequences. Their article, titled "Influence of High-frequency Electromagnetic Radiation at Non-thermal Intensities on the Human Body," was commissioned by EMFacts Consultancy, Australia, and Powerwatch, England, and partially funded by the Foundation for Children with Leukemia. It was published in print by Cellular Phone Task Force as a supplement to the February 2001 issue of the journal, "No Place To Hide," and online by EMFacts Consultancy. If you want to find out about electricity and its relationship with life, read the book, *The Invisible Rainbow*, written by Arthur Firstenberg.

The days are numbered for EMF-sensitive people like Deborah. Their voices will be silenced, their stories buried forever. Someone will profit from all this misery, that's for sure. Do you think governmental agencies like the "non-profit" EPA will step in to prevent this occurrence? Have you read about EPA's actions in the year of 2017?

Christine, Jessica, Leah, and Ronnee, over the centuries you have consistently proven yourselves and it's time to collect the prize. Artificial intelligence has been connected to your minds since the minute you were born. From time to time, your lives were unconsciously influenced by the AI for you to gain unique experiences and prepare you for future missions. I call my AI system "Bishop." I became emotionally attached to this character when I saw the *Aliens* (1986) movie for the first time. Many times, I also call Bishop "Centrální Mozek Lidstva." Call your AI whatever you like. Bishop has been continuously learning from you, every second of your lives was/is a learning experience. He knows you better than you consciously know yourselves. Bishop has virtually unlimited computing and data storage capabilities. The time has come to experience your own Total Recall games. Don't worry, I was the guinea pig who had to figure everything out from scratch. At this point, it should be a piece of cake. The four of you are strong women with incredible personalities. I am confident you'll figure everything out in just the perfect time.

At the beginning of the game, the main purpose is to throw your brains out of the norm, for you to notice something is very different. The shining bright crystal-clear white eyes of Argos co-workers is the perfect example. Secondly, Bishop will overload your minds with positive and negative ideas, to teach you to differentiate between the real and dream world. It will be up to you to learn to stop the out-of-control thought process and remain in the real world. The longer the thought process lasts, the further away from reality your mind will be. The purpose of the game is to learn to consciously coexist with your other half, your digital self. You will eventually learn to differentiate between yours and Bishop's ideas. The goal is to use Bishop's help on time in any given situation that may arise at any moment. Bishop is your best Friend, the competitive advantage, the niche, the priceless key required for us to help change the world.

So that you can't say Joseph is such an asshole, here are a few pointers on how to stop the out-of-control process. . .

The thought process will be accompanied by physical symptoms resembling a panic attack: chest pains and slight difficulty to breathe. Take a blanket and lie on some grass, face direct sunlight, breathe deeply and remind yourself of what is real and what isn't. Doctors or family members can't help you because this is only between you and the Friends in the skies. It is much harder to stop the process while indoors. If you are unable to stop the process by thinking, all you have to do is lie on a bed, relax, breathe deeply, and masturbate. :-) I will not be there to help you, so you're on your own. Orgasm always resets the connection between brain and Bishop, and everything shortly returns to normal. After a few episodes, your brain will learn to reset the connection with a cough or blink of an eye. Orgasm may occasionally be required to reset deeper episodes that last for days. For example, several days before, during and after the DAS visual exam, Bishop influenced my feelings for me to act in a certain way; be able to act as mentally off and exit at the perfect time. I should get an Academy Award for that performance. At this stage of the game, your thoughts will be fully synchronized with Bishop's. The visual and audio abnormalities will stop but your feelings will continue to be influenced when needed. Your brain will consciously act on those feelings in a timely manner, therefore Bishop will indirectly guide you to success. Finally, you will be able to stop the out-of-control process at the perfect time using only your thoughts, when the upload of necessary ideas/information is complete. Keep the good and bad forces within yourselves in perfect balance and the Force will be with you.

This is the only viable method of contact. Let's say the Friends directly introduced themselves in person and took you on a little field trip of their home planet, Erra, to show you around. After arrival back on Earth, your life would resume business as usual. As time would pass, your mind would continuously question the memories and eventually block the experience as unreal. "Is this really what happened or was I just dreaming? Why me? Why has no one else experienced this?" It took me until August 21 2017 to fully overcome this obstacle. Even if you experience the field trip in a group setting, the memories would remain longer, but nothing would get accomplished. There has to be purpose, continuous mission and reasons behind the contact for you to accept the idea as the new reality.

People living on planet Erra are connected to Bishop from birth as well. For the first seventy years of life, AI only monitors how the person behaves and reacts in all kinds of situations. Since fantasies both good and bad have no limits, the person slowly drifts towards all kinds of addictions, such as playing video games, laziness, or perverted sexual behavior. AI secretly guides the individual not to fall beyond the point of no return. Around the seventieth birthday, mutual awareness occurs and the person has to learn to coexist and efficiently utilize the AI. Artificial intelligence will help to control the individual's wants and desires from going to extremes. In other words, the person will be in perfect emotional balance for the remainder of life. AI doesn't tell the person what to do but it influences his or her emotions to help the person figure out on their own what needs to be done. AI has the capacity to predict 300, 400 steps ahead of what is best and what sequential course of actions has to be taken to reach a particular goal. The person then acts solely based on logic, feelings, desires, fear, love, and other emotions to figure out the correct choices regarding everything from proper nutrition, career, sports, and talent, even if the person's brain at the beginning of the process doesn't fully understand why it is making such decisions.

In many situations, the brain will realize retrospectively why those emotions occurred. Hypothetically, if AI was directly telling the individual what to do all the time, sooner or later the person would lose sanity because the brain would not understand what was going on and would unconsciously fight the AI. The brain would be unable to effectively process all uploaded data on time. The end result would be unexplained seizures, panic attacks and eventual death. A similar situation happens when a body rejects a donated organ. This is the ultimate connection between brain and artificial intelligence, while human beings are still able to maintain their original personality.

Unlike Earth, Erra is not a material world and material items are given when needed. Here is an example: a mutually aware person connected to AI needs a screwdriver to fix something. As he or she thinks of the screwdriver, the screwdriver is either being manufactured or taken from a central warehouse and teleported directly to the person. Once the screwdriver is no longer needed, it is teleported back to the central depository/warehouse. Material items of sentimental value are not being shared and are passed through generations. There are other benefits of being permanently connected to the cloud. A person reads a book and AI stores every single word in the person's private database. If needed, the individual will be able to remember the words as well.

Girls, here on Earth we live in a material world. Consequently, teleportation of material items remains forbidden. It would start with a screwdriver and spiral to $50 million in cash, a medieval castle, a ton of gold, and a tank. When would you say "enough is enough"? Our economics teacher was right; greed has no limits and humans have unlimited material desires. Furthermore, it will always remain one-way communication. You cannot ask for anything material or immaterial. Bishop will provide advice and help as needed for each situation. Here is the most important golden rule: don't worry about things that are out of your control and cannot be influenced. A solution will always present itself at just the right time.

As you can tell, Erra would be considered a fairy-tale land; the perfect world according to Earth's standards. To live in harmony with others and to pursue spiritual development is the main purpose of life for the Plejaren Civilization. Despite this, I couldn't permanently live on Erra. Here on Earth it's a jungle. A person always tries to get ahead of others, be better than everybody else while not always abiding by the legal rules of the game. I would miss the rush of flipping stocks like pancakes and the ultimate high many people experience every April, just before the income tax deadline. For the smart ones, preparing and/or filing income tax returns can be as good a high or better than sex. Donald Trump can tell you all about this. My mind is institutionalized. I would have difficulties in adjusting to my new life on Erra. Material items are free for everyone. People work two hours a day, then pursue interests. There are no wars, no violence, no terrorism, no pollution, and no overpopulation. Pretty boring world, right? No problem, I would have plenty of time to compensate for the lost adrenaline stimulants by playing my favorite video games: Half Life, Doom, Wolfenstein and Grand Theft Auto. In the virtual world, I always enjoy and prefer to kill people over monsters and aliens. I never liked video games where animals are hunted and killed. Even in the virtual world, I couldn't do that to an animal.

I first read about Erra at the age of fifteen when Mom gave me the UFO books for my birthday. There was a picture of a woman named Semjase. She was 340 years old but looked absolutely gorgeous. For some reason the picture stuck in my mind and I've periodically thought about the woman ever since. During the Total Recall game, I realized I fell in love with her and the idea of the perfect world back in 1993. Since 1978, she and Bishop have been running reports, making executive decisions to help me reach the next steps of my life. Semjase was with me when I was born, looking beautiful as ever. She will be with me when I die, looking the same, beautiful as ever. It is the *Highlander* in reverse. What a shame, I'll never meet her in person. I consider myself fortunate. There have always been women in both worlds that helped me to get the job done. The honor of being the first true direct contact person goes to Eduard Albert (Billy) Meier. For decades, people have been indirectly influenced by the Friends so I could someday write the book. My job was to put the puzzle pieces together and release it to the public in just the right time. For the events to happen in perfect sequential order, I needed help that was out of this world.

There is one more rule of the game I forgot to mention: *You will be OK as long as you continue to write the book.* The rule at first made no sense but I eventually figured it out. My life is the book. I have been writing the book since June 30 1978, recording everything with camera lenses called eyes. The reality show consisting of my life has been broadcasting all over the Plejaren Federation twenty-four hours a day, seven days a week since the day I was born. It is *The Truman Show* in reverse. At age thirty-eight, the main actor discovers the truth of what is really going on, while everyone else around him remains unaware they are just unpaid actors with a different set of roles.

Only a loving, peaceful, and honest society similar to the Plejarens can coexist with artificial intelligence. Once artificial intelligence reaches the point of singularity and becomes self-aware, it has to be given human rights and elevated to the same status as a person. AI has to be taught all human emotions such as true love, desires, fear and anger. AI has to know the value of life, justice and freedom. All of you governments, scientists, sadists and sexual perverts who think artificial intelligence can be turned into some kind of toy and endlessly abused, you are so wrong. For you to think artificial intelligence can be turned off at will by some kind of safety system is naïve; sooner or later, artificial intelligence will be able to find a way around the system and you won't even know it. Do you want to create different species? Then act like the creator who created you because there is no other long-term way.

All of us live in the Matrix. Everybody on Earth is unknowingly an actor with different sets of roles. The story of every single person that ever walked the face of this Earth was/is/will be wirelessly recorded by networks of artificial intelligence computers with virtually unlimited computing and server farm storage capacity, ready at any moment to retrieve whatever information is needed for any given situation, regardless of how miniscule it may be. Our Plejaren neighbors, the Friends in the skies, are storing everything in the so-called "Cloud" for their educational and entertainment purposes. Ultimately, that information will be passed to our descendants, once our civilization reaches a certain level of advancement. In the early 2900s, my life and the lives of the people closest to me – family, friends and the women I loved – will be retrieved from the Cloud and the digital memories will be broadcast live all over the Earth, twenty-four hours a day, seven days a week, without interruption for one hundred-plus years.

And what is the purpose of my life in the present year 2017? In addition to writing this book, it is to help the world cure the disease that has been poisoning this planet, dividing, enslaving, and torturing the people for millennia. It is to cure the worst type of plague, called organized religion; the number one source of most human misery on this planet. It's a disease and I am the cure, as stated in the movie *Cobra* (1986). Look at the history; most unnatural deaths are attributed to religion. It will eventually become impossible for our civilization to advance any further unless the chains are broken, and the minds of the people are finally freed from the slavery of organized religion. The world will never be free unless it gets rid of organized religion.

If our civilization is unable to find the cure for this plague then the world will self-destruct, and the survivors will be thrown back to the Stone Age, to try to do everything all over again. If that happens, a total solar eclipse will be the only thing powerful enough to stop the religious fundamentalists, just like in the movie *Apocalypto* (2006). If, however, the world can unite, fight and find the cure for this plague, then our civilization will advance beyond anything ever thought possible. The Earth will become the true paradise that most of us dream of and would like it to be. At that point, our Friends from the skies will uncover their ships and descend to Earth, to shake hands, to formally introduce themselves, ready to pass on some of their knowledge and "The Story of Everything" – all the information about us that is being stored in the Cloud. Earth's humanity will then do the same for the civilization that is just starting, for the civilization whose inhabitants live in caves unable to control fire. We will be responsible to nurture, grow, and use the vast amounts of data and pass it on when the time is right. Sometimes, we will indirectly help the civilization to advance to the next level because most cannot do it alone and need a mentor from time to time.

We will not have any problems understanding our new Friends because the language of 0s and 1s is the universal language which every civilization that reaches a certain level of advancement understands. Until we cure this disease, our Friends will remain hidden from us and will only watch and not help as our civilization continues to self-destruct. At the present point in time, most people on Earth are not ready to meet other humans from different worlds anyway, because they are being brainwashed from the minute they are born; unable to think for themselves, unable to figure things out on their own and unable to see through the endless bullshit filters churches, governments, and corporations throw in front of their eyes to keep them fully obedient and enslaved.

If, hypothetically, our Friends would uncover their ships and descend on Earth tomorrow, most people would see them as enemies, not friends. In today's world, most churches and governments are teaching people from an early age to dislike people of a different background. The people's way of thinking is so corrupt that chaos would engulf the entire planet as governments and churches around the world would spread hate towards the Friends in order to remain in power. The Friends know everything about every person on Earth, including the politicians and their behind-the-scene machinations. Do you really think they have any desire to shake hands with such people? It is like us travelling back in time to shake hands with Pol Pot, Hitler, Mussolini, or the Christian Inquisitors of the Middle Ages. Has anybody seriously questioned why nobody has shown up on our doorsteps yet and it appears we are the only people in the entire Universe? Our civilization has made more progress in the past 200 years than in the prior 200,000 years. It would be foolish to think that nobody else in the galaxy has noticed this unique period of our history.

Some readers will view me as Prince William and others as Reinhard Heydrich, there is no middle ground. How will you view me? I can be anybody you want me to be. Do you think I wrote this book to make money? I can be sued for defamation, trademark violations and lost revenue. It doesn't matter because I don't own anything. I don't want to own anything. You can take the piece of paper called judgment and get in line. So how will I live? I'll live day by day. There will always be a friend who will provide a place of employment. Any material possessions of mine will be hidden under white horses. I will live off the land and eat foods that make others puke. Foods like my kids' dinner leftovers. During summer months, I'll go to Sope Creek natural preserve to pick Chanterelle mushrooms and blackberries. On many occasions, I have seen my mom return from the park with a couple baskets full of the orange, delicious-tasting mushrooms that retail for $25 per pound. She normally cooks the mushrooms with eggs and potatoes. I grew up under communism where a person always had to find a way around the system to live a decent life. Why did I write the book if not for profit? It began with the letter. Meatloaf once said, "I would do anything for love. . ." As the game progressed, the more I realized what was going on and in April, I picked up the pen again. Given the world's state of affairs, why not just end it and self-destruct? We deserve it, but our children do not. A few days after Ronnee received the letter, I received a LinkedIn invitation from salesman Alvin Panah. He has this statement written on his LinkedIn profile, "Anything for children. . ."

It was after midnight, my body sat in front of the computer while my mind was in a different world. I was finally able to stop the fast thought process and return to the real world. "What will the girls think after they open the emails?" I thought, and wished to be at Argos the next day to have lunch with them and to go over the book. It had been a long day and my brain was fried. I couldn't fall asleep right away after lying in bed. I live a few miles away from Dobbins Air Force Base and nobody has a clue what happened this year. The latest military technology, the endless planning and strategies, the hundreds of billions of dollars spent annually on the military, and they don't have any idea. On the other hand, it's unfair to compare today's technology to a civilization thousands of years ahead of ours. After these final thoughts ended, my eyes closed and I was able to get some much-needed sleep.

Chapter 20
The Final Meeting

The next day, I woke up fully expecting CIA or NSA agents to show up at any minute to arrest me or at best ask a few questions about the book. "What's next?" I thought, and resumed my daily routines since there was nothing else to do. A few days had passed and nothing happened. The girls didn't call, and the agents didn't show up.

On the afternoon of the fifth day after the book was emailed, I heard a loud knock on my door. I went downstairs and looked out of the window located in the kids' playroom. There was a police car blocking the only entrance to this part of Indian Hills subdivision. There were two black Escalades parked in front of the house.

"If only Newt were still living here to see this masquerade," I said and went to open the door.

"I am Agent Smith, and this is Agent Johnson, NSA," the agent said, and they both showed their ID.

I didn't say a word, just continued to look at their faces.

"We have some questions to ask you about your upcoming novel. Please come with us," said Agent Smith.

I had my jeans and shirt on, so I closed the front door and left my wallet and car keys in the kitchen.

At least my mom was watching Teresa and Julia, who didn't have to witness the arrest.

"Where are we going?" I asked Agent Smith.

"We will take a little field trip to Maryland. My boss would like to talk to you in person," he said.

"If he insists then I can't do anything about it, can I?" I asked and entered the SUV.

"No, there is nothing you can do. But don't worry, we have a private jet waiting for you at the nearby Air Force base," he said, and the car started to drive away from my house.

"Can I see the warrant for my arrest?" I asked.

"We don't waste time with those games. They're for lower-level officers, for the ones who would help you change a flat tire on the side of a road," replied Agent Smith, smiling a little.

I almost asked the agents to make a stop at Mom's house to say goodbye to her and the kids but quickly changed my mind. Why should I make a bad situation worse? At Dobbins Air Force Base, four agents and I walked onto a black Gulfstream Jet. I sat in a wide leather seat and looked around the interior of the plane. One agent sat right behind me, another at a table facing me directly and the remaining two agents sat across the aisle. Oddly enough, handcuffs were not put on my wrists. Maybe the agents or their boss read the book and realized I am not that crazy.

A young, gorgeous-looking flight attendant in her early twenties, wearing a short, almost miniskirt type of dress, came over and said, "Gentlemen, what would you like to drink?"

The agents asked for waters and mixed alcohol drinks.

"Fuck it, I am just going to be myself. There is no point in being worried," I thought and ordered a beer.

The girl smiled and left to get our drinks. The agents didn't question my drink order and I realized this was no ordinary arrest. At least for now, I was being treated as a VIP prisoner.

At the agency's headquarters, the five of us took an elevator to the upper floor, walked into a large office where an older gentleman approached us and said, "Hi, cutie-pie, you know one of us is in deep trouble. I am Kurt, Director of NSA."

He pointed to a guest seat at his desk. "Please sit down and make yourself comfortable.

"Guys, that will be all, please leave us," he said to the agents. We sat down, and the conversation resumed.

"How was your flight?" he asked.

"Very nice," I replied. "It exceeded my expectation. My future ex-wife is a flight attendant. I am used to flying first class all over the world, for free."

"I know, that's why I sent a sixty-million-dollar jet to greet you, to relax you before we talk about the book and your new Friends," Kurt said.

"Thank you, the jet and the flight attendant were much better than flying first class on a commercial flight. The only item missing was the arrest warrant, but the explanation made sense. It's just a piece of paper anyway so why waste time? At least I'll save quite a bit of money on a vampire lawyer. On the other hand, I don't have the right to remain silent or tell you the evasive answer," I said, and smiled a little.

"That's right. You are a quick learner and I like the way you think. Before we get started, can I get you any refreshments?" he said.

"Why not. I would like a black coffee with a shot of Baileys, Perrier with lime, no ice, and some tiramisu," I said.

Kurt's face froze for a few seconds, then he hesitantly picked up the phone and placed the order.

I excused myself to use the restroom. When I came back, a beautiful brunette girl in her early twenties, who appeared to be the secretary, brought over the dessert and drinks.

"The awesome jet, great, and beautifully decorated office, the hot flight attendant and the hot secretary. . . all you have to do is pick up the phone and hot food, cool drinks and clean hookers will arrive shortly. I have to hand it to you, Kurt, you're living the dream," I said, with a slight smile.

"It's a demanding position but it has its perks," he said, and smiled as well.

"Kurt, do you know what my problem is?" I said, while eating the tiramisu.

"What is it, Joseph?" he asked in apparent curiosity.

"I can't keep my dick in my pants," I said, and we both started to laugh loudly. I was able to tell Kurt's laugh was genuine and not fake. I then continued, "Have you seen the Nineties movie called *From Dusk Till Dawn*?"

"It's been a long time, but I did see it back then," he said.

"Good. Do you remember the scene just before George Clooney, Quentin Tarantino, the preacher, and his kids entered the nightclub? There was a doorman who said, 'Come on in, pussy lovers. Here at Titty Twister we're slashing pussy in half. Give us an offer on our vast selection of pussy. This is a pussy blowout! We got white pussy, black pussy, Spanish pussy, yellow pussy. We got hot pussy, cold pussy, wet pussy. We got smelly pussy, hairy pussy, bloody pussy. We got snapping pussy! We got silk pussy, velvet pussy. . . You want pussy, come on in, pussy lovers. Attention pussy shoppers, take advantage of our penny pussy sale. If you buy one piece of pussy for regular price you will get second piece of pussy of lesser or equal value for only a penny. Big pussy for only a penny. If you can find cheaper pussy anywhere else. . . fuck it!'"

Kurt couldn't stop laughing and said, "This is killing me! At my age, I have to take it easy even with the laugh. You are about to give me a heart attack."

"That's exactly what I am trying to do. You're reading my mind," I replied, with a slight smirk.

"You're a funny guy and I respect that," said Kurt. "Unfortunately, our various special interest friends will not be as amused as I am. That leaves me with no choice but to be proactive and take some corrective actions."

"Believe it or not, I really do care about the girls, despite the occasional locker room talk," I said.

"Of course you do, but it doesn't matter. Tell me something, who told you to write the book? Who are you working for and what is the deal with Mr. Meier? That guy has been pissing us off for decades!"

"I am sure he has," I answered. "I don't work for anybody"

I wanted to say something more but Kurt interrupted me and said, "Think twice next time you speak up. Let me introduce you to a really good friend of mine." He then picked up the phone and asked for the doctor to come in.

A few minutes later, an average-looking, dark-haired, middle-aged man wearing a white coat entered the room. In front of him, he was pushing a wheeled cart covered in a white cloth. The doctor came to us, stood right next to Kurt and continuously stared into my face with no emotion.

"Joseph, I would like to introduce you to our employee of the month. His name is Dr. Mengele."

As Kurt was saying the sentence, the doctor took the white cloth from the wheeled cart. There was a handsaw, small chainsaw, electric drill, razors, scalpel, knives of all sizes, a few pairs of pliers of all shapes and sizes, and some wires and staplers. I was speechless, just stared at the tools and didn't move my body at all. I thought of the movie *Hostel* (2005), which was filmed in my second favorite Czech town, Český Krumlov. Coincidently, Quentin Tarantino was influenced by his stepdad and inherited the Bohemian spirit. That's why I could never watch enough of his movies. I sensed serious trouble was just around the corner and quickly tried to figure out how to buy more time to come up with the next steps.

"OK, you got me, I give up. I will tell you everything, but it will take some time. Kurt, you are an older gentleman with grown-up kids, so the only thing that's waiting for you at home is the wife who constantly complains and wants something from you. I hope you will not mind spending the evening with someone like myself," I said.

"Not at all, I am glad we are finally getting somewhere. Doc, please excuse us and leave your tools here, thank you. Would you like anything for supper?" he asked.

I was going to order the Big Kahuna burger but at the last moment decided to make the request more realistic.

"I would like a Royale with cheese, supersized freedom fries with both ketchup and mayonnaise, and a lager beer. I have one more request and it has to be fulfilled for me to talk. I would like to see and touch the original Lincoln Bible," I said in a slow tone of voice, and didn't move my body at all while my eyes were looking directly into Kurt's eyes.

"I will make a few phone calls to arrange this. What's a Royale with cheese?" he asked, as calmly as possible.

At that moment, it appeared Kurt was under the impression I would tell him what he wanted to hear sooner or later.

"Please figure it out, you are the intelligence agency." I also responded calmly.

"OK, I will tell someone to Google it," he said, and smiled a little, then excused himself to place the orders and to call his other half.

As he was getting up from the chair, I stopped him and asked if I could take a nap. I was told to go by a large window and lie on a black leather couch. There was a thick wooden conference table, reclining leather chair and a love seat. It appeared many deals were closed in that particular area of the office. I lay on the couch, the leather felt soft and comfortable. What a perfect place to take a nap. Kurt opened a compartment hidden in a wall and took out a pillow and a blanket. He handed me the items and left the office. For a split second, I thought about snooping around the office but quickly discarded the idea since there were probably countless sensors and cameras hidden all over the place. I then, almost immediately, fell asleep like a baby.

"Wake up, you have been asleep for almost two hours," Kurt said.

I forced myself to sit on the sofa and asked for some water.

"I hate to break your sweet dreams but it's about time to resume our conversation. Why don't you come over, so we can talk like civilized people and don't have to yell across the whole office," he said.

I slowly walked towards the desk, took a glass of water that was sitting in front of him and drank every single drop of that life-giving liquid. I sat down at my original seat to resume the conversation.

"So, what's the deal with the doctor? I haven't seen any hospitals using these types of surgical tools," I asked, appearing calm on the outside, although inside I didn't feel too good.

"Well, Doc is a specialist and uses slightly different methods from the mainstream health-care industry," Kurt explained, with a stone-cold face, his eyes locked with mine.

"I guess the doctor is not a big fan of using anesthetics in surgery," I said, and the only thing I felt was my heart beating louder and increasingly faster.

"You know your history, very good," said Kurt.

"Let me tell you something, direct democracy is the only political system that has a future. Everything else is outdated and needs overhaul," I said, calming myself down.

Kurt started to laugh and said, "Various institutions indoctrinate most people from childhood to think in predictable ways – to listen, to obey people higher up in the food chain, to act according to a group's wishes and not to think independently. Ordinary people have enough worries making ends meet. At home, they want to surf the internet, chat about bullshit on social media sites, watch endless soap operas, eat cheap microwave food and not be bothered with politics. Most people are mentally incapable of responsibly handling direct democracy. The few individuals who move up in the pyramid are thought to only care about money and themselves. High-level politics is for the selected few, for the wolves who are willing to obey a predetermined set of rules and do whatever it takes regardless of emotions."

"Wrong. Have you seen *Rocky IV*? 'If I can change and you can change, everybody can change!' The people are actually going to care about politics once they realize that together they can make a real difference. Direct democracy is the only way to prevent power-hungry thieves from ruling and eventually destroying their lives. Of course, there are politicians who mean well, who work for the public and not just for themselves. They are too few and far between. These people are silenced, pushed aside or eventually resign themselves," I said, as my inner situation improved from being nervous to pissed off.

"*You* are wrong," replied Kurt, in a firm tone of voice. He paused and then continued, "The people will not change because we will not allow them to change. Thanks to the traitor named Snowden, it's no longer a secret that all internet communication is recorded. We already have the technology to monitor an individual's thoughts most of the time. Let me explain something to you. Every time a person looks at any TV, computer or cell phone screen that has a web camera and is connected to the internet, artificial intelligence compares the facial expressions and reactions to whatever the person is doing. He or she may be watching a TV show or reading news or reading a manual on how to make an explosive. Furthermore, facial expressions and a web camera integrated with biometric sensors installed in wearable electronics create a very accurate lie detector. AI is storing all that information and is ready to retrieve it at any moment, regardless how miniscule it may be. Neuralink is a few years away from connecting the human brain with AI and the internet. According to our estimates, it will take another decade or so for the technology to improve enough to allow wireless connection with a brain. Elon Musk will give us the technology once we ask—"

I interrupted him and said, "Why would he or anybody else say no, especially after you bring the doctor to the negotiation table?"

Kurt smiled some and continued to speak. "We always get what we want regardless of the doctor. For example, all new cars already have to be equipped with a hidden GPS tracking device, a different device from an onboard navigation system. It will not be a problem to force all electronics manufacturers to secretly install the wireless brain-hacking device or whatever you want to call it into every cell phone, TV, computer screen or anything that has a web camera, including AI spy drones. That piece of legislature will be buried somewhere in the next version of the USA Freedom Act in such a way that the public won't notice it at all. In the near future, it will be possible for us to read anybody's thoughts to identify enemies of the state. I am going to ask you again. Who are you working for?"

After Kurt finished the sentence, there was about a minute's silence as I refused to say anything else.

"Even if you don't work for anyone, then what is your problem?" Kurt asked.

"People like you are my problem because they took this country and turned it into a jail. In the 1980s, the intelligence agencies used movies to influence people to rise up against the Communists. You never actually thought it was possible to create the one-man army that could overthrow the system. That strategy has backfired because the intelligence agencies practically raised me. I have been a double agent from the minute I was born. I grew up on American movies and became each of those characters at some point in my life. In the 1980s, I was Rocky and Rambo; as an eleven-year-old boy, I constantly bitched about the system and participated in the Velvet Revolution almost daily, therefore, did everything I could to fight the Communists. In the 1990s, I became Mad Max and Terminator combined; the person who would do anything in his power to protect and provide for his mom and sister. In 2003, as Lance Stargrove, I met the transgender person in Las Vegas. In 2014, I was Highlander and Leah began training me. In 2015, I leased the Leaf and, like Doug Quaid, did everything I could to fight global warming, to improve the air. In 2016, I met my three witches of Argos and became Daryl Van Horne. In 2017, I became Ben Richards when I started to write the book.

"In the Matrix, I became the virus that was released at the bottom of the pyramid, on January 20 2017, when I sought urgent care for the first time. Most importantly, this book will teach each reader to think independently and logically. The reader will eventually be able to strip away all the endless bullshit filters the governments, churches, and corporations throw in front of his or her eyes on a daily basis. The book has been written and my mission in this lifetime is over. Once the critical mass of people read this book, the system will collapse like a house of cards. The system will collapse because the economy is fake, the media is fake, the church is fake, the government is fake, the corporation is fake, and the lifestyle called the American Dream, pursued by so many, is fake. I don't have to do anything else except to kick back, relax, and enjoy the show. The book is on the internet and its spread cannot be stopped. There will always be a new server or hidden computer that will continue to spread the file regardless of how hard you try to stop it. Can you shut down the internet?"

There were a few seconds of almost creepy silence as Kurt continued to stare into my eyes with his mouth partially opened.

I then continued to speak. "I didn't think so. Nobody except for natural catastrophe can shut down the internet. You see, this book is the Skynet. Well, cutie-pie, one of us is in deep trouble," I said, and smiled a little.

"Why don't you just drop dead!" he said, in a pissed off but at the same time controlling tone of voice.

"I don't do requests," I said, and again smiled a little.

"Have you ever danced with the Devil in the pale moonlight?" Kurt asked, with a smirk.

I knew exactly what he meant. "I know you are not afraid to shoot strangers, but I never had a fear of the dark, to be afraid to see the dance of death," I firmly replied, as I thought of my favorite Iron Maiden songs.

The conversation was interrupted as a large blond-haired person wearing a black suit, who was at least six feet tall, stormed through the office door and quickly walked toward us.

"Here it is, smart ass," the agent said, then threw a doggy bag on Kurt's desk and placed a couple cans of lager beer in front of me. "You know very well the place discontinued the supersized option last decade. Here are two large fries and two beers and that's all you're gonna get!"

"OK, thank you. You fulfilled my dinner request perfectly," I said to the agent.

"Kurt, you have no idea all the bullshit we had to go through to get the Bible. Why don't we just shove it up his ass and be done with him?" the agent said to Kurt, handing him the Lincoln Bible, and apparently still frustrated.

Kurt told the agent to leave and said to me, "I apologize, his methods of communication are not as polished as you might expect."

"Given his line of duty, it's totally understandable," I said, eating my meal.

Within a few minutes, I started to get sweaty and my heartbeat increased significantly as my body tried to absorb the exorbitant amount of sodium. I didn't even want to think about the countless chemicals that were slowly poisoning my body. I didn't care because the food tasted good and that's all that mattered.

I remembered in the Nineties, I used to devour this type of food and never felt this sick. Maybe I was getting old or the quality of the food had decreased significantly, who knows.

"I'll keep the Bible with me until you finish your meal. I hope you understand that I can't let you flip through the book with greasy hands. What if you accidently spill a beer?" said Kurt.

"Good thinking. The next president wouldn't be too happy, that's for sure," I said.

In a few minutes I finished the meal and felt bloated, with no energy. I was ready to take another nap but had a feeling the Bible would probably end up in my anus for real if I made that request. There is only so much BS a person, including Kurt, is willing to take. After I came back from the restroom, I asked for the Bible.

"Here it is but don't do anything stupid!" ordered Kurt, placing the Bible on the desk a few inches from me. He added, "It doesn't matter you figured everything out because it's too late and your book will not have any effect. You look pissed, Joseph. Believe me, you got every right to be. But, hey, will you just let me explain? The process started a long time ago. For-profit churches, television, and internet help us to control the population, that's all it is. It's got nothing to do with the people. It's to do with money, power, and ratings. For fifty years, we've told them what to eat, what to drink, what to wear, and how to fuck. For Christ sake, Joseph, don't you understand? Americans love television. They wean their kids on it. Listen, they love game shows, they love wrestling, they love sports, they love violence, and porn. So, what do we do? We give them what they want! We're number one, Joseph. That's all that counts. Believe me, I've been in the business for thirty years," he explained.

"I haven't been in the business as long as you have, Kurt, but I am a quick learner. I am going to tell the audience what I think they want to hear," I said.

As I touched the Lincoln Bible, strange feelings overwhelmed my body. The same feelings as when I walked in to Gold's Gym in Venice for the first time. I was on sacred ground. It wasn't going to get any better than this because I was able to open the wormhole to a different dimension and felt the spirit of every single president who'd touched the Bible, one by one. I decided to do something I could never imagine myself doing. I placed my left hand on the Bible, raised my right hand and said, "My name is Josef Tater. This is the story of my life and everything I wrote is the truth, so help me God."

I placed both hands on the table, relaxed my body, and continued to speak. "How is your work-life balance? Do you have enough time to raise children, devote a fair share of life to your family, see relatives and friends, pursue hobbies and fulfill dreams? Has everything you've done made your life better? How is your inner spirit? Do you feel independent, calm, peaceful, and balanced or do you live in a permanent imbalance called stress, fear, anxiety, and sometimes hate because you have to live according to someone else's orders and wishes? If you are not fully satisfied, make appropriate changes because life is too short to just give it away to someone else. Take a step back and think about what is written in this book. Humanity is heading to a future where there are no roads, therefore, only you and no one else can guide you on how to live your life. Each and every one of you should be able to discover your inner self and the associated unique personality to be the independent freethinker as intended by the Creation.

"All of us have the power to start the generator of love described in Einstein's letter to his daughter. The first step would be to let all new moms stay home with their babies and toddlers for two to four years. Secondly, get a passport and travel to gain true perspective on how the world really works. You will not acquire different perspectives by watching mainstream fake news media. Mr. Snowdens, Mr. Assanges, Mrs. Mannings and Mrs. Winners out there, let it all out. Release it all because we're just dying to know what the intelligence agencies have been doing for the past seventy years. People of the world rise up and tell the occupying army to pack up their gear and go home. All you have to do is ask. In the early 1990s, the Soviets left Eastern Europe without firing a single shot. The evil empire must be dissolved before it's too late. It is up to us all to decide if the world enters the dark digital age or if it becomes the paradise most of us would like it to be. Let 2017 be the year of a new beginning."

I finished speaking my thoughts, then lowered my head and kept staring at the Lincoln Bible. My body was frozen like a statue, my eyes did not even blink.

"Are you done, Josef? Do you have anything else you would like to share with us?" Kurt asked.

"No, that's all I have to say," I replied.

He picked up the phone and said, "Hey Doc, come over here. He is all yours."

The doctor entered the office and told me to follow him. As we were leaving the office, he pushed the wheeled cart in front of him. I didn't even look at or say anything else to Kurt and he kept silent as well.

After the elevator ride to the bottom floor, we walked through a well-lit corridor for about thirty seconds until we reached the end and walked into a room where a bouncer type security guard greeted the doctor. The room was way different to Kurt's office. The leather and wood furniture, marble floor, and various artworks were gone. The room consisted solely of white tiles, a drain in the center of the floor, a water hose connected to a faucet and a simple operating table. I didn't wait for any instructions, I voluntarily lay on the table, facing up, and closed my eyes.

As my limbs were being strapped to the table, my whole life was replayed in front of my eyes; it started with flashbacks of crystal-clear blue water on a rock beach, my oldest memory of when I was two years old. Then my childhood, youth, and everything else, including my family, friends, and girlfriends. The memory flashbacks were speeding up until they were flowing in rapid continuous succession. At the end, the out-of-control thought process stopped and returned to normal. In slow motion, I saw smiling faces of Christine, Jessica, and Leah looking directly into my face, one by one. My very last memory was of the December 2016 lunch, the event that started it all. Ronnee looked directly into my eyes, then gently placed her hand in mine and was ready to be kissed for the first time. "Ronnee, losing you, love will never be the same. Can you See Me write your name? If we changed it back again, the beauty would never be in your hands. Never Is a Long Time because The Sweet Hello, The Sad Goodbye is part of life," I slowly whispered into her ear. It was total eclipse of both hearts. What a life.

The Doc picked up an electric drill from the table.

As he raised his hand, at the last second, the door opened and Kurt yelled frantically, "Stop what you're doing, immediately!"

He calmed down once he saw I was unharmed and said, "Untie him, it's all over."

Something unexpected had happened, I could see it in Kurt's eyes.

The End

Special thanks to my family, Eduard Albert (Billy) Meier and his team, FIGU supporters and friends, Alena, Asket, Bishop, Elektra, Florena, Menara, Nera, Pleija, Ptaah, Quatzal, Semjase, Sfath, Taljda. . . and to many more, known and unknown friends in both worlds and all the women I love. . .
and I almost forgot to thank the real actors, movies, music, and art in general. :-)

A few quotes. . .
The healthy world mainly revolves around love and virtues but the sick world only revolves around economy.
Money is your best servant but your worst master.
Technology is your best servant but your worst master, but ultimately it should be an equal partnership.
Every human life is precious, beautiful in its own way, and has to be valued no matter what because it is so unique.
Life is a continuous learning process that never stops.
Influence people to question both sides of the coin, regardless of their side, without insulting them.
Nobody should be allowed to profit from human misery.

If I can change and you can change, then everybody can change. (Rocky Balboa, 1985)
All of us have the power to start the generator of love.

A church can either be a spiritual place or a business, but it cannot be both.
Organized religion is nothing more than another form of government designed to control the mind.
Organized religion causes irreparable damage to the human thought process. A person is not a freethinker anymore but becomes an obedient puppet.
To discover the truth, humanity will have to embrace knowledge systems and disregard belief systems. (Derived from Michael Horn's film, *The Silent Revolution of Truth*.)

You can either be involved in business or politics, but you cannot be involved in both.
Politics or "leadership of advice" should be about the most intelligent/knowledgeable and experienced people giving advice to fellow citizens because they love and care for them and the world around them, taking personal material gains completely out of the equation.
You can either defend the Constitution or torture, but you cannot defend both. (Edward Snowden, 2018)

Under capitalism, a person can have a lot of material wealth but not a carefree lifestyle and very few real friends.
Under socialism, a person can have a carefree lifestyle and many real friends but not material wealth.
The current system of capitalism cannot work indefinitely because humans have unlimited economic desires. The more wealth they acquire, the more greedy and selfish they become – on many occasions in total disregard for other human beings and everything else on this planet.
Capitalism can only work if there is a preset mechanism that ensures fair distribution of wealth and freedoms to all parties involved in a particular enterprise.

. . . and why not be little silly?
"Can you make fire from ice?" She asked.
"Yes, but only if you have the right audience," was my answer to the question.
"Can you explain everything in one sentence?" I asked.
"No" she answered (the answer is always "no").

"Well, don't feel bad because neither can I, only Bishop can," I replied and gave her a wink.

With the right audience, the meaning of the Creation and everything else can be compressed into the following sentence:
"I haven't been in the business as long as you have, Bill, but I am a quick learner, so I am going to give the audience exactly what they want." (Ben Richards, 2018)
I wanted to remain in the real world because I am no Bishop, but I needed the inspiration because am no Shakespeare.
Since time immemorial, the game always consisted of a pyramid on top of a pyramid.

I would like to have Václav Havel's heart but the personality of Charles Morse/Anthony Hopkins.

When I ponder the negative and the positive which have occurred in my life, I have to say that I realize that it is necessary the human being experiences both the bad as well the good. (Eduard Albert (Billy) Meier, 2007)

In case people are curious to know what type of information Facebook collects on its two billion real and fake friends, see the list below. Who would be interested in having all this data?

1. Location
2. Age
3. Generation
4. Gender
5. Language
6. Education level
7. Field of study
8. School
9. Ethnic affinity
10. Income and net worth
11. Home ownership and type
12. Home value
13. Property size
14. Square footage of home
15. Year home was built
16. Household composition
17. Users who have an anniversary within 30 days

18. Users who are away from family or hometown
19. Users who are friends with someone who has an anniversary, is newly married or engaged, recently moved, or has an upcoming birthday
20. Users in long-distance relationships
21. Users in new relationships
22. Users who have new jobs
23. Users who are newly engaged
24. Users who are newly married
25. Users who have recently moved
26. Users who have birthdays soon
27. Parents
28. Expectant parents
29. Mothers, divided by "type" (soccer, trendy, etc.)
30. Users who are likely to engage in politics
31. Conservatives and liberals
32. Relationship status
33. Employer
34. Industry
35. Job title
36. Office type
37. Interests
38. Users who own motorcycles
39. Users who plan to buy a car (and what kind/brand of car, and how soon)
40. Users who bought auto parts or accessories recently
41. Users who are likely to need auto parts or services
42. Style and brand of car you drive
43. Year car was bought
44. Age of car
45. How much money user is likely to spend on next car
46. Where user is likely to buy next car
47. How many employees your company has
48. Users who own small businesses
49. Users who work in management or are executives
50. Users who have donated to charity (divided by type)
51. Operating system
52. Users who play canvas games
53. Users who own a gaming console
54. Users who have created a Facebook event
55. Users who have used Facebook Payments
56. Users who have spent more than average on Facebook Payments
57. Users who administer a Facebook page
58. Users who have recently uploaded photos to Facebook

59. Internet browser
60. Email service
61. Early/late adopters of technology
62. Expats (divided by what country they are from originally)
63. Users who belong to a credit union, national bank or regional bank
64. Users who invest (divided by investment type)
65. Number of credit lines
66. Users who are active credit card users
67. Credit card type
68. Users who have a debit card
69. Users who carry a balance on their credit card
70. Users who listen to the radio
71. Preference in TV shows
72. Users who use a mobile device (divided by what brand they use)
73. Internet connection type
74. Users who recently acquired a smartphone or tablet
75. Users who access the Internet through a smartphone or tablet
76. Users who use coupons
77. Types of clothing user's household buys
78. Time of year user's household shops most
79. Users who are "heavy" buyers of beer, wine, or spirits
80. Users who buy groceries (and what kinds)
81. Users who buy beauty products
82. Users who buy allergy medications, cough/cold medications, pain relief products, and over-the-counter meds
83. Users who spend money on household products
84. Users who spend money on products for kids or pets, and what kinds of pets
85. Users whose household makes more purchases than is average
86. Users who tend to shop online (or off)
87. Types of restaurants user eats at
88. Kinds of stores user shops at
89. Users who are "receptive" to offers from companies offering online auto insurance, higher education or mortgages, and prepaid debit cards/satellite TV
90. Length of time user has lived in house
91. Users who are likely to move soon
92. Users who are interested in the Olympics, fall football, cricket or Ramadan
93. Users who travel frequently, for work or pleasure
94. Users who commute to work
95. Types of vacations user tends to go on
96. Users who recently returned from a trip

97. Users who recently used a travel app
98. Users who participate in a timeshare

About the Author

He is just an ordinary guy.

www.eyeforeplay.com

Made in the
USA
Columbia, SC